Leviathan

John Gordon Davis is a Rhodesian with Welsh ancestry. He went to sea with a Dutch whaling fleet at the age of 18 and also sailed in British merchantmen, writing stories 'in the fo'c'sle head'.

In addition to his success as a writer, Davis is also a successful barrister – Crown Counsel in Rhodesia and Hong Kong.

He abandoned the law for full-time writing when his first novel *Hold My Hand I'm Dying* became a bestseller in 1967. Since then he has written three more novels – *Cape of Storms*, *The Years of the Hungry Tiger* and *Taller than the Trees*, in addition to a non-fiction title about the campaign to save the black rhinoceros, *Operation Rhino*.

John Gordon Davis now lives in Spain.

John Gordon Davis

Leviathan

Pan Books London and Sydney

First published in Great Britain 1977 by Michael Joseph Ltd
This edition published 1977 by Pan Books Ltd,
Cavaye Place, London SW10 9PG
2nd printing 1978
© Westminster N.V. 1976
ISBN 0 330 25278 X
Printed and bound in Great Britain by
Richard Clay (The Chaucer Press) Ltd, Bungay, Suffolk

For Shirley-Anne Millard

One day, at the beginning of the long hot summer of the Southern Hemisphere, a tall American with dark hair and blue eyes and a very tanned face, which ordinarily would have been identified immediately at most airports of the world, passed through the D. F. Malan Airport, Cape Town, South Africa, without prompting recognition, thanks to a forged passport, sunglasses, and a moustache grown for the occasion. From the airport he took a taxi into Cape Town, to a hotel. That afternoon he went down to the docks.

He bought a visitor's pass for the passenger liner *Canarvon*, which was to sail in an hour, and joined the throng of well-wishers crowding up the gangways. Once aboard, he went up onto the lifeboat decks. They were almost deserted. Through his binoculars he studied a large black ship moored against the adjacent pier. This ship was surrounded by many smaller ships, all identical to each other. The big ship was called the *Slava* and she was the pelagic whaling factory ship of the Union of Soviet Socialist Republics. The small ships were her hunting vessels, called catchers. The *Slava* and her catchers were calling at Cape Town to refuel and provision before they set out on their long journey to the Antarctic to kill whales. In earlier years at this time, the docks of Cape Town were always full of the whalers of Europe, heading south – the English and the Dutch, the Norwegians, the Greeks, the Russians. Nowadays it was only the Russian *Slava* that sometimes called at Cape Town on the way to the Antarctic, because all the other European whaling nations had stopped their killing.

The young man studied the *Slava* for a long time through his binoculars, making mental notes. There, in the stern, was the slipway up which the whales were dragged. There were the long cutting decks, where they were butchered up with flensing knives, blood flying and flooding out of veins as big as a strong man's arm. He could see the big vat holes into which the great chunks of meat were dropped, down into the cooking vats in the vast factory deck below, to be stewed up for their oil. And there were the bone saws and winches for ripping up and tearing apart the massive skeletons.

The young man looked at the cutting deck of the *Slava* carefully; then he turned his binoculars up to the bow and began to study the ship, yard by yard, noting its features. Then he fitted his telephoto lens to his 35 mm camera. He took twenty photographs of the ship, inching his camera down her bulk.

Then he left the passenger ship. He walked along the piers towards the *Slava* and took another twenty photographs of her with his small pocket camera.

Later that afternoon the young man returned to D. F. Malan Airport. He produced a forged helicopter licence and rented a Bell JetRanger helicopter, without pilot. He took off and circled over Cape Town docks and took more photographs of the *Slava*.

The next day, when the *Slava* sailed for the Antarctic with her fleet, the young man was on the end of the pier. He took a large number of photographs from all angles as she sailed past him.

The next day he flew back to America to rejoin a ship called the *Jubilee*, which was owned by a company called Magnus Oceanics, Inc.

part one

one

The corpse of Captain Lars Magnus should have been very white after two years of dying in a hospital, but the undertaker had given him a Hollywood tan and had fluffed out the beard to conceal much of the thinness of the face. In death he bore a closer resemblance to the image portrayed in his publicity photographs, of the Grand Old Man of the Sea, than he had in the last ten years of his life. And that was how Maxwell Hagen, head of Magnus Communications, had been describing him for the last thirty minutes in the crowded white chapel of the Frank E. Campbell Funeral Home, Inc., Madison Avenue, New York.

He was saying into the microphone, 'He was . . . the Grand Old Man of the Sea.' He paused. 'He was . . .' he paused again for emphasis, 'as the president of the United States described him in a telegram I received two days ago . . . a great American institution. . . .' A reporter flicked over the page of his notebook, and Maxwell Hagen paused once more, then put his hand in his pocket and pulled out a piece of paper. 'In fact I have here that telegram from the chief executive of our land. . . .'

Justin Magnus, sitting in the front row, closed his eyes and thought, *Please, Max*. He kept his eyes closed as Max read the cable very deliberately, ringingly; then he felt ashamed for being embarrassed. Max's pride in the telegram was touching. Justin was proud too, even though he was sure that aides to the president of the United States of America sent off thousands of condolence telegrams a year. The Old Man had been to the White House only once, although he had a lot of friends on Capitol Hill, but Max loved to speak as if the Old Man was always in and out of the oval office on oceanographic policy matters.

'He served *brilliantly*!' Max said. 'A veritable lighthouse sweeping the darkness of the environmental crisis that is descending on our world. . . .' Justin Magnus closed his eyes again; Max went on. 'Indeed "brilliance" is the word to describe all his works. . . .' Max looked out over the heads of the people; there were some very bright people there, some senators, film producers, several publishers, all of whom knew brilliance when they saw it, and Justin flinched inwardly and prepared himself for Max's elaboration. 'He made brilliant nature movies. . . . He wrote brilliant books. . . . He served the cause of nature brilliantly! . . .' Max lifted his eyes over the heads of the people and lowered his voice. 'But for all his genius . . . he had great humility. . . .'

Justin felt the young woman next to him looking at him, and he turned his head slightly to her. Her expression said, *Be tolerant, Justin.* He nodded. He looked at his younger brother, on the other side of the woman. Craig Magnus's eyes were red from the crying he had done, and Justin knew that he was a little drunk. Craig too seemed uncomfortable at hearing his father eulogized as a humble man in front of hundreds of people who, whatever their other opinions of the Old Man and his brilliance, knew him as flamboyant and arrogant. Justin sat there braced for Max to rhapsodize on the Old Man's humility, when, to his relief, almost too abruptly, Max finished his long eulogy. He stepped down from the rostrum slowly, his eyes blurred with tears and his face suffused with emotion. He turned to the coffin and bowed to it. Then he turned and sat down next to Justin in the front pew. He glanced at him, and Justin felt his throat constrict.

Justin whispered, 'Well said, Max. Thank you.'

The organist beside the rostrum was suddenly churning into the last hymn, the navy hymn. The assemblage was getting to its feet.

Justin felt his chin tremble. He took a breath and tried to sing.

Eternal Father, strong to save,
Whose arm hath bound the restless wave. . . .

Along the front pews the eleven crewmen from the *Jubilee* joined the singing. The hymn swelled up through the white chapel, and suddenly the emotions swelled up through Justin's throat and his eyes burned and then the tears were running down his face. He stood there, breathing through his mouth, eyes closed, trying to control the tears, his chest quivering with effort. He felt Katherine Robinson put her little finger into his hand and suddenly, with this sympathy, the emotion overwhelmed him and the sob broke up through his throat. He did not look at Katherine Robinson; he squeezed her finger hard once then let go. As the hymn ended, at the signal, he stepped forward to the coffin. He went to the head of it, then slid the lid closed. The undertaker appeared beside him and began to clamp the lid down. Max and Craig and three other *Jubilee* crewmen stepped forward and gathered around the coffin to join Justin as pallbearers. The crewmen were very tanned, and they looked bulky and awkward in their suits. Craig took up his position opposite Justin at the head of the coffin. His eyes were bright with tears. The organ swelled again as they began to carry the coffin down the aisle to the hearse that was waiting outside in the warm busy sunshine of Eighty-first Street.

Fifteen minutes later it was all over. The last hand had been shaken, the last press photograph had been snapped, the hearse's engine was running.

Justin said to Max, 'Will you go with the Old Man to the crematorium to represent Oceanics? What time's your plane back?'

Max looked surprised. 'Eight o'clock. But I'll have to leave for the airport at six and there are some things I want to discuss with you first. Aren't *you* going to the crematorium?'

'No. Craig will go to represent the family and bring the ashes back. The undertaker says he'll get them through in four hours.'

'I think you should go, Justin.'

'Maybe I should, Max. But I don't feel up to it.'

'We can talk in the car on the way to the crematorium. I won't have another chance, I'll have to go straight from there to the airport.'

Justin said, 'I don't feel up to talking business either, Max. What is it? Tell me now and I'll write to you from Bermuda.'

Max looked at Justin impatiently. He said, 'Then I'll come with you now to the *Jubilee* to talk.'

'Come to the *Jubilee* with pleasure,' Justin replied, 'until the ashes get there. We'll have a drink. But, please, I don't want to talk business. What do you want to talk about?'

Max became angry.

'A number of things. Number one, Why have you ordered Katherine to go back to the *Jubilee*? I need her out there in the Los Angeles office. Just all of a sudden you order her back. Without consulting me.'

Justin took a breath.

'I loaned Katherine to you for six months to help you set up the L.A. office. She's my assistant, not yours. I need her now with the humpback whales. We need a woman in the water, and she's the natural one. She's a name and face the public knows.'

Max stood there. His face was set. Justin always made him angry these days, Justin always won any contest between them. He won not only because he was the executive vice-president of Magnus Oceanics, which owned Magnus Communications, he won naturally.

Max said, 'Can I have her back when you've finished shooting the humpback footage off Bermuda?'

'Sorry, Max,' Justin said. 'Then I need her in Baja California for the grey whales. I also need her for the book.' He added, to compliment him, 'Your L.A. office is working very well indeed now. If you need an assistant, hire one; you're still within your budget.'

Max's resentment turned into discomfort. 'I'm asking you a favour, Justin.'

Then Justin understood. He was surprised at himself for not understanding earlier. He thought, *Oh God no, please Max, not Katherine, what's wrong with all those starlets out there in Holly-*

wood? We've got enough troubles without you being screwed up about Katherine as well. He had no intention of changing his mind, but he said, 'What does Katherine say about this? Does she want to stay out on the Coast?'

Max said, embarrassed, 'I believe so.'

Believe so? I see. He felt sorry for Max, Max did not stand a chance with Katherine. She was far too bright for Max. And far too young. Max could show a girl a good time around town for a couple of months and make her laugh. He could be a charming guy, but he was not nearly intellectual enough for Katie. He was exactly the right man to run the Hollywood end of Magnus Oceanics and he used to be a great man in the water, but he was not deep enough, and Katie had real brains. Justin decided this was no time to allow Max to confess anything. Katherine was too valuable. She was vital.

He said, and this was the truth, 'Max, I'm sorry, I need her with the humpbacks. And after that with the grey whales in Baja California. That takes up until end of February next year. Six months. After that, she can resign from Magnus Oceanics if she wants to and go to work for you.'

Max Hagen glared at him a long moment.

'Jesus Christ. You're always playing God, aren't you? Ever since you took over Oceanics.' Justin felt his heart go out to Max. He opened his mouth to speak, and Max whispered, 'This is my life you're playing with, Magnus, not just my job!' Justin started to speak again and Max snapped, 'She can resign any time she likes! She's a free agent!'

Justin said evenly, 'No she can't, Max, her contract calls for six months' notice and I'll hold her to it.' He stared at Max apologetically and Jesus Christ he felt sorry for him. The man was getting old and he was in love, or he thought he was.

Max said, 'Or six months' salary in lieu of notice! I'll pay it myself!' He turned abruptly and strode through the crowd looking for Katherine.

She was standing with some of the *Jubilee* crew under the yellowing summer trees on Eighty-first Street. Justin Magnus wanted to bound after him and get to Katherine first and say,

'Don't accept anything until you've spoken to me. You've got to come back to the *Jubilee* until January, whatever your relationship is with him.' But Max was already striding up to her. She looked at him, surprised at his sudden purposeful appearance. She was as tall as he, long legs and high heels. Justin saw him take her elbow and walk her away from the others, talking urgently to her. She looked lovely in black; she was wearing a black lace scarf over her blonde hair. Max was walking her down the sidewalk, talking to her, holding her elbow.

Ross Evans appeared at Justin's side. 'Back to the ship?' he said. He followed Justin's stare. 'What's going on over there?'

'He wants her to go back to the Coast with him,' Justin said, watching them.

Ross said, 'Oh God. Is this love or something?'

Justin nodded. Ross stared after them, then asked worriedly, 'You haven't even had a chance to speak to her yet, have you?'

Justin shook his head, watching them. 'No.' He added, 'Katie won't go for him. Not Katie.'

'I hope to God you're right. He can be quite a charmer.'

'Magnus Oceanics owns Magnus Communications,' Justin said. 'Oceanics could forbid Communications to employ her.'

'If she's in love with him, that won't work.'

'She isn't,' Justin said. 'She's far too smart for Max. She runs rings round him and she knows it. I know Katie.'

Katherine had stopped. Now she and Max were facing each other, thirty yards down the sidewalk. She was talking. Justin felt his pulse trip in anxiety. Then he breathed out. She had started to put her hands around Max's neck and kiss him, then she had changed it to taking both his hands. Justin knew what was happening. He knew Katie. If Katherine was going to accept whatever serious matters Max was proposing she would have given it much more than that. She would have given her wide Katie smile and almost certainly kissed him. Even outside the Frank E. Campbell Funeral Home. Katherine did not do anything by half measures, unless she had changed a hell of a lot in the six months since they put her on the plane to go to help Max straighten out the new Los Angeles office. Now she was talking, earnestly, kindly, and Max was listening wooden-faced. Justin turned away from the little drama taking place down the street. He knew what she was saying and he knew what Max was feeling, and it was like eavesdropping to watch them any longer.

A minute later he looked back again. Katherine was walking back towards them, her head down. Max was walking fast in the opposite direction towards Fifth Avenue.

two

Justin Magnus shared a taxi back to the pier with Commander Henry Thorogood and L. C. Singleton. He had sent David Cartwright with Katherine to her hotel to get her suitcases, and now he wished that he had picked someone else, in case she had any trouble with Max there. Max was quite capable of making a bad scene in public, and Justin wanted her calm for the proposition he had to put to her. Cartwright had been a dumb choice to send in the circumstances. Cartwright was no coward in the water, but he was a nervous young man, no match against any bluster. And Max could bluster. Cartwright had really been the worst choice. But the taxi was already at Twenty-third Street on Ninth Avenue and Katie's hotel was way back and across town, and the press and some of the people who had attended the funeral were already on their way to the *Jubilee*. He said to L. C. Singleton, 'When we get to the *Jubilee* you'd better take the taxi back to the Waldorf and make sure Katie's all right.'

L. C. Singleton clamped his wide, froglike mouth aggressively. 'You're referring to that little scene with friend Max just now?'

'Yes. I don't want her upset if I'm putting the whole deal to her tonight. Cartwright wouldn't be much good with Max.'

'Right,' L. C. Singleton said. 'I'll handle him.'

'Don't create a scene, L.C.'

'No. Very tactful, don't worry. Though it would give me great pleasure.'

'Maybe I should go?' Commander Thorogood murmured. He pulled on his handsome square-cut beard.

'It'll be all right,' Justin said. He had to keep himself from saying, 'No, I want you to help handle the guests and the press,' because that would have hurt L.C. L.C. was a diabetic and he got drunk rather easily, and Justin knew he'd had a few already. There was a general policy of keeping an eye on L.C. when the *Jubilee* threw a formal party, trying to manoeuvre him away from the booze as much as possible. L.C. was the ship's cook. He also knew a good deal about marine biology now. He was pleased Justin had selected him to go to the hotel to deal with Max, and Justin knew it.

'Noticed that little scene myself,' Henry Thorogood said. 'Gave me some alarm. Couldn't understand it, a stunning girl like that with Max. But she seemed to be giving him the old heave-ho.'

'Max is all right,' Justin said.

'Oh, yes . . .' the commander shifted his stocky body, 'as long as he stays off my bloody ship he's fine.'

They drove on in silence. Justin smiled, despite his tension. He loved that British Royal Navy accent. He thought, *You're solid British oak, Henry. Thank God for you.* Sometimes in the night the thought of the commander gave Justin a bit of extra confidence. The man exuded no-nonsense Royal Navy efficiency and dash. Like that beard of his. 'My bloody ship.' Justin had found him through the advertising columns of *Yachting World*: 'Retired Royal Navy submariner seeks executive position. Little commercial experience but accustomed to handling men.' And he had hired him in twenty minutes. Commander Henry Thorogood had had his fill of trying to survive on his Royal Navy pension and on what he could make farming a smallholding in Connecticut left him by his sister. 'Damn things just wouldn't grow under me, old chap. Suppose I spent too much time under damn salt water.' The 'little commercial experience' had been acquired trying to sell life insurance around Connecticut, equally unsuccessfully. 'No damn good with that sales pitch, old chap. Take or leave it, I wanted to say, just look smart about it. Damn fine thing, life insurance, I suppose. Never could afford it in the navy. Very high premiums for us submariner types. Suppose they thought we'd drown prematurely or something.'

The taxi turned off towards the Tenth Street pier, and there lay the ship.

The *Jubilee* was a handsome vessel. She was a hundred and eighty feet long, bigger than the average minesweeper. Her gleaming engines could drive her at thirty knots. Old Man Lars Magnus had spared no expense on her. She had all the gear a multi-millionaire impressario of the deep would put on his floating home and film studio.

In the aft hold was cradled a twenty-seven-foot Otter Mark Z submarine. Forward of that was another hold housing a Bell Jet-Ranger helicopter. There was a shop with tools that could turn out any piece of machinery that the *Jubilee* could need, down to the tiniest part of a camera. There was a film-processing laboratory and darkroom, temperature-controlled for developing colour film, and an editing projection studio. In the radio room, behind the bridge, was the finest radio and radar equipment and a bank of eighteen closed-circuit television sets, along with a bar and a big swivel chair, which had enabled the Old Man to sit and drink and see at a glance almost everything that was happening in almost every part of the ship. When his film crews were working he had made them set up closed-circuit television cameras underwater too, so he could see what they were doing and direct them over the aqua-telephone. He had copied Jacques-Yves Cousteau's design of a watertight headpiece for his divers, which was uncomfortable to wear but looked good on film, and into each helmet was built a telephone receiver and transmitter. In the very bows of the *Jubilee*, below the waterline, was a small steel chamber with a glass porthole, where a cameraman could lie and film, and a closed-circuit television camera was mounted at this porthole too, so that from his seat at the bar in the radio room, or from his seat in his office, the Old Man could see underwater the whole time. In the Old Man's day, especially in his last few years, when he was too old to dive himself, it was said on the *Jubilee*, and particularly by Justin, that you couldn't go to the goddamn lavatory without the Old Man watching you on one of his television screens.

The wardroom was directly below the bridge, the big windows looking out onto the foredeck. The wardroom was oak-panelled, and the furniture heavy leather. Across one bulkhead was another bar, a big mahogany one that the Old Man had bought intact in an old New Orleans whorehouse. On the opposite bulkhead was another bank of television sets. The Old Man's steward had served as barman, but since Justin took command, everybody served himself and paid for his own drinks, at cost, and kept his own tally in the ledger. The pretty stewardesses also were gone. Everybody cleaned his own cabin and sections of alleyways and decks, and meals were served buffet-style.

Justin had made everybody learn everybody else's job as far as possible. Everybody, including Katherine, could take the wheel and steer the ship under any weather conditions; everybody could man the radio and radar, everybody knew deck seamanship, everybody had a first-aid certificate and could dive and handle underwater cameras efficiently if necessary. Five of them could fly the helicopter in need; four of them could command the submarine.

In the three years Justin had been running the company he had made sizeable and very necessary economies. He had cut the shipboard administrative and editorial staff from four to three: Katherine Robinson, who handled Magnus Books and much of the film editing; Ross Evans, Justin's best friend since college, who wrote most of the papers for the scientific journals and supervised research; and Justin himself. The marine staff had been cut by nearly forty per cent, saving the company a hundred thousand dollars a year. And Justin had made much better Magnus films than his father had made and written better Magnus books. He had set up Magnus Communications in Hollywood to handle the film distribution – and to provide a face-saving way to get Max Hagen off the *Jubilee*. In three years, Justin had rescued Magnus Oceanics from the debt the Old Man had got it into in the last five years of his life and had made considerable money. And now that Justin was the majority stockholder of the company, he knew how he was going to spend that money and use his power, and he was glad with all his heart.

Most of the crew were in the wardroom, soberly drinking a bottle of Scotch with people who had come down to the pier from the funeral chapel. Katherine, Cartwright, and L.C. were not back aboard yet, and Craig Magnus had not yet returned from the crematorium with his father's ashes. Justin had stayed in the wardroom long enough to be polite, then had beckoned to Ross Evans, Steve Gregorowsky, and the commander to follow him. He led them to his suite, got out a bottle of Scotch, and poured big shots into four glasses. They each took a glass. Justin picked up his glass and turned to Steve.

'Well, Steve,' he said quietly, 'we leave for Japan tonight. You, Craig, and I.'

Steve Gregorowsky swallowed his mouthful of whisky and stared at him, his tough blue eyes surprised. Justin could not help smiling; it seemed the first time he had ever surprised Steve.

'Tonight? I thought you were leaving the Japs until we'd finished in Bermuda.'

Justin nodded. 'It's a golden opportunity. Both Japanese factory ships have just gone into Yokohama harbour to be refitted for the Antarctic. They're empty, everybody paid off for three weeks, the chances of hurting anybody are nearly zero. Meanwhile everybody knows we're here in New York. That we're sailing for Bermuda tonight. The Old Man's funeral and all – it'll be in the papers tomorrow. So tonight we sail for Bermuda, just as everybody expects us to. It's a perfect alibi. As soon as we're outside the harbour, Ross flies you, Craig, and me back to Connecticut by helicopter, puts us down on the commander's farm. Nobody knows we've come back. We drive to Boston airport. From Boston we fly to Mexico City. On the forged passports, of course. From Mexico we fly to Tokyo. We'll be there at noon tomorrow, Tokyo time.'

'Meanwhile,' Ross said, 'everybody thinks we're on the *Jubilee* steaming for Bermuda.'

'I see,' Steve said.

'It's perfect,' Justin said.

'It's the perfect time for it,' the commander said in his old British accent.

Justin was tired and taut. The last forty-eight hours were catching up with him. It helped to hear the old commander agree with him. He was the only professional saboteur among them. At nineteen during World War II the commander had been a rating in the Royal Navy's X-craft submarines, sneaking into German harbours and blowing up German battleships. At forty-nine he had retired as skipper of a nuclear submarine shadowing Russian nuclear subs that were shadowing NATO fleets.

Steve Gregorowsky spoke, his voice surprisingly soft for such a strong-looking, battle-scarred man. 'How do we get back to the *Jubilee*?'

'Same way,' Justin said. 'Right after we've done the job on the Japanese, we fly out on three different airlines. I've got the schedules and tickets here.' He indicated his desk. 'Craig goes by way of Vancouver. You go via Seattle. I go via Mexico City. We converge on Boston. Go out to the commander's farm. Fly the helicopter back out to the *Jubilee*. Which is now happily filming the humpbacks off Bermuda.' He looked at them. 'It's as good an alibi as we can possibly get.'

Ross's face was beaming. He sat up in his chair. 'It's all happening at last.'

'And the explosives?' Steve asked.

'They'll be there waiting for us. I've arranged it very securely. I'll pick them up. Alone. What you don't know can't hurt you.' He added, 'The same with the others. The rest won't know till we get back; even then we probably won't tell them. It's not that I don't trust them. It's just that they can't be accomplices to a crime they didn't know was being committed.' He turned and walked with his whisky to the porthole and looked out over the Hudson River. 'It's an elaborate alibi,' he went on, 'but it's worth the trouble. I want to give us every bit of cover we can get. If one of us gets caught because we failed to take a precaution, then all twelve of us, the whole of Magnus Oceanics, goes down.' He faced them and waved his hand. 'Sure, we could fly from Bermuda to Mexico City, using our own passports, then fly to Tokyo on the forged ones. Or fly tonight from New York to

Mexico City. But there's a good chance we would be recognized – certainly at Bermuda. And our alibi is weakened. It would be provable that we were not on the *Jubilee*. I don't want there to be *any* facts against us, none at *all*.'

'I agree,' the commander said. 'It's worth the trouble.'

'Sure,' Steve said. 'I'm not worried about going tonight.'

Ross slumped back, grinning. He had a prematurely balding head, studious eyes and eyebrows, and rosy cheeks. Ross was general manager of Magnus Oceanics. Justin smiled back at him. God, Ross was a good man. If Ross had his way the *Jubilee* would sail into Yokohama harbour with blazing cannons on its bows. And Steve. Sure Steve wasn't worried. Nothing worried the unflappable Canadian. His body had many scars, he gave the impression of indestructibility. Justin thought, *Craig won't be worried either, the only thing that will worry Craig is that he won't be staying in Yokohama long enough to get thoroughly laid, but he'll probably manage to squeeze one in.*

'Listen, Justin,' Ross said, 'there's one thing that bothers me.'

'Yes?'

Ross got up out of his armchair and paced across the cabin. 'I know you've vetoed this before, but I urge you to rethink it. Listen. I don't think that both you and Craig should go.'

Justin started to answer and Ross interrupted him. 'Hear me out. Listen. If something happens to both of you – God forbid, but if you're caught and put in a Japanese penitentiary for Christ knows how long they jail saboteurs – well, there's nobody to carry on Magnus Oceanics. And *then*,' he raised his finger, 'not only does Magnus Oceanics go under – because what'll happen to your shares? Who'll head the company? What about all our contracts for new movies? And books? Well, not only does all that happen, but also the Antarctic plan falls through. *And* all our other plans. *All* our work goes to hell.'

Again Justin began to answer, but Ross soldiered on. 'I haven't finished yet. I feel this is terribly important. To Oceanics.' He nodded. 'Oceanics' prosperity depends mostly on you. Now . . .' he held out his finger, 'I know you feel you've got to do this Japanese job because it's your idea, and therefore your responsibility – an officer leads his men and all that crap.

Well . . .' he shook his head just like the schoolmaster he used to be, 'it's not so. We're all in it now, right up to our necks, pal. We're all totally committed. If something goes wrong on the Japanese job, and you personally are caught, everything collapses. And it's no good, either, if you're caught and Craig comes back.' He shook his head. 'With all due respect to him, Craig cannot take over Oceanics, let alone the Antarctic plan, he's just too irresponsible.'

Justin said, 'He's not irresponsible, champion. He's just young and high-spirited.'

'Okay.' Ross held up his hand in a display of acquiescence. 'Young and high-spirited. Believe me, I think he's a great kid, he's a great diver and all that. But, Justin . . .' he looked at him with his earnest brown eyes, 'that kid cannot run this company. Now or ever. He's more of a goddamn playboy than the Old Man and you put together.'

Justin smiled faintly and said, '*De mortuis nil nisi bonum*, champ.'

Ross sighed. 'I'm sorry. Look, what I'm saying is send Craig to do the Japanese job. Fine. Let him make his bones, as the Mafia says. Do him good. Under Steve's leadership. They'll pull it off. What I'm saying is . . .' he stabbed with his finger, '*you* shouldn't go. Because you're the brains *and* the financial muscle. You control Oceanics. Christ,' he said, 'can you imagine any bank lending us money with Justin Magnus in a Japanese prison for ninety-nine years?'

'Oceanics doesn't need any money,' Justin said. 'But who do I send instead of myself?'

'Me,' he said. 'Listen. Send me. Seriously. It makes sense. I'm the helicopter pilot anyway. I can be in Yokohama and *you* can *really* be filming the humpbacks off Bermuda just like your alibi says.' Justin and the commander were both grinning. 'Seriously,' Ross said. 'Seriously.'

'And besides,' the commander said, 'you've never been to Yokohama.'

'Right!' Ross flashed a smile that broke up his incongruously businesslike face, and it made them all laugh. Then he said, 'My argument's valid.'

22

'You're the only married man,' Justin said. 'How would Mary feel about your going?'

'Mary and I have it all worked out,' Ross replied. 'She believes in this thing as much as I do.'

Justin walked to the desk and filled his whisky glass. He filled all the glasses. Suddenly he was very tired. Dear old Ross. Unathletic, chubby-cheeked Ross, who did well at everything by working at it twice as hard as anybody else. Ross had won a place on the Stanford University swimming team despite the fact that his kick was weak, by overdeveloping his arm stroke. Played varsity football by turning himself into a suicidal tackler. Got a regular Bachelor of Science degree in marine biology by working twelve hours a day whereas his roommate, Justin, got his cum laude working half the time. Ross had courted and won the most popular girl in their group, by dint of sheer determination. Down there in the water Ross was an excellent cameraman even though he still could not kick his feet properly and even though Justin knew he was very afraid of sharks, much more than a professional diver had the right to be. Justin smiled at him wearily. What Ross had omitted to say was that he could not bear to be left out of the glorious action.

'All right, champion.' Ross's face went grim with triumph. Justin continued, 'Craig doesn't go. You and I and Steve go. Craig,' he added, 'stays as insurance. In case something goes wrong.'

'I still think you're making a mistake,' Ross said. '*You* shouldn't go. What'll happen to the Antarctic operation if you get into trouble?'

'I've got to go. And that's that.'

Nobody said anything. Justin knew the commander would agree with him. It would not matter to Steve. Steve would feel he could do the job himself anyway.

'You haven't spoken to Katherine yet?' Ross asked, after a moment.

'As soon as Cartwright brings her aboard.' He added, 'She's vital. We'll have a hell of a job without her.'

Ross said, 'Your Russian's good enough for us to get by.'

'Like hell it is.' Justin shook his head. 'I wish it were, but it just isn't. I had one year of it, ten years ago. And got a C.' He stood there pensively, then nodded at the carpet. 'Sure, we could get by, I guess. But that's not the point. The point is this Antarctic operation has *got* to go like clockwork! Too goddamn much is at stake.'

three

Katherine Robinson had liked the name *Justin*, and the name *Magnus*, but put together she had thought the result a bit too much. Almost too dashing. And the numerous photographs of him she had seen before she met him did little to change the impression: there he always was, suntanned, lean, blue-eyed, and ruggedly clean-cut, always doing something clever or dangerous in the sea. And the curt business letters he wrote her, and the flamboyant, fulminating style of the nature books he wrote, and which she had to edit, made her think him arrogant. As his editor at Random House, since his father became ill and Justin began writing the books, Katherine Robinson felt she knew a great deal about Justin Magnus long before she met him, and what she knew she did not like much. The feeling had been mutual. Miss Smartass Robinson sitting in her ivory tower at Random House writing him endless letters telling him how to rewrite his books, which drove him crazy, and firing off deadlines by cable, which drove him crazier, was costing Magnus Oceanics a fortune. Her high-flying ideas of editorial perfection were keeping Justin Magnus out of the water.

They were both prepared to dislike each other intensely the day he strode through Random House's plush editorial halls and presented himself unannounced at her office and proceeded to have a conversation with her that very soon went something like this:

'If you're so smart why don't *you* write goddamn books instead of tearing other people's apart?'

And she replied, 'I can't write books, Mr Magnus, or I would. I'm only good at making good books better.'

'Were my father's books good?'

'Not *good*.'

'I beg your pardon?'

'They were only commercially successful.'

'There's a difference?'

'There's a big difference.'

'Okay there's a difference. I'm not a Philistine, although you think so. But did they tell the world about the wonders of the sea?'

'They did, in their way. I don't think you're a Philistine, I think the opposite. I only think you're rude.'

'You make me feel very rude indeed, Miss Robinson. Your letters make me climb the wall. Are my books commercially successful?'

'They are.'

'Do they make people aware of the need for conservation?'

'They do.'

'Better than my father's?'

'They are more beautiful.'

'Because you're my editor?'

'Not only because I'm your editor. I was your father's editor, too. You have more talent.'

'Are they more commercially successful?'

'As commercially successful.'

'Then *that*,' he said, 'is good enough for Magnus Oceanics, Miss Robinson. Oceanics can't afford me investing more of my time in the books. If my books get their message across, that's good enough for Oceanics. And that's good enough for Random House.'

'But not good enough for me, Mr Magnus.' She waited a moment, then said in a warmer tone, 'Your books are capable of becoming masterpieces. You have the vision; your father never had it. I'm not going to let that talent go undeveloped by letting you publish second-rate books.'

'Second *rate*?' Justin was furious. 'Aren't you a little young for your job?'

'Random House doesn't think so. Neither do a number of other publishers.'

'How old are you?'

'Mind your own business!'

'It is my business, if you're telling me what to do. How much do they pay you here?'

'Mind your own business!'

'It is my business.'

'It *is* your business?'

He glared at her. 'Maybe I'll give you a job. Write the damn books for me. These Magnus contracts are driving me crazy.'

'You'll give me a job, will you?'

Nevertheless she felt obliged to take him to lunch, as publishers do to their more important writers, to try to mollify him and iron out their differences and make him see her view. The Magnus series of books on ocean life were not particularly good, but they were quite important to Random House. The photographs in them were extraordinary and their educational value for the layman was considerable, and they had a large following. The books got a great deal of free publicity from the television series on ocean life that was Magnus Oceanics' principal product and that had made the names of Lars Magnus and his sons and the ship *Jubilee* household words. The publishers made a great deal of money very easily out of the Magnus books. Katherine Robinson had always liked them, not because of their literary quality but because of the wonderful creatures and places they told about; they stirred her romantic soul. Furthermore, she was an ardent conservationist; she applauded the effort the books made to awaken the public. In addition, Justin Magnus did in fact have a talent for writing. She nursed an editor's ambition of turning him into a great writer and his books into classics.

At lunch that day, at a flossy French restaurant called Le Madrigal, much patronized by publishing people with large expense accounts, she tried to explain all this to him. That evening he took her to dinner at a steakhouse, to continue their editorial discussions but really because she was a very pretty and charming young woman and very good company. He was getting to like Miss Smartass Robinson. They spent the next day in her office going through his manuscript, and they sent out for sandwiches for lunch, which they ate while they worked. That night he took her to dinner again. The next day he spent alone in his hotel studying her editorial work and trying to follow her advice in rewriting passages. He found it very difficult. The day after that he showed her what he had done, but she was still not satisfied, and he was about ready to quit.

Justin Magnus did not particularly want to be a writer at all. He wanted to make films about the sea and its life. He was an environmentalist, a friend of the earth, and if anything would further that cause he would do it, including the sweat of carrying on his father's tradition of producing Magnus Books. He had considered those books badly written, over-romanticized, over-commercialized accounts of the Old Man's adventures, only superficially educational and fainthearted on the subject of conservation. He had quarrelled bitterly with the Old Man over this, as he had over many of his father's films. He agreed that Magnus Books badly needed improving, but he had not bargained for this new editor and her extravagant ambitions. That day decided him. He simply did not have the time to trudge on alone with the books and all the other work. He needed to get back to his ship and get back in the water and get the company back out of debt. The next day he took Katherine Robinson to lunch again, but they did not speak of his manuscript. He tried to persuade her to accept a job aboard the *Jubilee* as editorial and managerial assistant.

Altogether it took him six months to talk her into it. Katherine Robinson had won her position at Random House the usual hard way, after years of being secretary and then assistant to full-fledged editors, and it had been a long time before she was allowed to handle a book on her own. Her title and position were precious to her, and she was not about to throw all that away lightly. But two attractive people of opposite sexes working together successfully can quickly develop a very close relationship, one of mutual reliance and an intimacy that is almost sexual in quality and extremely fulfilling. Between editor and author, this can be particularly intense. Between Justin Magnus and Katherine Robinson there developed a professional affinity so keen that they could easily have gone one step further and fallen in love with each other. But the relationship was too good and important to both of them to risk it by doing so.

It took six months and two more trips to New York, and many long working lunches and editorial letters and radio-telephone calls to talk her into it. Which was one of the smartest things Justin had ever done. Katherine was also a good swimmer and looked lovely on film. The graceful body of Katherine Robinson gliding through the underwater wonderworld with her blonde hair streaming silkily behind her, swimming through spectacular coral reefs, riding giant turtles, diving with dolphins, had become a very important feature of Magnus films. She also had very good business and administrative judgement. She was as natural an editor of films as she was of manuscripts. And she helped Justin turn his books into the works they should be, partly by taking much of the administrative workload off him and partly by editorial inspiration and discipline.

Justin Magnus was a most undisciplined writer. He had the gift of the gab and most of his books he did not write at all but dictated into a portable tape recorder, striding up and down his office aboard the *Jubilee* or on the decks, or sitting alone on a beach, bestowing upon the recorder his impressions of the ocean, his words soaring up on the wings of the sea gull or booming and crashing with the great surf on the rocks in the storms. Justin did not just try to educate the world, he thundered at it. Katherine Robinson disciplined him, her hand thrust sometimes despairingly into her hair, her red pencil sweeping, and by arguing and fighting with him, making him condense his vision without narrowing it, making him carry the reader along instead of grabbing him by the scruff of the neck. The words were all there. The hard part was persuading Justin Magnus to accept her cuts and make him do the rewriting. 'But they must *understand*! They must *see* and *understand* the terrible peril that nature is in.'

'They will see better if you hone it down! Your argument's great, as trimmed. It's irresistible, it brings tears to the eyes and a cry from the breast. . . .'

28

'I want them to wail and gnash their teeth and beat their breasts.'

'You overdo it, you'll turn them off! Like a preacher who rants too much. You also lose them with too much technical information sometimes.'

'They've got to be *educated*.'

'But not up to marine biologist standard! Let's put all that technical stuff into the appendix at the back, for the real marine biologists to read if they want to. And all those statistics. You want to reach the general public, make the average person aware. The same applies to your biblical arguments.'

'All that Bible stuff stays!'

'Sure it does! It's great. But then you go on too long. You've got to be a theologian to follow some of that stuff here. I don't know where you get it all from, especially since you don't believe in God.'

'Maybe the God I don't believe in wants it written in like that. The God I don't believe in is very smart and He doesn't mind if I overdo Him. He doesn't mind what I do as long as I get the message across. That biblical stuff is good strong stuff and it *stays*.'

Their meeting at the funeral chapel had been brief, and confused with emotions and people. As he opened his office door now to her wide Katie smile, he realized his sheer pleasure at having her back aboard, a friend returned. 'Hello!' He kissed her on the cheek and grinned. 'Come on in, Katie.' He closed the door behind her. 'How does it feel to be back?'

'Oh,' she said, 'I'm so happy! . . . I'm sorry it had to be under such sad circumstances.'

'Didn't you have a good time out there?'

'Oh, a great time! But Hollywood isn't the scene for me. This is where I belong.'

He nodded, smiling. 'Have a chair.' He went to the liquor cabinet and poured her a vodka and snapped the cap off a tonic. 'You look beautiful.'

Katherine did, although she was not, not really, beautiful. She was tall and full-bodied and blond and summery. Her face was perhaps too round and her mouth perhaps too wide to be beautiful. And then when she smiled she was ravishing, and her big blue eyes sparkled deep. Her eyelashes were extravagantly long. He handed the vodka and tonic to her. She held her glass up. 'To the Old Man.'

'The Old Man.'

He wanted to bend down and kiss her on the cheek again but didn't. He turned to the other armchair and sank down into it with his whisky. They looked at each other.

'Tell me about the whale film.'

'It's going to be the best we've ever made,' he said. 'We got miles of beautiful footage. And we've recorded wonderful sounds all through the Caribbean.' He inclined his head east and smiled at her. 'They're all waiting for you off Bermuda now, Katie – the humpback whales. All beautiful and friendly, calves and all. I want you in the water with them, like you were in *Dolphin*. All gorgeous in your bikini. Hanging onto their tails.'

'I can't wait.'

'You'll be terrific.' He knew her – he knew she could hardly wait. She was very like him. Katherine Robinson, daughter of a Boston Brahmin, former book editor, animal-lover, very good on film. He looked at her sitting opposite him, long legs crossed elegantly. Even the plain black cotton dress she had bought somewhere this morning for the funeral became her. She knew how to dress. Everything just naturally, instinctively, easily, to the greatest advantage. She always wore high heels, to make herself even taller. She took very good care of herself. Her body always looked thoroughly healthy. Well groomed, well nourished, well exercised, well sunned, with serenity and poise from well-being. God, it was good to have her back. But for all her appeal, for all the long stretches at sea, her presence had never caused any trouble in Magnus Oceanics, because she made sure of it. In particular she made sure of her good professional relationship with Justin Magnus, with whom she worked very well. Whom she admired, as a very talented and sexy man, with the softest heart. Whom she regarded as a notorious playboy and womanizer and whom she would not touch with a ten-foot pole. He started to say, 'Tell me about Los Angeles and Max,' and he changed it in his mouth. 'Tell me about the whale book, Katie.'

She leaned forward, her elbow on her knee. 'It's great, Justin. . . . And isn't it great to be back, talking shop?'

'Yes.' And it was.

She sat back in her armchair again and lit a cigarette and puffed hard. 'It's really a very good book. I finished my first edit the day before we left L.A. It's in my suitcase. Shall I get it?'

'No. Just tell me.'

'It's going to be superb. When it's properly edited. It's the best thing you've ever done.' She stretched out and looked up at the overhead. 'Your enormous feeling for whales. . . . The desperate plight they're in, the outrageous tragedy of it, the whole ecological crisis . . . and your whole Will-of-God thing.' She glanced at him, then went on. 'It's great. The sense of wonder about these marvellous, massive animals. It's almost brilliant. I mean that. It's tremendously powerful and compelling. A real page-turner. It arouses the most tremendous sense of moral outrage against what man has done in the last fifty years. The brutal butchery, the savage cruelty, the agony of it all. Oh God, Justin, it's horrific and marvellous.' She raised her hand and dropped it on her knee. 'It made me so furious at the Russians and the Japanese. And at the International Whaling Commission! You're going to have the whole world up in arms about whales with that book.'

He was delighted, though he knew from experience what was coming next.

'But?'

Her finger shot upward like a schoolmarm's. '*Aha!* But! But I've got to edit it like hell.'

He took a swallow of his whisky and sighed. 'Oh Christ.'

'You've done your usual thing of charging off on tangents all over the place with these mighty floods of words and facts that overwhelm the reader and give him vertigo and mental indigestion. But we can strip it down and polish it up – and it's going to be a classic.' She pointed towards her cabin. 'Read it again, with my edits. Keep an open mind. You're not going to like everything I've done to your book.'

'I'm not going to like any of it.'

'Trust my objective judgement. As your fervent advocate.'

He looked at her over his glass. She was. In the final result he did not doubt, or at least would not doubt when the time came. She made his books right. She had never let Magnus Oceanics down.

'If you're so smart,' he asked, 'how come you don't work for Random House?'

She sat back and smiled at him. 'It's going to be fine. Now tell me about the good ship *Jubilee*. How is everybody? What hair-raising escapades have you and he-man Steve and wild young Craig been having in my absence?'

'None,' he said. 'It's all been plain sailing. Just lovely gentle whales. No sharks.'

'Not a single shark?'

'Oh, they've been around. But we didn't take time out to film them. Chased them off the set. It's been very peaceful.'

'Thank God for that,' she said. 'Who's this new kid, Peter Webb? How's he turning out?'

Justin got up out of his chair and went over to the bar. He wanted to get on with it now, put the whole proposition to her, but he had to clear up another subject first.

'Spider Webb,' he said. 'He's great. He's exactly the sort of guy I need. Nature boy. Sharp as tacks. Tough as nails. Fearless. Spider loves every minute of it.'

'He looks very young,' she said. 'And tough.'

He was pouring a small shot of whisky into his glass.

'He's twenty-two, I think. But he's done a whole heap of living.' Justin walked back across the cabin to the desk and sat down on the corner of it. 'He's wandered all over South America, the Amazon, trekking through the jungle. He fancies himself as a survival expert, and I bet he is.'

'What's a survival expert do for a living?'

'Does just about everything. Snake-handler at a zoo and looking after the animals in a circus. He worked in the oceanium in Los Angeles training the dolphins for a while. That's how he ended up writing to me for a job. He *is* a survival expert, I think. He's one of these guys who really wants to have the ability to live in nature with just his bare hands. He's the only guy I know who can actually make fire, *every time*, in a few minutes, by rubbing two sticks together. He's showed us. And make good strong rope out of twisted tree bark. And he knows all the edible berries and leaves and roots and insects of the jungle as far as I can see, and he knows how and where to dig for water, and things like that. And he's an expert knife-thrower – sticks every time, and accurate. And bows and arrows and things. He's an expert with a lasso – he's shown us that, too. And he can make a boomerang that actually does come back. He's a fascinating kid. He's also a bit of a karate expert.'

She appeared suitably impressed. 'He fits in here okay?'

'Round peg in a round hole. Very quiet, though. But he loves it. He's very good in the water. Wants to know everything; he'll turn into a good little researcher if he reads a bit. He'll go up to anything in the water. Go anywhere. The darker the better.'

She laughed. 'Sounds like he-man Steve. And a few other idiots I know.'

'They usually work together in the water. Spider and Steve. They paired off naturally. Steve is Spider's hero. They're two of a kind.'

'Well, I hope you don't let him pick up Steve's bad habits. *Or* yours. That recklessness. I'm serious, Justin. You guys will get in trouble one of these days.'

'I'm not reckless.'

'Well, I think so. I suppose you're not too bad, but Steve? That guy gives me the creeps sometimes.'

'I thought you thought he was sexy.'

'He's not my type, but he *is* good-looking, in a spine-chilling sort of way.' She shook her head seriously. 'I mean that – spine-chilling. He's got this atmosphere about him. Those scars. Almost coldblooded. Almost as if he's got a death wish. I shudder to think of anybody working with him down there.'

Justin said, 'Steve hasn't got a death wish. He's just cocky. About danger.'

'No. You're cocky. Craig's cocky. But Steve? He's got something different. He looks for trouble, so he can get into it. Expose himself to it. Ross thinks so too; he's told me. Ross thinks

Steve's got a death wish, and Ross is pretty sane. Like with that hammerhead shark? And he just stood back politely outside the cage door as if he was outside the Ritz Hotel to let you go into the cage first? Even you said that was madness. It *was* madness. I saw it with my own eyes on the film, it was horrifying. The man's whole demeanour said to that shark, "Come on and kill me if you want." '

'No. Steve's got this psychic thing, he believes he can *will* things to happen, overpower an animal with his superior willpower. And maybe he can. He says he did it often in Africa and I half believe it.'

She said, 'Well, he's not indestructible. And I hate to think of anybody inexperienced working with him. I even hate to think of somebody as experienced as you working with him down there.'

Justin got up off the corner of the desk. 'Steve's fine.' He wanted to get back to the point, he did not have much more time. He said abruptly, 'Whales are not going to become extinct, Katie.' He turned and looked at her. She was surprised at his change of subject and tone. 'Not if I can help it, and I can. But I can really only do it with your help.' She began to say, 'My help?' and he took another breath and went on. 'But first tell me about Max.'

She was more surprised.

'About *Max*?'

He said, 'I'm sorry to have to inquire into your private life, Katie, but it may be important. Tell me about your relationship with Max.' He added, trying to make a little light of it, 'In a couple of sentences. Maybe a paragraph.'

She frowned. 'All right. You're thinking of that little incident outside the funeral parlour?'

He nodded.

'Okay. I had a great time in Los Angeles. Max was very sweet to me. He took me everywhere. Dining and dancing and sightseeing.' She added with a wisp of a smile, 'We also got the office straightened out, in the daytime. He's doing very well out there. And I also did find time to edit your book.'

'Go on.'

She raised one eyebrow. 'You mean, did we have a romantic affair?'

'Yes.' He was amazed that he felt a blow of jealousy. A *romantic* affair? As opposed to a purely sexual affair? Justin Magnus, no stranger to purely sexual affairs, was shocked and jealous that his beautiful personal assistant should have a purely sexual affair, and with Max Hagen of all people.

She said a little archly, 'I'm assuming you have a good reason for your questions, Justin. The answer is no.' He felt a twinge of relief; she added, 'or, not really.' She lit a cigarette and looked a him steadily. 'I mean that Max rather fell in love with me – or whatever you'd call it. But I did not do the same. I thought he was sweet, and fun; we had a lot of fun. He's still a very attractive male. He drinks too much, but he holds it. He's not the brightest guy in the world, but he can be very entertaining over a short period. But a permanent relationship with Max? . . . If the purpose of your question is to find out whether I'm going to quit the *Jubilee* and live in Los Angeles, the answer is no.'

'Does Max know how you feel?'

She sighed. 'Yes, I explained it to him some time ago. And several times since. And yesterday, when we got your cable for me to come back permanently, he was very uptight. And again today. He knows, the trouble is that he doesn't accept. He thinks I'll change my mind.' Her eyebrow went up again. 'I made a mistake, under the circumstances. I did sleep with him.' She added, 'Once.'

He was stabbed with jealousy. God, it could break his heart to think of it, beautiful Katherine Robinson, whom he had scrupulously kept his hands off, in bed with somebody else – with Max. He said, 'You don't have to excuse yourself to me, Katie.'

'I know I don't. I'm simply accounting for a small personnel problem you have. I'm sorry about it, because it's all so . . . unnecessary. I should have kept my cool. Now . . . tell me why the questions.'

'Tell me why I have a personnel problem.'

'*May* have,' she corrected. 'You know how Max feels about you. He can't stand you. No, not entirely true. But he's jealous as hell of your running the company, he feels the Old Man should have given the job to him.' She smiled. 'He thinks you're an upstart. You've thrown your weight around too much, your cuts in staff and budgets. And that you're getting too fancy with the type of film you insist on making. That's an extravagance, he says, the Old Man's type were good enough. The fact that you've got the company out of debt doesn't make it any easier for him. He says anybody could have done that. Especially him. Better. And', she said, 'he hates it that you got rid of him by shunting him out to Los Angeles.'

'We gave him his own company to run, for Chrissake. And he's doing well out there.'

'Sure he is. And Hollywood's his scene. He loves playing the big distributor. And he's good at it, he's charming, he's fun. Everybody likes him out there. And, of course,' she smiled, 'he has all those desperate little actresses who'll do anything to get noticed by big wheels like Max. And, my God, the sheer raw beauty of them! A girl like me doesn't stand a chance.'

'A girl like you, huh?'

'I'm serious. They're absolutely beautiful. And they're *every*-where. However. . . . And now, I'm afraid, Max has got a new hang-up about you: he's convinced that I'm in love with you. Or that we're having an affair. Or have had. Or going to. Or something. He thinks that's why I was so happy to come back. Et cetera.'

'He said all that?'

'Did he ever. He's as jealous as hell of you. Look. I like Max one hell of a lot. And he thought the world of the Old Man. But he's full of pride. He's got a grudge against you because you took over the company, because you overruled him so many times, because you got rid of him. And he's pushing fifty, and he's terribly conscious of his age and losing his looks, and so forth. He isn't really in love with me. He's been a happy-go-lucky bachelor all his life, the big outdoors man, he's as vain and self-centred as hell. Suddenly he feels he's getting old. The boss's son takes over and puts him out to pasture. Along comes a sweet young thing like me and I'm the first girl who doesn't tear off her pants for him and probably the first one he's had who's got any sense. And,' she said, shrugging, 'eventually I make a silly mistake one night. And from then on he was very possessive and thought he was head over heels in love. If another man paid any attention to me he got very uptight.'

Justin exhaled. 'How did you handle it?' He added, 'I'm sorry, Katie.'

'You might as well hear the whole godawful story; you've heard this much. I had to make my feelings clear to him, it wasn't fair to him to be kind. In brief, I said I thought he was great but I wanted a platonic relationship with him, et cetera. He took it very well, actually. But he said he was dead serious, and that he would wait. Meanwhile, we'd just continue to be friends. . . . This was about a month ago.'

'And how did that work out?'

'Not well at all. He got more possessive. And moody. He started talking about marriage.'

'Marriage? *Max?*'

'He doesn't really mean it. Trouble is, he thinks he means it. Anyway, it got very tricky. Especially around the office. Everybody must have known. And especially at nights, going everywhere, and me trying to keep my distance.' She stopped and then said after a moment, 'He wouldn't take no for an answer. I began to plead a few headaches. Actually it *was* giving me a few headaches. Then he began to phone me in the middle of the night to see if I was out with somebody else. One of those situations.'

'Oh.'

'Then he started in about you. Then your cable came. Then he *really* got bad. About you. He said all sorts of things. Including calling me a whore.'

'Good God.'

'He'd got a bit drunk. Afterwards he said he was sorry. He was also upset about the Old Man's death.'

'Max is old enough to take a setback without making a fool of himself, particularly around the office.'

'He quieted down. But he's very upset. I don't know, maybe it's just his pride. And because of you. Here you are ordering his life around again. It's just that he hasn't really grown up. Or something.'

Justin snorted. 'What did he say today?'

'He asked me to come back. I tried to be nice about it. Then he said he was going to fly out to Baja California in December while we're filming the grey whales.'

Justin studied his cigarette. 'That's what I'm afraid of.'

'Why? And why all these questions?'

He sat up and leaned towards her.

'Because Max is the only guy in this company I don't trust. I've got rid of all the others. He's screwed up about me and he's bitter. And now he's screwed up about you as well. And about you and me. And Max is the kind of guy who bears grudges, as you say. He's a goddamn Scorpio and they're great ones for grudges. Max won't miss an opportunity to bring me down.' He paused. 'That's why I asked the questions.'

She looked puzzled. 'How can he bring you down?'

'Because we won't *be* in Baja California, Katie. And that's why I don't want him to come flying out there in December to see you. Baja California is just our alibi. We're going to be in the Antarctic.'

'The *Antarctic*?'

'We're going down to the Antarctic. To sink that fucking Russian whaling factory ship.'

She stared at him, absolutely astonished.

'And that's where you come in, Katie. Because you speak Russian. I tried to find someone else who could speak Russian and I thought I found one, but in the end I didn't feel I trusted him. We need you, Katie.'

She was still staring at him, incredulous. Then her mouth slowly opened and she whispered, 'God! So you're really going to do it!'

He stood up. She sat in the armchair.

He said quietly, 'Now listen to me please, Katie. Without interruption until I've finished. I'll answer all your questions later. In a short time Craig will be back with the Old Man's ashes and as soon as he's back we're sailing, and as soon as we're deep sea, Ross, Steve, and I are going off in the helicopter for a few days, we'll rejoin you in Bermuda.'

'Fly to Bermuda in the *helicopter*?'

He said patiently, 'Please, Katie. Yes, the helicopter. Bermuda's only six hundred miles and we've fitted extra tanks, now she's got a range of over nine hundred.' He held up his finger. 'I can't tell you where we're going, it's strictly confidential. So is everything else. I'm telling you what I am in complete confidence.'

She nodded, anxiously.

'Beginning of December,' he said, 'the *Jubilee* sails for the Antarctic. We're telling the world that we're going to Baja California. In fact we *will* go there for a day or two, just to establish our alibi. When we get to the Antarctic we'll locate the Russian fleet. And here's where you come in, Katie. You're vital to enable us to find the Russians. Because you will listen in to their radio talk, and the fleet will be giving their navigational positions to each other the whole time.'

She looked at him, eyes wide. He went on. 'Having located them, you're still vital to us. To keep us abreast of where each ship in the fleet is and particularly where the factory ship is, the *Slava*. When everything is favourable, some of us – not you – go to the *Slava* and sink it.'

She cried, horrified, 'You'll *kill* people!'

He held up his hand. 'No, Katie. We won't kill anybody. It's our express purpose *not* to kill anybody. I'll explain how in a minute. They'll have plenty of time to get off into their lifeboats.'

'How are you going to get them off – the *panic*, for Godsake! – you're *bound* to kill people.'

'Please, Katie. Listen to me. I'll explain it. I'll answer your questions afterwards. We've worked it out with military precision and nobody is going to get killed. We are *not* terrorists. Now listen to me. . . .'

She sat there in the armchair, staring, her eyes following him. He paced up and down the cabin outlining the plan to her. She rested her forehead in her hand, in awe. She just could not believe it. Yet she could see Justin meant every word he said. And that he was speaking for the whole *Jubilee* crew.

When he had finished, she raised her head and looked at him, then put her head in her hand again. 'Oh my God, Justin.' She shook her head in her hand. 'Oh my *God!*'

He stood there, watching her. Then he turned and paced away across the cabin. Then he came back to her. She continued to sit with her forehead in her hand. He hesitated a moment, then he bent down and kissed her head. And oh God yes, the sweet Katherine smell of her. She lowered her hand slowly and looked up at him with big, blue, alarmed eyes. He straightened up and looked down at her. He said, 'We're going to do it, Katie. We're all absolutely committed. You can't dissuade us. We've figured out every minute detail. The only question is, Will you help us?' She was staring at him, frightened. 'We really need you, Katie.'

She looked at him desperately and breathed, 'Oh my God!'

'Without you, we'll still do it. But it will be much more difficult and dangerous. For everybody, us *and* the Russians.'

She closed her eyes. 'It's *you* guys I'm worried about now!'

'Sinking that goddamn ship is the only way to stop the bastards from killing the last of the whales, Katie. We've tried everything else. Boycotts, campaigns, United Nations pressure, the United States government, even the secretary of state himself. But those bastards won't stop, Katie. They won't stop unless we make it *commercially impossible* to continue whaling. And the only way we can do that is sink their goddamn expensive factory ship. They can't hunt whales without their factory ship to process them. It won't be worth the expense of building another one because there are so few whales left.' He watched her. 'It *is* the only way, Katie. We have to make whaling unprofitable for them. By sinking their factory ship. If we don't do it, they'll hunt whales until the last animal is dead.' He looked at her urgently. 'Probably the most wondrous animals the world has ever seen. Some as big as thirty elephants, the biggest creature ever to have lived on this earth. With minds possibly equal to man's. And the kindest and most gentle of creatures. And man has butchered them by the cruellest method, almost to the brink of extinction. Next year it may be too late, Katie. And once whales are gone, they are gone. As George Small says, "The miracle of their creation will never be repeated." '

Her eyes bright with anxiety. 'Let me think, for God's sake.'

'Think well, Katie. We need you. . . . The whales need

you. . . . The *world* needs you, to save whales for mankind.' He paused, then added, 'Without you we may come to grief. Then the whales *will* become extinct. And the world *will* lose whales. Forever.'

She was mesmerized. He said, 'Tell me when we get back to Bermuda. But remember, Katie . . .' he held out his finger, 'unless we have the guts to do this, whales will soon be extinct. And the miracle of their creation will never be repeated.'

He let the words hang, then he turned and looked out the porthole and saw his brother coming back along the quay.

Craig Magnus and Black Bob Clark were a little drunker, because on the way back from the crematorium they had stopped their taxi several times to have a few drinks, sitting hunched, staring into their glasses, softly singing spirituals together. Now they were slouching moodily along the quay, pensively singing, Craig carrying the Old Man's ashes in a big urn under his arm, like a watermelon. The ashes would scarcely have filled a cigarette box, but Craig had bought the biggest urn he saw.

four

Craig Magnus had no authority in Magnus Oceanics to hire or fire anybody, but it was he who, three years ago, had hired Black Bob Clark, on the spot, at an Evangelist meeting outside a bar. Black Bob's only qualifications for the job of underwater movie star were his experience as a beach photographer and his big beatific smile as he raised his hands and sang his praise to the Lord in his deep brown voice. Craig Magnus loved black music, and he had joined in lustily as he tumbled out of the bar, and Bob Clark had given him a joyous smile of welcome that had almost stolen Craig's heart for the Lord. Craig had known the Old Man wanted a black man on the crew because it was good for the TV ratings. Craig took responsibility for Bob – called

Black Bob to distinguish him from Bob Matthews, the *Jubilee*'s electronics expert, who was then dubbed Hi-fi Bob – and turned him into an excellent underwater cameraman.

Craig went up to his brother's office aboard the *Jubilee* and put the big urn of his father's ashes on the desk. Next to the urn was a copy of a written statement that had been issued to the press.

Justin Magnus, who has been acting president of Magnus Oceanics during his father's long illness, now officially assumes leadership and legal control of the company.

The company policy will continue to be that of documenting, in film and books, the wonders and beauty of the oceans and all their creatures, concentrating on the need for conservation.

Magnus Oceanics is presently engaged in the making of a film about whales, the largest creatures ever to have lived on earth, and the imminence of their extinction at the brutal hands of man, principally the Russian and Japanese whaling companies. Magnus Oceanics hereby urges the public to help the Save-the-Whale Campaign by joining in the boycott of Russian and Japanese goods.

The *Jubilee* and its crew sails today for the coastal waters of Bermuda, to continue its filming of the humpback whales. Thereafter the *Jubilee* will proceed to Baja California, the remote lagoons off the Mexican coast, to film the annual migration there from the Arctic of the grey whales.

The *Jubilee* was steaming evenly down the Hudson River in the New York sunset, heading for the sea. The dark suits and blazers had been taken off and the crewmen were back in their sea gear, which was anything they liked provided it was clean. Justin and Craig, however, were still in formal dress. They still had a private ceremony to perform. The Old Man's ashes had to be scattered. It would be done when the *Jubilee* reached deep water.

Justin sat on the corner of the desk. Craig sat on the sofa, holding his glass of whisky, staring at a porthole. His eyes were dull from old crying. Justin studied him, and he could feel his own eyes burning. Craig was so sentimental and Justin loved him for that, and for many other things. He thought, *God, he's good-looking, wish I looked like that*. Craig was not yet twenty. He was the image of the Old Man and he had all the Old Man's charm, and more. He was very much like his father but differed from him in a number of important respects: he had a very soft heart, which his father had not had. He had never done a day's real work in his life, whereas his father had come up the hard way. Craig earned his salary honestly enough, diving and filming, but it was all sport to him. He was thirteen years younger than Justin, and he had grown up as his father's darling. He had never worried one moment about money, his own or the company's. His salary was all pocket money to him, to be spent in high living when the *Jubilee* hit port. He was perfectly happy to let his older brother run the company. Justin could do all the worrying and Craig would go along anywhere for the ride and sheer fun of it and do as he was told. The only managerial duty Craig was enthusiastic about was that of social secretary, and at this he was superb. When the *Jubilee* arrived in port, Craig Magnus could be relied upon to find a dozen pretty girls in a very short time and be the life and soul of the party. But he was very subdued now.

Justin said, 'Kid?' Craig turned his head slowly. Justin wanted to embrace him. 'Listen, Craig. Last night I made a will. I left all my Oceanic shares to you.'

Craig looked surprised at this depressing talk but his eyes were lifeless.

'Thanks. Maybe I better do the same. And leave all my shares to you.'

'I want this company to stay in the family as much as possible. I control it now anyway, even without your shares voting for me, because the Old Man left you most of the cash and me fifty-one per cent of the shares. Do you understand how his will worked?'

'Yes.'

Justin went on, 'But you never know, I may have to pledge some of my shares one day to raise cash, and the control could slip from my hands.'

'You can rely on my shares if a shark gets me. And while I'm alive, I'll vote for you. And lend you cash.'

'Thanks, kid. I know. But the point is this.' He looked at him soberly. He did not feel like having this heavy conversation. 'You may find yourself in control of this company one day, sooner than you think, and it's time you learned management.'

'Well,' Craig said, 'if you get bumped off in the Antarctic job, there's every likelihood of me getting bumped off at the same time, chum. In which case there's not much point in worrying about who gets whose shares.'

'No, I'm not thinking of the Antarctic operation. I mean the Japan operation.' He looked at him. 'We leave tonight, kid. But I'm sorry, I'm not taking you. I'm taking Ross.'

Craig gaped at him. 'Why aren't you taking me?'

Justin held up his hand. 'No arguments, please. Just listen. I'm not taking you because if anything happens to me in Japan you must be able to take over the company.'

Craig said indignantly, 'If *that's* what you're worried about, then it's *you* who shouldn't go to Japan! *You're* the brains of this outfit! *I* should go with Ross and Steve.'

'Please, Craig. That's that.' He couldn't help smiling at his brother's indignation. 'The point of all this is tomorrow morning crack of dawn you start going through all the account books of this company with Katherine. She'll explain them to you; she's got to catch up herself.' Craig looked blackly at him, insult added to injury. He went on, 'You're going to start a crash course in management, Craig. Every aspect of the business.'

'Okay, so I'll take a crash course in management! But why the hell can't I do that after I come back from Japan?'

'Craig.' Justin suppressed his smile. 'Not only am I your employer, I also now stand *in loco parentis* to you – *legally*. I'm your guardian, strange though that may sound to you.'

Craig was astonished. 'Hey,' he said. 'What is this? You going to start telling me what time I come home at nights?'

'Hell no. You can keep on burning the candle at both ends and screw yourself into an early grave, just as long as you're in the water on time and provided you know how to run this company if something happens to me. Listen, kid. I've worked goddamn hard to bring this company up. And the Old Man before me, starting from nothing, one goddamn fishing boat and a box camera. Now we're worth a fortune. And now the Old Man's gone and you know how we're going to spend it. We've got a mission in this life, Craig. And if we can't do it with the pen and the picture we're going to do it with the goddamn sword! Now listen, kid. That our work continues and gets practical results is far more important than glory. And certainly far more important than any fun and adventure we have. . . . This is a very serious business, Craig.'

'I know it is, for Chrissake, Justin.'

'And if something happens to me, you're going to goddamn well carry on or I'll haunt you to your grave. And to ensure that you're able to carry on, you're not taking any unnecessary risks. And you going to Japan is an unnecessary risk. Ross can do it.'

'And, besides, I'm your kid brother who you've got to protect?'

'Yes,' he admitted. 'And that's that. I've got to go because it's my plan. But it would be the end of the company if both of us landed in a Japanese penitentiary for life, or side by side at the execution block. And that's that.'

Craig started to ask a question, but Justin plunged on, 'Now you know all the underwater stuff, and you're an excellent cameraman. But you know nothing about topside management. The accounts, for a start. The necessary maritime law and company law. And contracts. Insurance. Costs. Our profit-sharing scheme. Investment of profits. The Los Angeles office. Distribution. Sponsors. Advertising. Public relations. Equipment. Depreciation. Income tax. We're going to get a whole lot bigger and make better movies and expand. Maybe two ships. The more powerful we are, the more clout we'll have and the more good we'll do. We're going to do a hell of a lot of things we couldn't do while the Old Man still officially ruled the company from his deathbed.'

'He was great, Justin.'

Justin slid off the desk and walked across the cabin.

'Sure he was, kid. I loved him as much as you did, although you don't think so. It's only that I was the one who had to argue with him, not you, you were too young to know what was going on.'

'And spoiled,' Craig said. 'Go on, say it.'

'And so was I. We were both born with silver spoons in our mouths. But I had to work with him and then take over the mess he left when he got past it. We were bankrupt, Craig. He was great, but he was old-fashioned and he'd come up the hard way and he regarded the sea and his movies as a way to make money and lead the Hollywood life.' He was sorry he had said that, he went on quickly. 'You and I are luckier than he was, Craig. We can afford to have more ...' he was going to say integrity, 'to be more altruistic. Philanthropic. Conservationist. The Old Man gave us the opportunity to be that. And, by God, we're going to do it. Right?'

'Right,' Craig said. 'You don't have to convince me.'

'Right.' Justin turned towards the shelves lining the cabin. They were full of his zoology and marine texts and the complete set of Magnus books in a dozen languages, and scientific reports and journals.

'I wouldn't wish writing on my worst enemy. But I want you to read them all again and get the hang of the format and depth. Because I want you to start taking over some of the writing. Even if it's only the technical stuff and captions.' He turned to him. 'Those Magnus books are worth a hell of a lot to the company in money and in promoting our policies. You've got to be able to do it.'

'Christ, I couldn't write a book, Justin. Make Ross do it.'

'You're going to start. Those books sell themselves with the magic word "Magnus" on them.'

Craig said with a wry grin, 'Do I get to sit next to Katherine while she edits them?'

'Not very close, I'm afraid.'

'She'll hit the roof if I try to write. You're her fair-haired boy, she'd quit, that's why she's here.'

'Bullshit.'

'Come on, she's crazy about you. Didn't you see her face this morning when she saw you again? Okay,' he said, 'she's not crazy about you, she's too smart to let herself go with a bastard like you.' He added, 'Wish she was *my* assistant.'

Justin let it go. 'At the moment you're a jack-of-all-trades and master of none. To run this company you've got to be able to do everything.'

'Like our new president?'

'Just like our new president.'

Craig sighed and turned away to the liquor cabinet. He poured himself another whisky, then turned back to his brother. 'Okay. But you're not cutting me out of the Antarctic operation.'

Justin smiled. 'No, I'm not.'

Craig raised his glass. 'To the Old Man,' he said.

'The Old Man.'

The sun was setting. The last lights of New York harbour were sliding past the porthole.

At eight o'clock that night, on the Atlantic swells, Justin and Craig, standing alone together on the stern, scattered the ashes of Lars Magnus on the sea. At ten o'clock the helicopter was winched up onto the *Jubilee* deck from its cradle in the number two hold. Then Justin went to Katherine's cabin to say good-bye. He kissed her cheek and said, 'Think well, Katie.'

Ten minutes later, with Ross Evans, Steve Gregorowsky, and Justin Magnus aboard, the helicopter chopped up into the night sky.

part two

Many times they had tried to kill her. They had killed all the rest of her clan, every year more and more, kill, kill, kill, until she was the only one left that she knew about, and she went alone calling, calling, but she heard no answers she needed. Now she was a beautiful young blue whale eighty feet long, which is as long as a railway car, and she weighed ninety tons, which is the combined weight of one thousand men, and her tongue was as big as an automobile and it weighed nearly as much as an elephant, and her heart weighed as much as a horse. She was nearly five years old and she had lived nearly all her life without the company of other blue whales. Now she had reached sexual maturity, and she knew by the great urgent feeling in her belly that she wanted and needed a male blue whale to mate with and to love and to live with forever.

From time to time during those years she had found a few other blue whales in the millions of cubic miles of the oceans, and she had joined them joyfully, but she had then not reached sexual maturity. She had lived with them in the warm sunny South Pacific during the winter; then at the beginning of the summer they had headed south to the Antarctic. For a little while they fed on the Antarctic abundance, gaining half a ton in weight a day. Then, always, the whalers had found them and hunted them and shot them with their harpoon cannon, and every time only she had escaped.

She had found other kinds of whales at the Antarctic in those summers, finbacks almost as big as she, and the smaller humpbacks, and sei, and minke, and the sperm, but no other blue whales. She had stayed with the finbacks and the humpbacks and even sometimes with the sperm, and they had accepted her feeding among them, and they even understood many of her sounds, and she theirs, but she knew they were not blues like her, and all the time she was making her calling noises, calling for blue whales to hear. She heard no answers back. At the end of the summer she knew it was time for blue whales to leave the Antarctic, ahead of all the other kinds of whales, and she headed north for the warm South Pacific, calling, calling. But there were only a few hundred blue whales left in the world, because the whalers had killed so many, the greatest animals ever to have lived on this earth, and there were many millions of cubic miles of ocean between them, and many continents and islands in between.

She heard many noises, of other kinds of whales, and fish, and of ships, and the sounds of the sea breaking on shores, but no sounds of blue whales. When she swam near the surface she could hear, and her cries could be heard, for fifty miles through the sea. Much deeper, between the warm surface layer and the dense cold layer, is the sound channel of the seas, and there she could hear for four hundred miles. If there had been no faraway noises of ships to interfere, she could have heard and been heard for four thousand miles, so exquisite was her hearing and echolocation. Sometimes she dived down deep into this sound channel to send out her cries and to listen for answers, but mostly she swam near the surface, blowing and calling, blowing and calling, and all the time her great heart crying out for a mate, for a male blue whale to love and live with. All through the winter of that year she swam the South Pacific looking and calling, and all the time the urgent feelings in her belly and her heart aching. Then, at the end of the winter, when the spring was coming, she heard an answering cry, and her great heart lurched.

The bull was three hundred and sixty miles away across the Pacific Ocean when he heard her. He turned his body towards the faraway cries, and he answered, and then he bucked his back and beat his flukes and he started swimming as fast as he could towards her. And she bucked her back and beat her mighty flukes and she swam as fast as she could towards him, all the time making her urgent crying mating noises, calling to tell him that she was coming and to tell him to keep calling her, so they could find each other in the vastness of ocean between them. Thus the two great beasts swam desperately, joyfully, across the vast Pacific Ocean towards each other, beating their tails and blowing plumes of breath and sucking in immense lungfuls of air and then ploughing back under again, swimming and bucking and beating and coming up and then ploughing under again, and all the time making their *here-I-am-here-I-am* crying noises.

For ten hours, all through the night, the two animals swam towards each other under the sea, calling, calling, and their cries were getting louder and clearer all the time. When the very first greyness began to come into the east they were only twenty miles apart, calling and calling and galloping and galloping, and they were exhausted now. The sun came up over the Pacific, flaming golden pink and orange and red. Now they were only seven or eight miles apart, seething and gushing and blowing and ploughing under again and galloping their weary backs and tails and calling. And now their blows on the surface were sprays on the golden red early morning South Pacific, and now their callings were clear and loud and near, near, near, not more than a few miles away. Now the female's pounding heart was crying out joyfully for the great male blue. She was driving herself, driving herself to find the whale she had been seeking so urgently. She galloped and swam crying out, 'Yes, yes, here I am, here I am.' She lifted the front of her body out of the water enough to see and now she saw his blow, his weary gushing spouting up out of the sea just a mile ahead, and her heart gave a leap. Then they saw each other.

Coming through and up and out of the vast ocean gloom, his dark shadow galloping. Then he burst into the sunlit water in front of her. Massive streamlined male beast nearly one hundred feet long with the big curved smiling mouth, and he was beautiful, absolutely beautiful, and her heart surged in joy. Two mighty beasts with upturned smiling mouths, galloping exhausted towards each other, then both swerving and surging to the surface. Two huge bodies surging up out of the sunny ocean and blowing plumes. Then they turned around and went racing back to each other and blew again, huffing and puffing and milling about and sliding against each other, bumping and rubbing and then surging back and rubbing and bumping, and all the time making their joyful welcoming squeaking noises, absolutely delighted with each other under the South Pacific sun.

After about two hours they copulated. Massive lovers, giant blue streamlined bodies, great surging tails, great flipper arms each as big as a man, and great bursting hearts. When they were ready to make love she dived down under the sea, calling him, running from him, coyly bucking her back and tail, and he galloped down after her joyfully. Pounding down on top of her back making his desperate amorous persuasive noises, and his nine-foot penis was out thick and strong and bursting, and as it bumped against her as she squirmed, it was massive bliss. She dove and bucked and squirmed and wriggled, throbbing coy provocative giant, and he swam down after her, on top of her and beside her and underneath her, desperately trying to seize her body in his flippers and thrusting his great penis at her, trying to jab and thrust it into her huge delicious body. He bucked and jabbed and bucked and thrashed his tail and tried to grab her with his flippers, and she rolled and twisted, escaping him. He dove and bucked and grabbed after her all the way, and he was desperately willing to dive down with her into the deepest blackest abyss of the ocean and right down into the hottest bowels of the earth itself just as long as he could get his flippers around her beautiful body and stab his bursting penis into her.

He followed her all the way down down down to one thousand feet. Then suddenly she rolled her belly over towards him. She let him grab her body with his flippers, and she stretched out her flippers and grabbed his body also, and they beat their giant tails and went surging bucking up towards the surface, belly to belly, clutching each other with their flippers and with the long smiles on their mouths and the joy for each other in their hearts. They broke surface together in a vast blowing and amorous crashing, and she rolled over onto her back and slapped her flippers on the surface and slapped at him. And he slapped at her with his flippers and came surging on top of her, bucking his back and thrusting at her belly with his penis, and she rolled over onto her side slapping him joyfully, resounding love slaps, and clutching him with her flippers. And he thrust his great penis but he missed and it skidded off her belly. He thrust again as they rolled and wallowed, clutching and slapping each other, and again he missed the place and his penis skidded off her. She rolled on to her other side, and he rolled with her, bucking and slapping and clutching and crashing and thrusting and missing and skidding and sliding. She twisted and arched and rolled and wallowed under and up, and he followed her all the way, thrusting and missing again and again, for it is very difficult for a male whale to find such a place with such a bulky member sixty feet away from his eyes, and of course he could not look to see what he was doing because whales have no neck to bend, and he had no hands to help himself with, he could only thrust. It was a very difficult and happy business.

After a long time they got it right. Clutching each other with their great flippers and rolling and sinking and splashing and thrashing and quivering and trembling and thrashing, and all the time making their desperately happy squeaking noises, massive lovers in the middle of the South Pacific sunshine.

five

They flew on the same plane, sitting separately, and arrived at Tokyo airport early the next afternoon. They went through customs with forged passports, without acknowledging each other, then left for downtown Tokyo by different taxis. Later that afternoon they went to different sports shops and bought the flippers, the face masks, and the breathing apparatus, then took different trains to the port of Yokohama. From Yokohama station each went to the waterfront red-light area and checked into hotels patronized by American servicemen.

Later, at different times and by different routes, two proceeded to the docks. The third rented a car and went to a building near the docks. There he took delivery of nine limpet mines from a man who specialized in supplying stolen war materials to guerrilla movements all over the world.

The two men at the docks spent an hour inspecting a large canal. The canal began as a dirty tidal creek winding down from the city of Yokohama and entered the docks between warehouses, contained by vertical concrete walls. Then it opened into 'A' Basin, where a number of vessels were moored, among them the big whaling factory ships. They were almost identical, differing only slightly in size. Both were almost empty at this time because they were refitting for their long Antarctic whaling season; the crew were all on leave and the yardworkers had quit for the day.

At exactly one a.m. the same night, when the tide was nearly at its height and the canal at its fullest, Justin Magnus stopped his rented car outside a bar called the Queen of Hearts and Ross Evans came out of the bar and climbed into the front seat. They drove straight for two blocks, then down a side street and stopped near the Cupid Bar for Steve Gregorowsky, who got into the back seat. On the floor were three scuba tanks and other gear. The car then drove through a dozen different streets and stopped at a warehouse alongside the canal. In the parked car, the three men started tearing off their clothes, under which they all were wearing swimming trunks. They got quickly out of the car and hefted the scuba tanks onto their backs and buckled the harnesses and strapped on the weighted belts. Each then took a canvas bag containing three limpet mines and padded to the black concrete canal wall. Each put on his face mask and flippers, held the canvas bag to his chest, and dropped silently into the cold, dirty blackness and was gone.

Underwater there was only the faintest gleam of light above them, from the night sky. The three men swam, each carrying his canvas bag of limpet mines, which, in the water, were neutrally buoyant, for a little over a thousand yards, carefully following the canal wall in the darkness. Then suddenly the wall curved away, and they were in the 'A' Basin.

They had to follow the dock, to which a line of ships was tied, end to end. They swam the length of the line, passing beneath the long black shadows of the hulls, one after another, keeping count until they came to the shadow that was the bow of the first factory ship. When they were well under it, they used their small waterproof flashlights for the first time. They rose in the murk until their hands touched the keel, then worked their way along it, towards the two big propellers and the two big rudders that were underneath the slipway.

Two men each pulled a limpet mine out of his canvas bag and set the small timing dial for twenty-four hours. They carefully felt for barnacles and weed, and there were none, for both ships had just been scraped. Then each carefully placed a mine just forward of the stern tube of a propeller shaft. The limpet mines clung to the steel plate by their magnets. The third man placed two limpet mines fifty feet forward of the stern tubes, then rejoined his companions. Then they went deeper again and swam to the next factory ship and planted five more mines. Then they turned and swam back to the mouth of the canal.

When they got to where the car was, they wriggled the scuba tanks off their shoulders, took off their masks, flippers, and belts and tied them to the scuba tanks, and dropped them to the bottom of the canal. Then they reached up and grabbed ring-bolts in the concrete and pulled themselves over the canal wall. They hurried to the car. Twenty-four hours later, the mines exploded.

They exploded with an eruption of the sea and a great muffled thud that shook the big ships from stem to stern and made the men on deck watch clutch and fall and lights flash out, and the concrete dock trembled. They blasted big gaping holes through the thick steel plates into the bilges and bowels of the ships so the black sea went roaring in. The explosions crashed through the vital stern tubes and twisted the rudders. The nine limpet mines exploded simultaneously, with a booming that was heard way beyond the docks; then there was the shocked yelling and shouting and outrage. The dirty black sea went boiling up into the engine rooms, and the massive sterns began to sink, and the high bows that were built for cutting through pack ice began to rise up out of the water. And all the time the yelling and the shouting and the outrage and the sirens.

At the same moment the three young men were in different airliners in the airspace of the United States of America.

six

Bermuda was about forty miles off. The *Jubilee* was cruising slowly, looking for whales. There were lookouts with binoculars in the crow's nest and on both wings of the bridge, on both sides of midships and on the stern. The sun was shining bright on the blue crystal sea and beaming deep onto the white, shimmering sand below. In tow behind the *Jubilee* were four inflated rubber speedboats, called Zephyrs, and in them were all the cameras and sound-recording equipment, ready. On the stern deck were spread the divers' aquasuits and scuba tanks.

Katherine Robinson was on the bridge in her orange bikini. She would not wear an aquasuit because they wanted her golden body on film. In her hair she wore an orange ribbon, tied in a bow across the top of her head. The tails of the bow hung down her shiny blonde hair, and when she swam they would stream out behind her and look very pretty. She was leaning on her elbows on the bridgewing rail, looking at the horizon through binoculars. Craig Magnus was standing near her, watching her out of the corner of his eye, and he groaned happily under his breath. It was the first time he had seen her in a bathing suit for half a year, and come to think of it, this was the first female body he had seen in the flesh for quite a time; apart from New York, the *Jubilee* had not been in a port for over a month. Craig thought, *Justin's crazy. He could have her if he wanted to.*

Well, maybe not. Not just like that anyway. Nobody would get Katie easily, she was far too smart. *No easy lay, not Katie,* Craig thought regretfully. In fact, she intimidated him. She was so goddamn sophisticated and – regal? *Regal* was a bad word for her but somehow it got the impression across. But on the other hand she was so friendly, and that smile of hers was all for you and it made your heart turn over. And you could say almost anything in front of her, and she could drink and joke with all of them on board, without inhibiting anything. Maybe she was just plain off limits. It had been very distracting working with her these last few days on the account books. Anyway, he wouldn't dare make a pass at her. Maybe she was the only woman in the world he wouldn't dare make a pass at. But, *oh.*

Craig eyed her, happily sex-bothered on the bridgewing of the *Jubilee*, when he should have been looking for humpback whales. He wouldn't make a pass at her for another reason too: in some indefinable way she was Justin's. That didn't mean she and Justin had a sex thing going, they didn't, but they were so close working together all the time. Big brother would skin him alive. But he couldn't understand why Justin didn't carry her off to bed forever.

Katherine Robinson had not been concentrating very well, either, the last few days. Nor had she been sleeping well. She could not stop thinking about the decision Justin had thrust upon her, she could not yet even adjust to the enormity of the action to be taken. And he was not around, here, to discuss it further.

Nor was Ross. They had disappeared, both of them, the two most important people, on some secret business probably to do with sabotaging the Russians – and just left her hanging, with a load on her mind. Sometimes she felt she could kick Justin for just zapping it to her, then disappearing. And Ross. She badly needed to talk to Ross about it. The right-hand man, he was so sensible she sometimes thought he should be *the* man except he didn't have Justin's creative genius – or Justin's creative *conceit*, his self-confidence. But Ross *was* sensible and he was in on this sabotage thing with Justin; that gave it a bit more sanity.

She did not want to talk to anybody else about it, not even to the commander. She adored old Henry Thorogood, but somehow she didn't want to talk to him about it; he was so Royal Navy and professional it was hard to argue with him or even doubt his opinions on technical matters. She bet he was the one who had helped Justin formulate his plan, he was the one with wartime submarine sabotage experience.

And it was no good talking to Craig about it; he would follow Justin to the ends of the earth. Katherine turned from the sea and walked slowly through the wheelhouse. She moved pensively through the radio room and went down the stairs into the wardroom. She wanted to talk to somebody *ordinary* about it, somebody at the end of the plan, not its hot centre. For example, L. C. Singleton. She went into the galley. 'Hello L.C.,' she said.

'Hello, darling.' L.C. beamed his wide froggy smile. 'Want some coffee? No whales yet?'

'Not yet.' She leaned back against the edge of the table. 'Yes please, L.C.'

He was getting it for her already. He was pleased she had come to talk to him. And he could tell her tension and he knew why. He did not blame her. But she was vitally important. He hoped she was going to confide in him so he could do his bit. Justin had ordered nobody to pressure her. As far as he knew she had confided in no one.

She said, gazing at her coffee, 'Why're you here, L.C.?'

L.C. said carefully, 'The *Jubilee*'s the only home I know. I've worked on one *Jubilee* or another for nearly seventeen years.'

'But why're you going on this Antarctic operation?'

L.C. paused before answering. He cut a slice of bread. 'Because I agree with him. About the whales. And his whole philosophy.' He waved his knife. '*Not* just because I'm a company man. I *agree*. I know a lot about marine life, you know.'

'I know you do,' she said.

'And so do you.'

'Oh yes. I do.'

He wanted to say, 'Well, then . . .?' He didn't. In the silence, he cut another slice of bread.

She knew what he was thinking, and she smiled wearily to herself. She did not want to discuss it any more. What she really wanted to blurt out was, 'Yes, but. . . .' But what? 'But good God! What a colossal thing to do.' What would he say to that? 'Of course it's colossal, but the problem is colossal. . . . If you care about the problem – and we *care*, don't we?' And she would say, 'Yes of course I do, but. . . .' But what? 'But what about the *danger*?' The *danger*. It was a demeaning thing to say. Oh God, you either believe enough to do it in spite of the danger, or you don't. Maybe the thing you profess ardently to believe in isn't worth the personal danger. Let the world go to hell, let the world go to shit, and I'll protest my beliefs loudly, until I'm endangered.

And danger to *whom*? *These* guys, her friends, her shipmates. *They* would go despite the danger, even if she didn't go. There was no question of dissuading them, so it was only her own safety she was chewing her lip about. And that was an unworthy thing. She took a deep breath, and L.C. glanced at her and waited. She was not going to say anything, and L.C. decided to try to rub it in a little.

'Those lovely Magnus books,' he said. 'What a contribution to science, really. And to people's education. About our philosophy, I mean. What we *stand* for.' He looked at her and gave her a smile that was meant to conceal his purpose. 'You've turned those books into masterpieces. Editorial work I know about – and *you* did it. No doubt about it. Justin admits it. He says he can't do it without you. And he's right.'

She thought she knew what he was doing but she couldn't help smiling and feeling almost tearfully warm. And proud. Because it was true. She said, to shift the subject from herself, 'Some of the best photographs in some of those books are yours, L.C.'

L.C. also knew what she was doing, but he was pleased. 'Oh,' he wagged his head, 'I'm not much good with the camera. Some of the animal ones, yes. While everybody else was off at the wars doing the heroic stuff. I know more about the biology part of it. And about developing.' He glanced at her. 'I'm pretty good at printing. Even that bad-tempered little bastard Hi-fi Bob has to admit that.'

She was feeling better. And she definitely did not want to talk about herself anymore.

'I don't know whether you like Hi-fi or not.'

'Hi-fi? Can't stand the little prick. Excuse me, bastard.'

'Come on, L.C.,' she said, 'I don't believe you.'

He glanced at her, then gave that strange grin of his, which never showed his teeth. He knew what had happened inside her and he understood. He was enjoying talking to her anyway.

'Bob's a good guy at heart. Just a born grouser.' He shook his head theatrically. 'Maybe you can't blame him, looking like that.' Katherine smiled and thought that a little ironic, coming from L.C. 'He wouldn't be happy if he didn't have something to cuss about. And there's plenty to cuss *him* about. *Somebody's* got to keep him in his place. Justin's too soft with him.'

There was something about the way he said that which disturbed her. L.C. did not look in the least bit gay, but often a click of the tongue, a toss of his head, a gossipy tone, the choice of a word, gave a hint. But when he bawled out somebody, like his arch-enemy Hi-fi Bob Matthews, he sounded like a sergeant major. Katherine had once asked Justin if L.C. was gay and he had said bluntly, 'No.' But then Justin would not let anybody down with something confidential.

She said, 'Bob amuses Justin. But I have trouble making him out.'

Cutting sandwiches, L.C. replied, 'He and I joined the old *Jubilee Two* about the same time. He used to be just the same with the Old Man. Justin was just a teenager then. Craig was a babe-in-arms.'

She was sitting on the edge of the galley table now. 'What was *she* really like? The Old Man's wife.'

L.C. shot her a look.

'What wife? *She* wasn't a wife, poor darling, she was a *house-keeper*. The Old Man had his wives in all the other ports. *And* sometimes at sea. Particularly when Justin was younger, before he properly understood what it was all about. When Justin got bigger he had it out with the Old Man one day about all these women. He was only fifteen then, but strong as an ox. It was during one of his school holidays. You could hear them bawling each other out all over the ship. Justin threatened to give the Old Man a thrashing. They didn't talk for days afterward. But the Old Man was more discreet after that.' He smiled. 'After *that* he used to ship his favourite mistresses out as his secretary, quote unquote. I don't think one of them could type. And as actresses, supposed to be for filming. Some of those hungry starlets from Hollywood. I don't think one of them could dive five feet, but they looked good in bikinis. And *those* were the days, my dear,' he touched her arm, '*before* bikinis.' He guffawed, delighted with his joke.

Katherine really liked L.C. And she liked hearing about the old days. And about the young Justin Magnus.

'Those were the days,' L.C. said, going back to his sand-wiches. 'The Old Man was a real terror with the ladies. And that wasn't the only thing Justin used to fight with him about. When he got old enough to have his say he didn't hold back.'

'What sort of things?' She really wanted to know.

'Work, mostly. Justin was always criticizing the Old Man for being overcommercial. "Sensationalism", Justin called it. "Hollywoodese." Justin said he didn't concentrate enough on conservation and scientific things.' L.C. pointed with his knife into the wardroom at the bookshelves. 'I swear, by the time he was fifteen Justin knew all those marine books inside out. He could run rings around his Old Man when it came to the books. *And* to practice.' He shook his head. 'He was *very* good.' He cocked his head reminiscently, almost like an actor. 'Some of the wonderful discussions we had around that wardroom table. . . . And some of the arguments? I remember once Justin saying to the Old Man, "You've violated your natural duty to protect the sea!" Aiming his finger like this. He was only seventeen. That was the time the Old Man was about to accept a contract from the oceanariums to capture live dolphin, for training to do tricks. Justin wouldn't hear of it, even though each dolphin was worth two-thousand-odd dollars, I think, and the contract was for a hundred animals – nearly a quarter of a million bucks! Justin shamed him into turning it down. A quarter of a million . . . back then. Justin was quite right, of course. And a dolphin only lives a few years in captivity, it's terribly cruel. Another time the Old Man shot a film about the thrills of spearfishing. Justin was at school. When he saw it he nearly blew his top. They had other rows, too, about extravagances and about the Old Man's drinking. Especially when we couldn't afford it. By the time he was twenty Justin knew this business inside out.'

'Did they really get on *very* badly? He's pretty close-mouthed about his father.'

'He adored his mother,' L.C. said. 'The Old Man *was* over-commercial. And extravagant. And when he got older he went downhill badly. They quarrelled a lot. Justin was usually right. He saved the company, didn't he?' He shrugged. 'The Old Man couldn't do without Justin. And he knew it. He was proud of him, actually. But Craig was his darling. Spoiled him rotten. But he's turned out a good kid. He's got a heart of gold. *And* tough. Oh yes,' L.C. wagged his head, 'and brave. You've seen those shark movies, especially that hammerhead? Black Bob and Craig? They're fearless, those two. Out of the cage, hiding behind the propellers, filming that shark attacking Justin and Steve. Justin chewed their balls off afterwards for risking their lives – excuse me.'

'It's all right,' she said, smiling.

She went back to the bridge. She felt a lot better after talking to dear L.C. But she still had not consulted anybody. And she did not want to. She felt almost ashamed to, after talking to L.C.

She went back up to the sunny bridge. Commander Henry Thorogood was fiddling with the radio in the radio room as she passed through. David Cartwright was on the bridge, Spider

Webb was at the wheel. In his swimming trunks Spider looked very tough, broad-shouldered and bulging-thighed. He gave her a shy blunt-cut smile and she gave him her wide dazzling smile back, distractedly. She saw the purple tattoo marks on his big hairy arms. God, he reminded her of Steve Gregorowsky. They both had the same sort of raw appeal: muscular, strong, brown-backed.

Spider had a big scar from something that had obviously entered through his left breast and come out his right breast. It was from an underwater spear gun, that's all she knew, and that after the accident Spider himself had pushed the barbed spear all the way through both breasts to get it out. She did not think she wanted to know any more. It shocked her to think about it – she could almost feel the teeth-clenched, grunting agony as Spider got up on the rock and shoved the long spear through his bloody body. That was Steve-like, almost.

She thought of Steve's scars. He had two bad ones that twisted up the insides of both his thighs and disappeared into his swimming trunks. That was from the great black rhinoceros, in Africa. And the big terrible double crescent of scars on his right hip and buttock, from the hammerhead shark; those scars disappeared *down* into his swimming trunks. The bad joke on the *Jubilee* was that Steve was still a bachelor, despite his good looks, because he was too embarrassed ever to take his pants off. It made her flesh cringe to remember it: the terrible thrashing of the great killer animal as she watched from the safety of the *Jubilee*'s deck. Afterwards she saw Craig's film of the incident, Steve standing back outside the cage door with almost a bow and a sweep of his hand to let Justin get into the cage ahead of him. Maybe it was arrogance, but she called it death wish, and she was damn sure she was right. She put her binoculars up to her eyes and looked at the sea.

She tried to make herself stop thinking about it, but everything brought it back. The sea, the beautiful mysterious dangerous sea, and soon she was going to enter it again for the first time in six months, and where was Justin? She was not the born, natural diver everybody thought she was. The sea, to enter the sea, to go down there, it did not seem right, almost unsafe, to enter the sea without Justin Magnus in command, *there, around.* Where'd he go? Mysteriously gone, and gone with Steve, Steve with his death-wish scars. What were they doing? And Ross, thank God for Ross, but where was he?

She thought of David Cartwright and lowered the binoculars to look for him. He was standing on the opposite bridgewing in his white tropical shorts, white socks, white shirt. Commander Thorogood insisted that his deck officer dress. Cartwright was tall and skinny and his thin arms and legs seemed white too, although they got brown, and his thin, reedy, nervous music-master's face with its big Adam's apple and little moustache also seemed white, though it patently was not. David Cartwright had grown his moustache only since joining the *Jubilee.*

Katherine wanted to talk to him because he was sensible also, in a nervous, birdlike way. And yet he too was in on this plan. And he was religious – she had seen him reading *Science and Health with a Key to the Scriptures.* He was a Christian Scientist and she felt a sort of affinity with him on that alone because the Mother Church was in Boston. She made up her mind to be straightforward about her problem with David Cartwright. She walked through the wheelhouse and out onto the bridgewing. He had his skinny back to her, looking through his binoculars. She said, 'David? May I have a word with you?'

He turned, nervously surprised, eyes darting. 'Yes, Miss Robinson—'

'*Please* call me Katherine.' All the same, she almost had diffi-culty calling him David, he was such a shy, formal young man. He did not invite familiarity. Familiarity was almost unfair be-cause he could not be familiar back; it was almost like teasing him. She crossed her feet and her hip jutted. She frowned at the deck and took a breath. She wanted to say, 'Listen, Dave, tell me person to person and no bullshit what do you think about this Antarctic operation because I'm scared shitless.' And that wasn't right, either.

She heard herself say, 'David? I wonder. . . . Could I ask? . . . I mean . . . why are you going on this Antarctic operation?' She kept herself from saying, 'You of all people. You're not a macho like Steve and Spider and Justin, you're more like me.' Instead she said, 'Why isn't it crazy? I mean – it's crazily dangerous.'

Cartwright looked at her uneasily, his skinny hands clasped in front of him. He said, 'About the dangers and the technicalities, Mister Magnus suggested we refer you to Commander Thorogood, he's the expert. . . .'

She had to restrain herself from saying, 'Goddamnit, David I don't want to talk to the commander!' She said carefully, 'All right, about the technicalities. But please tell me why *you're* going.'

'Why? Because it's *vital*. To save the whales. . . . And it's a vitally necessary stand to take on behalf of the whole environmental crisis. . . .' He stared at her, having run out of words to express the obvious. Then the nervousness came back. 'I support Mister Magnus,' he ended. 'In everything he's trying to achieve.'

Of course, she thought. *The obvious. It was the obvious answer – that's why I'm here too, that's why we're all here.* It's just that everybody else seemed to have more *guts* than she somehow had. *That's it, guts, courage, the courage of your convictions*. She wanted to blurt out, 'But do you think I should go, David?' but it seemed pointless. What would he say? 'That's a decision you've got to make for yourself, Miss Robinson.' That's what she had to do and she was damn sure that's what Justin had instructed them to say. Discuss it with her, but don't try to persuade her; she's got to make up her own mind. But she wanted to *talk* about it: *I don't know what to do, David.* And what would he say? Back to square one. She said, for something to say, 'You really love it here, don't you, David?'

Cartwright was not sure where this conversation was going. 'Oh, yes,' he said.

She just wanted to talk, now; about anything. 'You're a Christian Scientist, aren't you?' There was something comforting in that fact.

Cartwright blushed suddenly. 'Yes, I am.'

To keep the conversation going, she said, 'Their Mother Church is in Boston, where I live. Some of my friends are Christian Scientists. They're all very serene, happy people.'

'Oh,' David Cartwright said. 'Yes, Boston.'

'You believe in faith healing?' She really wanted to know.

Cartwright cleared his throat. 'Well it's not exactly faith healing, as such.'

'What is it then?'

'We believe that God made man perfect in His own image and likeness. Therefore all man has to do to achieve perfection, in mind and body, is to . . . is to believe in and seize that simple truth – it's called the Truth, you see – and then he will be perfect too.' He glanced at her. 'In mind and body. Of course it's much more complicated and sophisticated than that,' he added apologetically.

She looked at him. She was sure he had never had a girl friend. She felt sisterly towards him. 'I'm quite religious too,' she said. She added with a small laugh, 'Presbyterian. Tempered with modern science and Women's Lib. Though I don't know if I'm saved or not. Not according to Black Bob, anyway.'

'Oh?' Cartwright said.

She went on, 'The Evangelists tend to be a bit tough on their fellow Christians. But Bob's a quiet one. But he's very devout. When he does talk about it, he's quite impressive in fact.'

'Oh,' Cartwright said, 'I didn't know that.'

God, she thought, *it's hard to get him to talk*. She wanted to know and she wanted to talk. 'According to Justin, that's why Black Bob's with us. Something to do with the End of the World and the Battle of Armageddon and the Garden of Eden. . . .' Cartwright nodded but did not seem about to comment. She pressed on, 'Has your religion got anything to do with why you're doing this job? I mean, apart from your interest in marine biology.'

Cartwright's Adam's apple went up and down. 'That's it,' he said. 'Marine biology.' He glanced at her and then added, 'I always wanted to be a marine biologist, but I couldn't afford it. I went to sea instead, as a cadet.'

It was hard to imagine. 'Doesn't a cadet officer have to spend two years before the mast and go scrubbing bilges and be bellowed at by the bos'n's mate?'

'Yes.' He smiled tentatively. 'Something like that. It depends which company you join.'

'Did you enjoy it?'

'Got to be done.'

She thought for a moment he had picked up some of the commander's clipped manner of speech, and maybe even his accent. 'How long are you going to stay with us, David?'

He said without hesitation, 'As long as Mister Magnus will have me. My contract's for one year. It'll be up in April. I hope he'll renew it.'

She smiled to herself. This was the way it was. She knew how everybody felt, she knew all the answers they would give. So she had to make her own mind up. But what upset her was where was Justin to talk it out with – and Ross? She heard the commander call. 'Craig!' He was beckoning.

Craig turned and walked into the bridgehouse. The commander led him into the radio room behind it and faced him. His craggy robust face was beaming behind his beard. He indicated the radio and whispered, 'Confidential, of course, but I've just got it on the BBC World Service. . . .' He beamed, 'They sank those Japanese whalers! No loss of life! And no arrests made, quote unquote!'

Craig looked hard at the commander, then he clenched his fists overhead.

'Jeez! Oh, Jeez!' He spun around, unable to contain himself. 'Hey! Hey! Hey! How about that! Jesus, can't we tell somebody?'

The commander grinned. 'Justin said only you and Miss Robinson.'

Craig bounded for the door and shouted out to Katherine. 'Katie, come here.'

She turned and came into the bridgehouse.

'Come here.' Craig pulled her into the radio room and closed the door, beaming. She was looking puzzled. Craig said, 'Tell her, commander.'

The commander was beaming too. 'Mr Magnus asked me to tell you, very confidentially, if and when I got the news on the radio – and I just have – that the three of them succeeded in blowing up the two Japanese whaling factory ships in Yokohama harbour! Without loss of life. And no arrests made by the Japanese authorities.'

Craig exploded. 'Ain't that fantastic! Oh, Jeez, isn't that fangoddamtastic!'

Katherine was thunderstruck.

'They blew up the Japanese whaling factory ships?'

Craig cried joyously, 'Blew the bastards sky-high! Blew them to Kingdom Come! Ain't that fanfuckingtastic?' He raised his arms to the heavens and did a spin around. Katherine was staring, incredulous, shocked. 'Oh my God!' She smiled uncertainly. 'Oh God. . . .' She added, still shocked, 'Where are they now?'

'According to the BBC the explosion took place at approximately midnight last night, Japanese time. That would be approximately six o'clock last night by Bermuda time.' He consulted his watch, 'Nineteen hours ago. They'll be approaching Boston now, if not already there.'

She turned to the commander, still shocked. 'Why Boston?'

'The helicopter's parked on my little farm,' the commander said proudly.

'Oh Jesus, that man.'

'Isn't he something?' Craig burst out. 'I'm getting some champagne!'

'What about the humpbacks?' the commander said. Craig was already bouncing down the stairs to the wardroom below. The commander said to Katherine, 'He really is to be congratulated – Justin.'

'Oh yes! I just can't believe it! It's extraordinary! I'm just so . . . impressed. That's the word – *impressed*. He didn't tell me.'

'Nor anybody else except Craig and me.'

She was suddenly grinning too, sparkling.

'It's marvellous! Just as long as he gets away with it—' Abruptly her grin dropped. 'They're bound to be suspected. He's made such a fuss about the whale issue. What about their passports?'

'Forged ones,' the commander said. She closed her eyes. *Thank God.* 'There's a forged passport for everybody on this ship, he got them while you were away. Including for you.'

'*Me!*'

Craig came bounding back up the stairs with two bottles of

champagne and a fistful of glasses. The commander said diffidently to Katherine, 'I know Mister Magnus has spoken to you
about the next part of our operation – the, er, Antarctic. Soli-
citing your, er, help.' He looked at her, 'Your Russian language
ability is crucially important to us.'

'Can that wait till he comes back?'

'Of course,' the commander said. 'But in case you have any
questions, or anxieties . . . about the safety of the operation – or
the morality of it – Mister Magnus asked me to help you, by
discussing it.'

She said, 'Morality of it, no. But *anxieties*?'

The champagne cork popped. 'It's going to go like clockwork,
Katie!' Craig said, delighted, 'We'll sink that goddamn Russian
factory like a stone.' He was pouring the champagne. He gave a
glass to her and one to the commander and held his own glass
high.

'Like a stone,' the commander echoed.

'Stone.' Katherine gulped at her champagne.

The commander said with a cough, 'If you do *not* join us, Miss
Robinson, I suggest you'll be a damn sight more anxious. Because without your assistance the operation is fraught with
difficulties – and dangers. Whereas *with* your help monitoring
the Russian radio, it will be plain sailing.'

'Plain sailing!' Craig agreed. 'She's coming, commander!
Magnus Oceanics expects this day every man and woman to do
his or her duty et cetera.'

'When *will* they get back here?' Katherine asked. 'If they're
in Boston now. . . . I pray to God they're in Boston.'

'They are!' Craig said. 'Getting plastered to celebrate.'

The commander said, 'If they leave more or less straightaway,
seven hundred miles at a hundred and fifty miles an hour. . . . In
five hours.'

'They won't,' Craig said. 'They'll get plastered. They've got
it coming to them! They'll show up tomorrow morning.'

seven

It was a beautiful day. The sun shone golden bright. The commander said over the loudspeakers, 'Echoes entering my sonar screen from the southwest,' and they all swung their binoculars to look.

Then Spider Webb shouted from the crow's nest, 'There they blow!'

And ten miles away, almost dead ahead, they saw the faint gushing spouts of the whales, then another, then another, then half a dozen more.

Craig said cheerfully over the loudspeakers from the bridge, 'All right, folks. Get suited up while we close with them.' He turned and said to the commander, 'I think we should have a bit more steam, don't you, admiral? I'm sorry – commander.'

Henry Thorogood gave him a look. He knew some of them called him the Admiral behind his back because of his jolly-hockey-sticks Royal Navy accent, and normally he did not mind it, but he didn't like young Craig being too familiar – nice lad and all that, but a bit too full of you-know-what at times, the Old Man had been far too soft on him by all accounts. In Justin's absence Ross or Steve was in charge of filming operations and the commander did not much care for taking orders from young Craig.

'Very well,' he said, and rang up the telegraph to half ahead. Spider was climbing down the mast from the crow's nest, everybody was going aft.

Craig flicked the intercom switch to the galley and said, 'Sorry, L.C., to the stern, please.' He called to David Cartwright. 'Stern, please, Dave.' Because Justin, Steve and Ross were away they were shorthanded, and David Cartwright and L. C. Singleton had to help by driving the Zephyrs.

When he got to the stern they were pulling on their rubber aquasuits. They were black with a single yellow longitudinal stripe down the side, which looked good on film. When they were doing extensive underwater work, especially where there were sharks, they used different suits, ones with special plastic tank harnesses and airtight helmets that made them look like spacemen, and radio-telephone devices built into the helmets to enable them to speak to each other underwater, and with the *Jubilee*. But not today.

Craig said, 'Katherine comes with me in Zephyr One. With Dave steering. L.C., you steer Black Bob and Spider in Zephyr Two. Hi-fi takes himself.'

'How can I record anything with all these motors going, anyway?' Hi-fi Bob said. Bob Matthews was short and scrawny with freckles and ginger balding hair and glasses; he was in charge of all electronic equipment and sounding recordings, at which he was a master craftsman, and he was the ship's complainer, at which he was also very accomplished.

Black Bob said to him, 'Then just record the engines, Hi-fi, an' it better be good.'

'If they stop and play, shut down your goddamn engines.'

Craig said to Black Bob, 'You go around behind them, come up on their tails, jump in, and roll the cameras. Katherine and I will meet them head on and try to get them to stop and play. Let's go.'

Hi-fi Bob's Zephyr was fully loaded with intricate machinery with wires and dials that only he was allowed to touch. They climbed into their Zephyrs.

David Cartwright started his engine. They pulled away from the *Jubilee*. Craig looked ahead. He could not see any whale blows. He flicked on his two-way radio and said above the engine noise, 'Zephyr One to *Jubilee*. Are they still dead ahead, commander?'

The commander came back, 'About four or five miles ahead. They've got some calves with them.'

'Got that, Bob?' Craig asked.

Black Bob's voice came over the radio, 'Yeah, four or five miles ahead.' His Zephyr swept across the bows of the *Jubilee*, L.C. at the helm, and roared off towards the horizon at an angle to the whales. L.C. liked driving the boats at times like this; it made him feel like an aquanaut.

Craig shouted to David Cartwright, 'About half-throttle until we're a couple of miles off, then cut right down.'

Cartwright opened the throttle and the big rubber bows came up and started going smack smack smack. Katherine sat on the gunnel, blonde hair flying, her face into the wind, watching for the whales. The champagne had worn off but she was still both stunned and exhilarated. She could not believe that they had done it, but she *did* believe it all right. My God, this was for real! Craig shouted to her over the wind and engine noise, 'Go down to about thirty feet. Then when you see them coming, zoom up towards the leader's nose with your arms upstretched, wide like this.' He held his arms up. 'Esther Williams stuff, legs together, just your flippers moving. I want to try to film you going into his smile. Don't worry about his flipper, he'll be careful not to bump you with it. Then if he keeps going, just wash down his flank. Watch out for barnacles on him. And watch out for his flukes. Okay?'

'Okay.'

'Duck under his flukes gracefully. Sort of swoop. Then reach up like an angel and try to grab the tip of a fluke and hang on. You'll have to be fast to grab his tail. Kick your feet hard. But gracefully, like an angel.'

'Easy – particularly like an angel.'

He smiled. 'Then just play it by ear. Just do what *you* think will look good. Try to curve your body around, like you did in *Dolphin*. Some ballerina stuff. Just look good.' He added, 'That won't be hard.'

'Oh no,' she shouted. 'Easy.'

'Are you scared?'

'Yes. Just a bit.'

Cartwright called over his shoulder, 'Humpbacks won't hurt you,' but they did not hear him.

Often people did not hear David Cartwright because he spoke very softly. He had been with Magnus Oceanics only eight months and he was overshadowed by all the personalities – except perhaps by shy Victor Gardner in the engine room – but Justin valued him and knew he would never be tempted to boast or confide. Justin had needed a second qualified bridge officer for his Antarctic operation and had known it was not going to be easy to find one in a hurry who could be trusted to keep his mouth shut forever. Like a godsend, David Cartwright had come to Justin Magnus through the Friends of the Earth Society. He was a fourth officer in the merchant marine who really wanted to be a marine biologist. If he was too late for that, he wanted to work for Magnus Oceanics or Jacques-Yves Cousteau. Justin had given him use of one of the *Jubilee*'s laboratories, and now he was studying marine biology on his own, from Justin's library. Cartwright was a very contented young man now, but he was so shy and nervous he seldom showed it. He was watching for the whale blows intently as he drove the Zephyr. They blew in a series, one after the other, then several at once, three miles ahead. There must be about a dozen of them, he estimated. Zephyr Two was way ahead, and he saw it begin to drop back into a wide sweep behind them, and Bob Clark and Spider putting their air tanks on their backs. Craig shouted to Katherine, 'Tank up.'

She crouched down on one knee and wriggled her arms into the harness, then swung it onto her back. She buckled the straps and weights across her stomach. Then she wrestled on her flippers. Craig watching her out of the corner of his eye as he tanked up, her long legs. She leaned over the gunnel and rinsed her face mask in the rushing sea. Then she scanned ahead for the whales, facing into the wind, and she was very excited.

The other Zephyr was coming up behind the whales now, slowly. Bob Clark and Spider Webb were sitting on the gunnels, each holding a big underwater camera, searching the sea in front of them. Now they could see the big dark shapes distorted in the water just ahead. There were more than a dozen of them. The Zephyr moved right up on top of them, engine purring, then a little in front of them. Then the leading dark shape came surging up towards the surface to blow, and the others began to follow, and it was as if the world was rising up through the sea. Then the first one broke surface, in a great seething rush of massive shining black living hide, then there was the great sighing gush of its animal breath and the plume of steamy spray rose high and rainbowed, and Spider and Black Bob rolled off the gunnels into the water.

They rolled over the side with cameras whirring into the

crystal blue clouds of turbulence, and suddenly there all about them were the immense bodies slowly swimming through the cold blueness, great knobbled wings of flippers outstretched, like smiling airliners – fourteen great cows and bulls and seven calves loping beside their mothers – and there was nothing in the world but their streamlined animal bodies in the blue crystal sunshine and the great buffeting turbulence of the sea from their tails swirling, and then they were pulling away from the cameramen.

Zephyr One was about eight hundred yards ahead of them now. 'Cut the throttle right back, Dave,' Craig told Cartwright. The bows sank down, the motor just sputtering. He said to Katherine, 'Goggle up, gorgeous.'

She pulled the mask down over her nose and sucked it on tight, then she put the mouthpiece in. She grinned nervously at him around it. She sucked on the mouthpiece, then nodded. Craig said, 'Go,' and she rolled over the side in a flash of golden legs and crystal bubbles into the sea.

Suddenly she was in the other world, weightless, the sudden taste of compressed air and the roaring of her breathing, and then she was flying again. And it was blue and beautiful and free, bright sun-shot misty blue and clear, fading into blue infinity. She kicked and dived down ten feet, then looked around for Craig. There he was ahead, with his camera. He beckoned to her and swam down to twenty-five feet, carrying the camera in front of him in both hands. She dived down and came alongside him. The reefs were beautiful, all the colours. He dived down another ten feet, to about thirty-five, and she came down with him, then he signalled her ahead. She waved in the underwater wonderworld about her and swam; he watched her go, long smooth full-bodied woman, legs flipping against each other and her long gold hair streaming behind her. She was fifty feet ahead of him when out of misty water came the great dark shapes.

Came looming and looming, massive blurred shadows streamlining slowly out of the infinite blueness, bucking their tails way behind them in the mistiness, great mottled animals with the great smiling mouths and the little gentle beautiful eyes. Fourteen mighty humpbacked whales nearly fifty feet long came swimming towards and above them out of the crystal sea, and the seven calves bucking their tails faster. Craig had the camera up in front of him, filming the whales looming towards them. Then Katherine kicked her legs and held out her arms, and she went streaming up through the water, up to meet them.

Curving upwards into the path of the leading whale with her arms out to embrace the massive smiling animal, up up up into the path of the creature looming enormously bigger and bigger on top of her. The whale moved his great hulk away so as not to bump into her, and rolled a little onto his side and lifted his flipper up so as not to knock her, and it passed over her head in a living shadow and slipped past her and there was nothing in the world but its awesome animal body right against her, flesh and hide, and its massive shadow. She was washed down the side of the great living body, overwhelmed by the huge livingness of it. Now the mighty tail was looming up towards her, slowly beating. She was facing the tail, ready to duck and grab, and the whale suddenly arched its giant flukes upwards and out of the way so as not to bump her. Great friendly beast curving itself out of the way so as not to harm her, and the great prehistoric animal flesh sailed over her head. She kicked and reached up desperately and grabbed the tip of the mighty fluke with both hands and hung on tight, and suddenly there were whales everywhere.

Whales all over the place, whales to the left and whales to the right, whales above and more below, the sunlight blocked out by the great bulging bucking shapes. Shadowed above, below, and all about, and the surface was splashing silver, bubbling, fuming blue and white among the massive flesh, and somewhere up there the young woman was hanging on for dear life. The whale lightly shook his tail, which had the power of five hundred horses, and the little creature with the streaming hair hung on.

And it was as if the great whale decided not to shake Katherine Robinson off his flukes but to dive down and around and up again to play with her, to give her a ride. He hesitated a moment, then he arched his back and dived shallow with hardly a beat of his tail, then came slowly, gently around and back the direction he had come, and the other whales dived with him. Then the whale lifted his smiling head and glided up towards the surface with all the whales bucking and cavorting about him, and Katherine Robinson hung on to his tail all the way, arms and legs outstretched and hair streaming behind her. Craig was trying to keep the camera on Katherine when there was a great bucking shadow, and a rush of water knocked him sideways. Fifty feet of whale galloped past him up towards the silver surface and broke through with a mighty blinding crash of silver blue. The body went galloping through into the sunshine in joy and playfulness, gleaming animal bursting up into the sunshine with a smile on his knobbly face. Then he crashed down onto his side and the sea flew silver in all directions. The rest was very confused.

Suddenly there were whales leaping all over the place, flying for joy and surging flukes waving in the air and crashing down. And somewhere in the middle was Katherine Robinson of Boston, Massachusetts, still hanging on. Craig spat out his mouthpiece and bellowed, 'Katie, let go!' and all he could see was whale flukes everywhere but no Katherine Robinson hanging to any of them. He trod water hard and tried to push himself up out of the sea, and he bellowed at the Zephyrs that were careering around trying to herd flying whales about like cowboys. He rammed his mouthpiece back and dived again into the mass of galloping joyful giants, then he saw her.

She was way down there at fifty feet, still hanging on to the monster with the smile on his face, gliding up towards the silver surface, fading into the misty blue. Craig shoved his camera up desperately filming the disappearing beauty of it. Then the whale's head broke the surface and Katherine let go. All the whales were disappearing now. Blurred beating shadows again, going, going. The whole thing had taken perhaps two minutes.

She broke the surface and spat out her mouthpiece and shoved up her mask, watching them go, the tops of their backs breaking the sea, and then blowing, grandmothers and grandfathers and calves and all, their great tails slowly beating under the sun-shot blue sea. Katherine watched them go, panting, smiling all over her wet face, and the joy in her breast, and she was glad with all her heart for what she was going to do.

eight

The helicopter came rocking down onto the deck, blowing wind everywhere. Justin jumped through the propeller blast down onto the deck and ducked and scrambled out of the wind. Victor Gardner, the chief engineer, was standing at the engine-room doorway, smiling self-consciously. He stuck out his hand to shake Justin's, and he shuffled his feet and said into the helicopter noise, 'Home is the sailor, home from the sea and the hunter home from the hill. . . .' Commander Thorogood was up on the bridgewing and he gave Justin a smart salute. The helicopter blades settled down and Steve and Ross climbed out. The Zephyrs were still several miles away, heading back to the *Jubilee*.

Justin went striding to his suite. He took a run across his cabin and threw himself on his back onto the big double bed, arms outstretched. Then he drummed his heels on the mattress with delight. Then he jumped up. He stood with his hands on his hips, joyous. *Christ, it felt good! And God, it was good to be back!* He wanted to do a little dance all to himself. He strode back into the office, flung open the refrigerator, and grabbed a can of beer. He snapped off the cap and lifted the can to his bristly mouth and gulped, then pulled the can away with a smack of relish. He flung himself into one of the armchairs. Then he jumped up and went to the telephone on his desk to call the bridge. As he reached for it it buzzed, 'Magnus!' he sang into it.

'Good afternoon!' Commander Henry Thorogood said. 'And congratulations.'

'Thank you,' Justin said happily. 'I was on my way up to see you, I just want to shower and change. Any problems?'

'No,' the commander said. 'We only got it on the one o'clock news. Everybody aboard suspects it's you, but we've admitted nothing.' He added, 'We had a radio phone call from the *New York Times* a couple of hours ago.' Justin felt his pulse trip. 'Wanting your comment on the Japanese sabotage.'

He felt his stomach turn over once. 'Who handled it?'

'I did,' the commander said. 'I said you were in the water, unavailable. I gave them the prepared press statement.'

Justin breathed out.

'Okay. That's fine. If they call again I'll talk to them, to prove I'm here.'

The commander said, 'Katherine knows it was you. As you authorized.'

'How did she take it?'

'She was terribly impressed, I believe she said. We cracked a bottle of champagne.' He paused, then added, 'I think she's going to go along with it.'

'Well. That's great. We'll crack a few bottles of champagne tonight. Is she coming back to the *Jubilee* now?'

'I think Craig's coming back now, with her.'

'Call her on the radio and ask her to come in now, I must talk to her. Tell Craig and the other Zephyrs to keep following those whales and get some more footage before the light goes.' He did not want to talk to them yet, he did not really want to talk to the commander either yet. He said, 'Turn around and follow them slowly.'

'Jolly good,' the commander said. 'And jolly good show to you!'

Justin laughed. Solid oak, that's what you are, admiral, solid British oak. He felt bad for not inviting him down for a drink. He knew the old boy was bursting to hear all about the jolly old Japs. 'Thanks, commander. See you soon.'

He slammed down the telephone and took a big gulp of his beer. Then he drank it down. When he finished the beer, he strode into his sleeping cabin and turned on the shower. He slung off his clothes and stepped into the hot needlepoint spray and groaned, 'aah!' It felt glorious. He was more tired and tense than he realized. He scrubbed himself vigorously, sing 'Oh What a Beautiful Morning', then switched the shower to cold and yelped at the blow of it. He stood under it for a minute, then stepped out and rubbed himself dry singing 'The Surrey with the Fringe on Top'. He pulled on a pair of slacks, ran the comb through his hair, then decided to shave. He got himself another can of beer and plugged in the electric razor. He had shaved only around his mouth and one side of his face when there was a knock at the office door.

'Come in!' he shouted.

He went barefoot into the office. The door opened and Katherine Robinson walked in. She was radiant.

She was still in her bikini, her hair still wet, her eyes sparkling in her round face. She leaned back against the door and shook her smiling head at him, and she half laughed, 'Oh thank God.'

He stood in the centre of the cabin and looked at her. She had never seemed so beautiful. He wanted to take her in his arms and hug her tight.

'Thank God, you're back! When they told me what you'd been doing. . . !'

He laughed and opened his arms wide and stepped towards her, and then she was suddenly in his arms and he was holding her against him. It was the first time he had felt her almost naked against him, and it seemed the most wonderful feeling in the world and she was giggling, 'Oh God, Justin, you're a crazy man – I've never known a saboteur before!' That seemed the funniest thing they'd ever heard, and they were laughing and clutching each other. The feel of her cool, smooth body in his arms was extraordinary and she was saying into his shoulder, 'And I've just had the most marvellous experience. . . .' And then she was leaning back in his arms with his hands around her waist, and her eyes were shining. 'I had the most fantastic ride on a whale's tail – and that animal *liked* me! He was playing with me because he *liked* me! It was the most fantastic feeling, flying deep down into the water and then swooping up, and all the time this fabulous, friendly animal so big he could have killed me with one flick of his tail, but instead there was this wonderful feeling between us! And he knew it and I knew it, and he was being kind to me like a huge grown man to a little child, giving me a ride on his tail because he knew I was loving it and he was understanding me; he understood and he was loving me hanging on. Oh God, it was the most beautiful feeling of kinship and – *love*! Sort of brotherly love.'

And he knew and understood what she had felt and was feeling, and there was the strongest feeling in him also, seeing her excited like this, and all he wanted to do at that moment was kiss her, feel her beautiful body against him in his arms again. And he knew what he was almost definitely, desperately, going to do.

She rushed on, 'And then all the whales started leaping everywhere. All I knew was there were these gigantic figures swimming up all around me, and my whale swooped along with me hanging on – it was the most wonderful thing!' Her eyes were bright with tears. 'And, oh God, I understand how you feel about whales, about the whole of nature.'

'Are you coming to the Antarctic with us, Katie?'

'Oh yes!'

And he pulled her to him and hugged her tight, and, oh God, the feel of her smooth naked back under his hands, and the glorious soft curve of her hip, and her skin, and her breasts pressed against his chest, and her arms around him and her face laughing against his; it was the happiest, most sensuous feeling, and then he was kissing her. He was ready to pretend it was just a sort of half-kiss of gratitude if she protested, and he felt her laughing mouth resist one long moment, then it yielded, and they were kissing.

Kissing each other first softly hard, and then he groaned and her arms went up around his neck and she felt his heart beating against her and she breathed into his mouth, and they were kissing each other hard, their bodies pressed close together, her shoulders and breasts and belly and hips and thighs tight against him, and the sweet warm smell and taste of her and the lovely taste and feel of her wide sucking mouth and her golden skin. Then he broke the kiss and looked at her, and they both knew it and what they were going to do, and there was no surprise any more, only urgent human happiness, and he kissed her again, more gently, and his fingers went up to the little buckle of her bikini top and unclipped it, and the top slipped forward off her shoulders, and, oh God, the glorious, beautiful, naked feeling of her breasts pressed against his chest as she kissed him with her arms tight around his shoulders, and her naked belly and her thigh and the glorious naked feeling of her under his hands, and the joy.

nine

When he woke up it was not like that. They had made wild glorious love only once, and afterwards, lying panting and sweating on top of her, in her arms, nothing seemed to matter, whatever were the complications. Then somewhere, almost straightaway, he had passed out asleep. When he woke up, lying there with his eyes still closed, all he knew at first was the feeling: *Oh Christ, what have we done? Oh God, how do we handle this one, how and why why why did you do something silly like that after all this time? You know how important she is to you, how can you run this company without her – now what have you done? You've gone and ruined that relationship; you've gone and ruined that first-class relationship. . . .* Then he opened his eyes and looked for her and she was gone.

The sunset was streaming in the portholes. He looked – there was not a sign of her. She had even smoothed out the bedspread around him, puffed up the other pillow. He looked around: no note, not even a cigarette stub in the ashtray, not a sign of her. He collapsed back on the pillow and stared at the overhead. He lay there a long time, trying to think it out, but what he really wanted to do was to make love to her again.

He sat up. He wondered what she was thinking. She did not want to get hurt. Involved and then hurt. She thought him an all-time womanizer, thought he'd break her heart. No way was she going to get involved and get hurt. No way was she going to risk wrecking their good professional relationship. She was a professional, a career woman, she loved it here, she was not going to risk wrecking that. The woman is always the loser, she would think; she would be the one who would have to go if she had an affair with him and it went wrong. He looked around the cabin. She was gone, as if it had never been. He did not even know if she had slept, as he had. She was giving him this opportunity to pretend it had not happened. She had left no sign of herself, to tell him that she would also pretend that it had never happened, that tonight at dinner she would not embarrass him, that tomorrow they could work again together and he need have no fear of her and trouble.

That was smart. She was smart. He did not want to have to run this company without her. She was indispensable. She was so smart and sensible that he could telephone her cabin right now and say, 'Listen, Katherine, what are we going to do about this one?' And she would say, 'I think we better cool it, Magnus. This was a dumb thing to do. Too much is at stake. I don't want to lose this job. Or my heart. Anyway, how can this company run without me?'

He lay back on the bed, closed his eyes. He was not thinking any more. He was only feeling.

ten

They had a wonderful time that September, following the humpback whales off Bermuda. It was going to be one of the best films Magnus Oceanics had ever made. The whales were summering, mating, and suckling, before continuing their long migration north. With the first clear sun in the mornings there were usually whale spouts to be seen within half a dozen miles of the *Jubilee*. Sometimes whales played and slept around the ship all night and the crew could hear their sighing blows and their flukes slapping the water, and sometimes they could feel whales rubbing themselves against the keel.

Half an hour before sunrise the alarm clock went off at Justin's bedside. She felt for it in the dark and snapped it off. He was already awake, at work in his office next door. He was an early riser; when there was work to do he was always suddenly wide awake at five o'clock, no matter how late he went to sleep. When he heard the alarm ring he got up from his desk and went into his cabin. He sat down on the edge of the bed.

'Hello, beauty.'

She smiled her lovely early morning smile at him. 'Hello.' He bent and kissed her, and the warm, sweet, naked-woman smell of her made him happy.

He went and made some coffee. She was sitting up in bed when he came back, brushing her hair, her white breasts shaking as she stroked. She smelled of toothpaste. A toothbrush was all she kept in his cabin. 'Now I can kiss you properly,' she said.

He kissed her, and he felt swelling of his loins. Even to touch her the smallest bit made him feel like that. She said, 'The mornings are the best time to be with your lover. Why do you get up so early, Magnus?'

'Your lover or your love?'

'Same thing. I guess with me they have to be the same thing or it doesn't work.'

'It's working okay between us, huh?'

'Is it ever. When are we going to cool it?'

'Maybe we better start today.'

'Let's not spoil a beautiful day. How about tonight, after we've done it a few more times?'

'Maybe you're a sex maniac.'

'And I'm beautiful and my daddy owns a brewery.'

'I better cool it, I guess,' he said regretfully.

'I'm busy cooling it all the time. Haven't you got the message, Magnus? You must be dumb.'

'So are you. You got us into this,' he said. 'It's all your fault. It always is.'

'Shaking my ass at you all the time?'

'God spare me from dumb blondes shaking their asses at me. I'll never hire another one.'

'You'd better not!'

He laughed and bent forward and took her in his arms and hugged and rocked her, and she was laughing over his shoulder. And then they were kissing again and he was pulling off his shirt. She shifted over in the bed for him and he pulled back the blanket, and there lay his beautiful naked assistant, golden in the lamplight.

Afterwards they sat up and drank the coffee, which was now

cold, and smoked a cigarette. Then she went back to her cabin. She looked out of the office door first, into the alleyway, then gave a quick smile and waved over her shoulder and dashed out.

He did not see her again until breakfast, where they were very deliberately normal, even distant with each other, and almost never caught each other's eye.

A few times they slept in her cabin to vary the pattern of their movements. Her cabin and the principal guest cabin were immediately behind his suite, and they were very comfortable but considerably smaller, and they had only bunks. After a while she always came to his cabin, for it had the big double bed. Their discretion was elaborate. She did not come to his cabin until it was safely late, and she left early in the morning, which fooled almost no one for very long. In the company of the others they treated each other casually. But in the water he had her working with him most of the time, and his concern for her safety and comfort were more than one would expect. One day Craig came up to him on the foredeck. They were alone.

'Hello, kid,' Justin said.

Craig said, 'So. You and Katie have got together at last.'

Justin was surprised. Craig was smiling, but barely.

'What makes you think that?'

'Aw, come on. The way you treat her. You always take her in the water with you, on your camera, always giving her a hand with her gear. She's not paralysed.'

Craig's tone did not sound like banter, it sounded like resentment. 'I'm teaching her,' Justin said.

'Come on. She knows how to suit up and tank up and climb in and out of Zephyrs; she's been in several films before *Whale*.'

Justin stared at him, astonished. He thought, *Oh so.* But it was hard to believe. *Craig was jealous.* 'Something wrong?'

Craig was embarrassed, not smiling any more. 'No,' he said. 'Just curious.' He tried to smile. 'You're my brother, aren't you? I'm entitled to know.'

Justin did not know whether to let it go or not. Craig jealous? Of him? He put his hand on his shoulder.

'What?' It seemed the first time Justin had ever seen his brother blush.

Craig asked: 'Are you in love with her?'

Now Justin was embarrassed. He was going to say, 'I don't know yet, Craig,' but he said, 'Yes,' and then added more truthfully, 'I think so.'

He saw the flicker in Craig's eyes and his heart went out to him. Craig looked at him directly, now that it was out.

'You think so? After all the women you've been through?'

Justin still could not believe it. Craig? Who had been screwing everything he could get his hands on since he was twelve without a care in the world? He said, 'Yes, that's right.'

'After all those women, and you've been working with her for two years and suddenly you're in love with her?' He hesitated, then it came out in a rush, 'And? Are you . . .' he was going to say 'screwing her' but changed it to 'sleeping with her?'

Jesus. He was going to say, 'That's none of your business, kid.' It was almost funny. 'Kid,' he said finally, shaking his head, 'what is this? I'm sorry if this upsets you, Craig.' He put his hand on Craig's shoulder again. 'Would there be anything wrong if we were?'

Craig was blushing. He looked at the deck.

'No. Of course not.' He said defiantly, 'Not if you treat her right. She's not one of your usual broads.'

Justin stared at his brother.

Craig blurted out, 'She's wonderful.'

'I know.' He was very touched. 'She *is* wonderful. And I'm your brother. And she's nine years older than you are.'

Craig was still blushing. He clapped Justin on the shoulder. 'Forget I said any of that.'

Justin nodded. 'Sure.'

Craig was trying to smile. 'Forget I said it. And for Chrissake don't tell her I said any of it.'

'Sure. But she'd be flattered.'

Craig glared. 'Promise?'

'Sure.'

'Okay.' He thumped his brother's shoulder again. 'You're a lucky bastard, Magnus.'

'I know.'

'She's really something. I wish I was twenty-nine. Okay, I'll go now,' he said.

eleven

In the night the great beasts slept and sometimes they also played, and then the starlight was filled with their gushing, spouting, splashing. Night was the best time for the sound and electronics engineer to record whale songs. His rubber boat rocked quietly all by itself out there in the moonlight, a mile from the *Jubilee*. Hi-fi Bob sat festooned with wires, his complicated recording machines with the banks of dials and indicators in front of him, listening to the songs of the whales going onto his recording tapes, serenity on his usually grumpy face.

Justin rowed quietly in the moonlight out towards Bob's boat, with Katherine in the stern, facing him. Behind them the *Jubilee* lay twinkling, anchored. The moon shone big and bright, the sea ahead a great wedge of sparkling silver all the way to the horizon. Suddenly there was a great surge beside them and the Zephyr lurched.

A great slow heaving surge and the mass of black broke the water right beside them. Justin raised his oar so as not to knock the whale, and Katherine cried, 'Hello, boy!'

She held the side of the rubber boat to steady herself and leaned far over the side to try to touch the great black disappearing arc of hide.

'Oh,' she said, 'isn't it terrific to be so close to them?'

'It is.'

She made her hand into a fist, to express herself. 'It's so . . . primitive, somehow. Atavistic. Know what I mean?' She looked at him earnestly. 'Here we are right among them, this is how it

86

was at the beginning. When man lived right among hulks of flesh and blood and brains like this, they were an intrinsic part of his life, and he survived and coexisted with them and only hunted enough to keep himself fed. Do you know what I mean?'

'And the world was clean.'

'Yes. And the world was clean!' Her eyes were bright. 'And young. And everything flourished in its right place. And there was room enough for everything. And man was only part of the balance of nature. . . . That's what that creature makes me feel like – the world before the battles long ago.'

'And it wasn't so long ago,' he said. 'Only fifty years ago. Even twenty-five years ago the world was still young. After World War Two. There were whales everywhere. And the world's human population was *half* what it is now.' He nodded at the sea. 'That whale probably remembers those days.'

Then there was a mighty, seething, rushing sound in the silver moonlight and the sea parted on the other side of the boat, and a great knobbled head rose straight up out of the sea and she cried, 'Look!' It rose up up up, five feet above the sea, the huge head of the animal with the curved smiling mouth. The eye was staring at them, the black smiling head glinting silver black just six feet from them. For three long seconds they stared at each other, the immense animal and the two human beings. Then he sank back into the sea and was gone.

'Oh God.'

He knew what she was feeling because he felt it too. She slumped against the gunnel, eyes closed. She put her hands to her hair and rumpled it in joy.

'I'm so lucky . . . so privileged to have been here and seen it and felt it! There are millions of people who would appreciate that animal being right there but *I was there*! I saw him, I felt him!'

He smiled at her. 'Yes.'

Sighing, she put her hands together and sat there, gazing at the moonlight, looking for more words.

He said, 'The sadness of it, almost. Because of the danger it's in, of being destroyed by man. I mean the great beauty of it makes you want to cry.' He looked at her. 'It's so magnificent and close to the real essence of life that it seems the only way to express your appreciation of it, to cry.'

'Oh, yes.' She sat back and looked at him, not smiling. He understood. That was wonderful, that he understood.

Hi-fi Bob's Zephyr was silhouetted against the moonlit sea. Justin drifted his Zephyr up against it. Hi-fi Bob had seen them coming from a long way and he ignored their arrival. The sound engineer could be a most silent man. He had his earphones on and he was turning a dial on the recorder with irritated concentration. Justin tied the Zephyr's painter onto Bob's oarlock. Then he carefully reached into Bob's boat and lifted out two sets of earphones. He passed one set to Katherine. There was a small mouthpiece attached to each set, to enable listeners to talk to each other above the sounds coming through the earphones. Justin tapped Bob on the arm, and Bob turned with a scowl. 'What?' he demanded.

'Sound, please, Bob.'

'What?' He could not hear with his earphones on but he knew very well what Justin wanted.

'Sound?'

With a grunt, Bob snapped the auxiliary headphone switch. Suddenly the headphones were flooded with sounds.

It was the song of the humpback whales, coming up alive from the silent moonlit deep. It came in a thousand different modulations, long trills and high-pitched sighs and lilting moans and mewings and whoops and janglings and squeals and creaks and groans. It came from the deep, silent world of the ocean, the eerie haunting melody of another world. Katherine had heard a recording of whale songs before, but it was awesome to hear it come alive from the deep itself. She listened enthralled, eyes closed. It was like hearing a mountain speak.

As she listened with her eyes closed she could almost see the sounds come furling up out of the blue depths, from way way down there and from over there where the ocean sank away into dark infinity where neither the sun nor the moonlight reached.

Justin said quietly over the intercom to her, 'Listen carefully now. They're starting a new song. If you listen you'll notice that each song has a number of units, or themes. And there's always the same number of phrases in each theme. They repeat each phrase over and over but each time it's changed slightly, until the final phrase is completely different from the original one. Listen.'

She listened hard, then she began to hear the pattern, the themes, the ululating phrases repeated over and over with the change each time. She whispered over the intercom, 'Is this a chorus? Is this one whale or several singing together?'

'Several. A choir. That's another wonderful thing.'

'Oh God, it's wonderful. A choir. . . .'

They listened in the moonlight to the long song of the hump-back whales. Then a new note came into the chorus, a lone gentle series that went *ta-ta-ta-ta-ta*, then *trrrrrr*, and Justin spoke again.

'Here comes somebody new. That's his surprised voice, he's surprised to echolocate us up here and he's curious. He'll prob-ably stick his head up in a minute to look at us.'

As he said it the surface of the sea bellied up, ten yards away, and again a great silver black head rose glinting up up up in a slow rush, as big as the front of a taxi cab. For five seconds he stood on his tail in the water, watching them with unabashed curiosity. Then he subsided.

She sighed deeply. 'Oh. Oh. Oh.'

For another twenty minutes they listened to the songs. Then Hi-fi Bob spoke for the first time and his voice was gruff to con-ceal his self-satisfaction. 'These animals *come* to me. From all over.'

Justin said quietly over the intercom, 'I know they do.'

It was true. If there was a sound going on under the water, Hi-fi Bob was the man to pick it up. Day after day Bob rowed out from the *Jubilee* all by himself and set up his equipment and lowered his hydrophones deep into the canyons with an uncanny instinct for the right place in all the square miles of sea about him, and for the right depth. And it did seem that all the creatures of the depths came in on him, obligingly making all their mews, grunts, squeaks, rattles, songs, clicks, and thumps. It was said on the *Jubilee* that Bob Matthews may be the grumpiest man on earth, but down there in the water he was Saint Francis; that the only time Hi-fi Bob was not cussing was when he was rocking all by himself in his sound Zephyr, which was the only time he was happy. Justin had another theory, which was very close to the truth, which was that Hi-fi Bob Matthews was one of the happiest men on this earth because he enjoyed cussing, and that since he was either cussing or recording the sounds of sea animals all the time he was a very happy man indeed.

Bob Matthews was always threatening to resign from Magnus Oceanics and get a job in the Hollywood studios, where he could have named his own price. He had been threatening that for the last seventeen years, ever since Justin could remember. The fact was that Hi-fi Bob Matthews had a way with, an attraction for, and a knowledge of sea creatures that he could never abandon. Justin Magnus had seen this charm equalled only by his own grandfather, who had the ability to call wild birds out of the skies and forests to gather around him and eat out of his hand. It was a very rare quality born of a closeness to nature and a magnetism for its creatures, and love of those creatures, which Justin did not completely understand. He knew he himself had it a bit, but not as strongly as cussing, sweating, balding, freckled Hi-fi Bob Matthews.

Bob said, 'The record of this is going to be worth a fortune. And I *mean* a fortune. Never heard anything like it.'

Justin said, 'I think it is, Bob. What depth are you?'

'Sixty feet,' Bob said. 'Eight thousand cycles per second.'

'It's absolutely beautiful,' Katherine said. 'How do they do it if they haven't got any vocal chords?'

'No vocal chords,' Justin said. 'Squeezing their breath through their respiratory systems. Their blowholes. And their larynx.'

'Why do you think they're doing it?' she asked. 'I mean, what's going on in their minds?'

'Anything could be going on in their minds,' Justin said, 'but

90

I think this is simple happiness. Don't you think so? Communicating it to each other. Like men singing as they work.'

'Listen to this,' Bob grunted. He was turning a knob. Above the whale song came a new sound, a croaking.

'What's that?' she said.

Justin said, 'That's either a little sea horse or a squirrel fish. Or an ordinary croaker. Must be very close to the hydrophone. He makes that noise by strumming his muscles against his swimming bladder. The bladder amplifies the sound, like a drum. Hear it?'

She had her eyes closed, concentrating, an intent happy expression on her face. Justin went on, 'Drummers do the same thing. A toadfish also grunts like that, with his swimming bladder. When two males meet each other, they growl. Same system.' He smiled. 'But when a female toadfish passes his nest he whistles to her.'

'How the hell does he do that?'

'Like a bird, almost. I don't know, I'll look it up. But I think he must force air out of his swimming bladder, through his throat or nasal passages. Bob?'

'Yeah,' Bob said. 'I reckon.'

'Grunters also use their swimming bladders for amplification, but they make the noise by stridulation. Grinding their pharyngeal teeth. Filefish do the same thing, but theirs is a much more metallic sound. So do porcupine fish, but they can only do it when they're inflated, so presumably they only do it in anger. Or fear.' He added, 'Hell of a frustrating life, the porcupine fish's. Can only express anything when he's uptight. That's probably why he looks so miserable.'

They grinned at each other. She said, 'I want to swim with you with the whales.'

Later, after Bob had gone back, they swam together in the moonlight, the glorious satiny feel of nakedness in the sea. They came slowly together, holding on to the rubber boat, and kissed, and her arm went around his neck and she clung to him and opened her legs to him in the water. Then they broke the embrace and without a word he pulled himself up into the boat. She pulled herself up after him, the water rushing silver off her. She sat on the rubber gunnel dripping water, looking at him, then he reached out his hand to her and she took it.

He knelt down in the bottom of the boat. She came down beside him, then lay on her back, looking up at him. For a long moment he looked down at her, his beautiful woman lying down for him in moonlight. He slid down beside her and took her cool wet smoothness in his arms and he kissed her nipples. They were hard erect, and she sighed. He sucked her big hard nipple – the taste of salt sea was on her – and she groaned and stretched up her arms around his broad neck. He came down on top of her, and she opened her legs to him and moved her hands to his buttocks and drew him slowly, blissfully, sweetly in to her warm wet sweet depth. It was the most irrepressible feeling of joy, and she kissed his mouth, and he looked into her eyes and said, 'I love you, Katie.'

She looked at him a long moment, her eyes wide and serious, then she gave a big, slow sigh and whispered, 'I love you too, Justin Magnus.'

twelve

In the warm sun-shot turquoise waters off Bermuda, the *Jubilee* followed the whales slowly, the Zephyrs cruising far afield, filming them in the sunshine; and Katherine swimming with them, through the misty sparkling blueness. Justin took far too much film footage of Katherine, but it was good footage that fired his imagination of film series to come, and anyway that was not why he was doing it. He was doing it for the sheer beauty and joy of her, the artist's pleasure of creating something beautiful. And the nights were long and sultry, and starlit and moonlit.

Their discretion was still elaborate. She still did not sit next to him in the wardroom at the end of the day's work when most of them had drinks, or at the mess table. But it was an open secret. Halfway through that September Ross said to Justin, 'You're a lucky man. Meaning, Katherine.'

'I know it.'

Ross was sprawled in Justin's armchair. They were both still in their swimming trunks, hair matted, salty, drinking a beer. 'Why don't you come out in the open with it? Why doesn't she move into your cabin? It's big enough.'

Justin shifted in his chair.

'Maybe we will soon.'

'What does she do? Sneak off with the sunrise? That's a hell of a way to live.'

'Why the sudden anxiety about my domestic comfort?'

Ross sat up. 'I don't like it,' he said. 'It's a dangerous thing you're doing. Do it properly or not at all.'

'Meaning?'

'Hell, meaning that she's important to Magnus Oceanics. She's essential to management, really. And on film, now. I hope to hell you both know what you're doing. If the relationship goes sour, she goes. It's always the way. Then we'll have to replace her. And that'll be a hell of a job.'

'I know it.'

'Well,' Ross said restively, 'why doesn't she move into your cabin? Because you're playing it cool, huh?'

'Maybe we both are.'

'What do you mean maybe? *You* know what's happening, you can tell me, I'm very concerned about this, for Oceanics' sake. And for her sake. I'm not worried about *you*, you bastard.'

'Thanks, pal. Me, a bastard?'

'Well, I must confess you've steadied up a little over the last few years,' Ross said, 'but you've still got a terrible track record for loving 'em and leaving 'em. You're a cool customer. And that's not good enough for Katie.'

'Are you telling me to get married?' Justin asked with a smile. 'Is this something you and Mary have figured out for me? The recommendation of a happily married couple?'

'What I'm saying,' Ross said, not to be amused, 'is don't play it cool with that woman. Or Oceanics will lose her. Do it properly or not at all.'

'Maybe Katie's playing it cool,' Justin said. 'Have you thought of that?'

'Of course she is,' Ross said. 'Who would blame her? With your reputation? She doesn't want to break her heart. She also doesn't want to lose her job. But I think she's only cooling it to play it safe – I'm a very good judge of character. Henry Thorogood thinks the same, incidentally, though he's too proper to mention it. This is a serious matter, Justin.'

'I know it is. But I don't much like us being a subject of discussion by everybody.'

'What do you expect? Everybody likes her.'

'What are the others saying?'

'That you're a very lucky guy,' Ross said.

He knew he was. And he knew it was a serious matter. And he knew he was happy. It seemed he had never felt so good and strong and happy in his life.

They were careful, but everyone knew. Victor Gardner, down in the bowels of the engine room, in his little workshop, even wrote Katherine an ode. She found it pushed under her cabin door early one morning. It was a lovely little ode, and scanned perfectly, and its purpose was to wish her well. She went straight down to the engine room to thank him, into the hot, oily, shining hammering. 'Thank you, Victor!' she shouted, beaming. She threw her arms around him and kissed him on the cheek.

'Oh nothing, nothing.' Victor gave his craggy, shy smile. 'Come into my parlour. It's quieter.'

Victor was only about fifty years old, but he looked much older, with a hawknosed face and heavy pouches under sad eyes and grey hair that he was always smoothing self-consciously. Once upon a time, somewhere, there had been a wife, but nobody knew anything about her. On the *Jubilee* he was very seldom seen. He had most of his meals down in the engine room and sometimes even slept in his workshop. And he wrote poetry there.

He led Katherine into the little workshop. There was the bunk he had rigged for himself, high above his gleaming lathe, and his shelves of books and his kettle and teapot and the little foldaway table. 'It's a lovely ode,' she said.

'Oh no, no.' Victor shook his head and he did his peculiar little shuffle that might be the very beginning of a preoccupied dance step. 'It's only a hobby.'

'We never see you,' she said. 'Why don't you come up topside more?'

'Oh, I'm very comfortable in my shell,' Victor said. 'Don't worry about me. I like it down here. My machines need me. And it gives me plenty of time to fiddle with my odes and things.'

'I'm touched. I've never had an ode written to me before.'

'Well,' Victor said, embarrassed, 'it wishes you lots of love.'

She would not move into Justin's big cabin yet, but one day she would.

On the thirtieth day of September, the *Jubilee* film crew hung in the water from their Zephyrs, their filming over, masks pulled off, watching the last pod of humpback whales slowly leaving, spouting, mothers and fathers and grandparents and calves gambolling, heading away. Justin clung to his Zephyr and reflected: *The holiday is over . . . and now begins the serious business.* October and November. At the end of November the Russian whaling fleet would arrive at the Antarctic. He clambered up into his Zephyr and sat there, dripping, watching the last of the humpback whales leave, and he turned his whole mind to what he was going to do.

It was a Magnus tradition to have a party at the end of a film job. If they were near a port it was usual to invite the local dignitaries and press and whatever women that Craig could muster; it was good publicity. Justin had intended to sail for Hamilton, Bermuda, late that afternoon and anchor off the yacht club that evening and go on the town. The next day they would take on fuel and provisions and have the party. But when he got back to the *Jubilee* that afternoon there was an apologetic Commander Thorogood to greet him.

'I'm sorry, but Max Hagen just radio-telephoned from Los Angeles.' He added, 'For Miss Robinson. And then you.'

'What the hell did he want?' Justin demanded.

'He's flying out to Bermuda tonight.' Justin's eyes widened. Henry Thorogood went on, 'That's my fault. I was taken by surprise. If I'd known I'd have said that we were sailing tonight for Panama. But he asked very naturally, very conversationally when we were finishing here. And I told him probably today or tomorrow, then we're putting into Hamilton thereafter for provisioning and the party.' He looked apologetic. 'Then he asked for Miss Robinson. I said she was in the water. Then he asked for you, said he had some urgent business to discuss with you. I said you were in the water, too. Then he said fine, he had to come to see you, he would leave on tonight's plane for Hamilton.' He shook his bearded head once. 'I'm sorry.'

'Damn! Damn, damn, damn!' Justin said. 'I don't want him snooping around this ship when we're stuffed to the eyeballs with explosives and limpet mines!'

'Mea culpa,' the commander said. 'I should have been on guard.'

Justin waved his hand, exasperated. 'Nor do I want him giving me a long lecture on how I should be running the god-damn company. Nor getting uptight about Katie.' He thought. 'Look, telephone him right now before he gets on that goddamn plane. Tell him you've just spoken to me on the radio, I'm five miles away in a Zephyr, we're *not* going to Bermuda, we're going direct to Panama tonight – in one hour, in fact. Tell him I'll call him back tomorrow, but try to find out what the hell he wants.' He looked at the commander. 'But for God's sake stop him coming here. Tell him that the helicopter's under repair. That's it – the starter motor's out, Victor's repairing it.'

Twenty minutes later Henry Thorogood rang Justin in his cabin. He had just spoken to Max. He said, 'He's most upset – angry in fact. He thinks you're trying to avoid him.'

'What did he say?'

'He refused to tell me what he wanted. I told him we're going straight to Panama in one hour. He didn't believe me, he sort of said uh-huh, as if he was expecting that. He asked for Miss Robinson again, I said she's in the water. Then he said he'd call back in an hour and just hung up.'

Justin stood in his towel, dripping from his shower. 'Max is just the kind of guy to check up on whether or not we went to Hamilton. Maybe we had better go direct to Panama. Have we got enough fuel?'

'I anticipated that question. Yes we have. I agree with you.'

He thought for a second, then said, 'I'll brief Katherine,' and hung up. Then he phoned Katherine, who was showering in her own cabin, and explained it all to her.

An hour later she came into his cabin. Max had just telephoned her. She said, 'He didn't want to speak to you at the end. He just hung up on me.'

'What the hell's his problem?'

'Me. The same thing. He wants me to quit here and go to work for him.'

'Oh.' For some reason he felt relieved. He didn't know why, what else was he expecting? That Max suspected that he had done the Japanese sabotage and was sleuthing on him? That he somehow knew about the Antarctic operation? That was impossible – it was just tension. 'What did he say about coming to Bermuda?'

She said, 'That's what he's decided to do. He said he didn't believe we were heading straight for Panama because the grey whales don't get to Baja California until December. He said you were trying to avoid him. He said he wants a showdown between us, between him and me.'

Again he was relieved.

'God,' he said. 'The man's forty-eight years old. Hasn't he learned to accept a setback gracefully yet?'

She sat down and said flatly, 'All his life he's had his own way. The great good-looking Max Hagen in the Magnus films.'

Justin smiled. Katie was perceptive, but he wasn't sure that Max Hagen was not in love at last.

He said, 'So he's coming to Bermuda anyway?'

She sighed. 'He said he was coming at his own expense, you couldn't stop him. He said you were hiding something from him.'

'Hiding something? What?'

'I asked him what, all he said was I was covering up for you. Then he slammed down the phone.'

Justin felt the tension come back. Hiding something? Max knew. Oh Jesus. Or Max thought he knew, Max suspected something. But how the hell could he know? He couldn't know – or he couldn't have any grounds for suspicion. But they sure as hell couldn't have Max making a scene in Bermuda and spoiling everything. Justin made up his mind.

'Well, we're not going to Bermuda.' He picked up the phone and buzzed the bridge. 'Henry? Hotfoot for Panama.'

'Yes,' the commander said, 'I think so.'

'And I don't want Max showing up there either, on vacation. When he calls again, tell him we're taking twenty days to get there. By then we'll be clear through Panama and into the Pacific, under any weather conditions. Max will be furious, but what the hell.' He added, 'We'll bunker and reprovision in Acapulco. That's a good place to show the flag anyway. Lots of tourists. And we'll be obviously heading north to Baja California.'

part three

thirteen

She lay off Acapulco harbour, all lit up in the hot sunset, one hundred and eighty feet of swift ship, with white superstructure and hull of midwatch blue. The funnel was floodlit, and her lights sparkled in the water. Around her were clustered many pleasure craft, small boats, and yachts. The Zephyrs did a taxi service back and forth to the jetty, and the wardroom and the decks were full of the beautiful people of Acapulco, mostly tourists. Craig Magnus had done very well. There were two journalists, one a Mexican whose name Justin did not catch and the other a *New York Times* reporter on vacation, a young woman named Snell, whom Justin had met before.

The party was a great success. Early on, at the formal stage before his guests got too drunk, he gave his speech. He had prepared it carefully, to establish their alibi that the *Jubilee* was heading north and going to disappear into the lagoons of Baja California for several months to film grey whales, and he delivered it well. Then he launched into an impromptu impassioned plea to his audience to support the Save-the-Whale Campaign, which developed into his favourite fiery lecture. Justin Magnus had a flair for the theatrical and he spoke with a histrionic fervour designed to put the fear of God into his audience. 'If the oceans should die, as they will unless we stop polluting the continental shelves with sewerage and industrial waste, unless we stop oil pollution coating the sea and preventing oxygenization . . . if the oceans should die, a charnel-house horror will ensue. First will come the colossal stench of the decaying organic matter, rising off the sea. It will be impossible to live along the coasts of the world because of the stench, and everybody will be driven far inland. And with the rotting vegetation on the top of the rotting dead sea, the vital evaporation process will stop. The climates and rainfalls depend on evaporation, and when it stops there will follow droughts and terrible famine. And with the death of the algae in the seas and with the death of the vegetation on the land because of the terrible droughts, there will come about a shortage of the oxygen we breathe, for oxygen is made by vegetation, and there will follow worldwide breathlessness.

'The oceans keep the balance between the different salts and gases upon which our very lives depend, and when the oceans die, the carbon dioxide content in the atmosphere will rise and rise until it forms a shroud around the world. And from this a greenhouse effect will develop – the heat rising upward from the earth will be trapped beneath the stratosphere making the air and sea temperatures rise, and then the polar ice caps will melt and flood into the seas, and the level of the rotting sea will rise one hundred feet in a few years, inundating many of the world's major cities.

'If the oceans should die, man will die within fifty years, trapped starving on high mountains between dead rotting seas, starving and gasping for oxygen. . . .'

It was a good, moving speech, and it held his audience rapt. He was gratified to see that the two members of the press appeared to be getting it down verbatim. As soon as he finished, Miss Snell, the New York reporter, came up to him. 'Do you mind if I ask a few questions, Justin? I'd like to do a feature story. It's so lucky I was here when you were.'

'Sure.' He was also glad to get a story in the *New York Times*. But he didn't feel like being interviewed, he wanted Ross to help. 'Ross,' he called. Ross came over. 'This is Ross Evans, our general manager. He'll handle some of the questions.' The Mexican journalist came up to them when he saw Miss Snell getting to work.

Miss Snell said, 'Apropros of your speech about whales, what do you think of the recent sabotage of the Japanese whalers in Yokohama harbour?'

Justin was ready for it. He said, 'I'm delighted.'

'Have you any idea who did it?' the Mexican asked.

Justin grinned at him. 'None. I presume they're people who feel outraged by the ruthless Japanese slaughter of whales to the point of extinction, regardless of world opinion. Regardless of the enormous cruelty, the terrible animal suffering that whaling entails.'

'But why specifically are you delighted?' Miss Snell said.

He took a breath. He would answer the question his way. 'Because man has butchered the great whales almost out of existence. Over two million whales have been slaughtered in the last fifty years alone, Miss Snell. To the point where now *all* eight species of great whales are in danger of extinction!'

He studied her face and again he had the despairing feeling that one can never properly impress people with those facts: whales are remote, the words *extinction* and *millions* unmeaningful abstracts. And once again he was reminded, as he was every time he wrote a book or shot a foot of film, *You've got to educate them.*

'The blue whale, Miss Snell, the greatest animal *ever* to have lived on this earth of ours – bigger than any prehistoric monster – the blue whale is already at the very brink of extinction!' He looked at her. 'Only *a few hundred* are left in the whole wide world.' He waved his hand. 'So few they cannot even find each other to breed. The northern right whale is the same. These species are all commercially extinct already. The finback whale, the second biggest after the blue, is also being driven to the brink of extinction. So is the southern humpback. Now they're killing off the smaller great whales – the minke and the sei.' He glared at Miss Snell without meaning to. 'Because whales are in danger of extinction, Miss Snell, *that's* why I'm delighted about the Japanese whalers being sunk! Because whales are magnificent animals! Because they're beautiful. Because they're so intelligent – many scientists say they are as intelligent as man. And once these magnificent animals are gone, they are *gone*. The miracle of their creation will never be repeated.'

He waited for Miss Snell to get down that quotable quote. Ross nodded encouragingly, Justin continued. 'And why?' He looked at them both. 'Why is it necessary in this modern day to slaughter whales like this? What for?' He said it bitterly, 'To make *shoe polish*, Miss Snell! And lipstick! And pet food for cats, and dogs! And so the Russians can feed their mink and sable to make furs for rich capitalist ladies. Even though there are plenty of cheaper commercial substitutes for the ingredients of shoe polish and lipstick and the contents of kitty and doggie food cans – without destroying one of the wonders of the world.'

The Mexican said diffidently, 'Whale meat is also an important part of the Japanese national diet, Mister Magnus.'

'Bullshit. Forgive me, but bullshit.' He looked at Ross. 'Can you handle that question, please?'

'Certainly.' Ross cleared his throat and said earnestly, 'That's what the Japanese whaling authorities claim. But in fact whale meat constitutes less than *one* per cent of the Japanese people's protein intake. Less than one per cent. The rest of the whale meat goes into catfood cans for export. And the Japanese are massive exporters of fish, which *is* the most important part of the Japanese national diet. If they can afford to export fish they can afford to stop eating their one per cent of whale flesh.'

Justin caught Katherine's eye across the room while Ross was talking. She tried to give him a warning look.

Ross went on, 'But no, they keep on killing. That's why we're pleased this has happened, Miss Snell. Every other pelagic whaling nation has given up whaling. The British, the Dutch, the Norwegians, the Greeks. They've all urged the Japanese and Russians to stop too. The United Nations has called for a moratorium on whaling three times. At the United Nations Conference on the Human Environment at Stockholm in 1972, they voted fifty-three to nil for a halt to whaling. Again at the United Nations Environment Programme in Geneva and Nairobi, they made unanimous calls to stop whaling. The Russians and Japanese just ignored these international pleas. There have been repeated demonstrations and picketings and organized boycotts of Japanese and Russian goods by conservation groups. *All* to no avail. That's why we're happy.' He added, uncharacteristically for Ross at a press conference, 'Because nothing else has made the bastards stop whaling!'

'May we quote you saying that?' Miss Snell said. ' "Bastards"?'

'Certainly,' Ross said.

'What about the International Whaling Commission?' the Mexican asked. 'Haven't they done a great deal to protect the whale population?'

'The International Whaling Commission?' Ross was enjoying himself now. 'You know what they are, don't you? They're not part of the United Nations. They're just a club of whalemen formed after the war in a so-called effort to quote regulate whaling and preserve whale stocks, unquote. Every whaling nation joined – and why? Because under the commission's charter every nation had the power to veto the commission's regulations. So the Russians and Japanese joined just so they could veto any regulations that cut down on the quotas of whales to be killed each season. And the commission itself was completely ineffectual. They knew whales were being shot out of existence and they did *nothing* to stop it. They hired independent statistical experts to advise them on blue whale stocks. The experts told them that the blue whale would soon be extinct unless totally protected – and the commission took another five years to implement the advice! When the blue whale *was* commercially extinct, not worth hunting any more, *then* the Japanese and Russians withdrew their veto. The commission created a whale sanctuary. Big deal! Where? In an area where it's known there are hardly ever any whales. The experts also advised the commission that the blue whale was not sexually mature – couldn't reproduce itself – until it was eighty-four feet in length; yet the commission ruled that a blue whale may be shot when it reaches only seventy-four feet in length – *when still sexually immature.*'

Justin took over and said slowly, 'The International Whaling Commission obviously considered the blue whale too valuable an animal to be allowed to live.'

Miss Snell got that down. She looked at Justin expectantly; she wanted Justin Magnus to talk, not Ross Evans.

Justin went on, 'Now the blue whale is almost extinct. Now

the whalers are driving the next biggest, the finbacks, to the point of extinction. Next it will be the sei and the minke. And they not only hunt in the Antarctic but also in the whole Pacific. The Japanese also hunt with a Chilean company off the west coast of South America in the Humboldt Current, which is the migrating route for Pacific whales to the Antarctic. On the average, every fourteen minutes a great whale is killed, do you know that? Every fourteen goddamn minutes! A long, slow, agonizing death. They even tried to hunt the Californian grey whale in its annual migrations down the American coast to their breeding grounds in Mexico. Those bastards will stop at *nothing*. Unless they *are* stopped.' He glared at them both, then nodded with satisfaction. 'And now somebody has at last had the guts and common humanity to try to stop them.' He looked at Miss Snell. 'That's why I couldn't be happier with what happened in Yokohama, Miss Snell.'

He decided to wrap it up. He had said more or less what he wanted to say and what was expected of him. He saw the commander waiting to speak to him. He could not see Katherine. The Mexican journalist said, 'What do you think is going to happen to the Russian whalers?'

This was the one he did not want to talk about. He pretended to misunderstand.

'They'll have less competition for the remaining whales, so I presume they're delighted, too.'

'I mean do you think the saboteurs are likely to sabotage them, too?'

He looked surprised that he should be asked it. 'I've absolutely no idea.'

'But you must hope so.'

Justin looked at him and tried to look grimly amused. 'Put it this way. My heart does not bleed for the big Japanese banks and industries and manufacturers of motor cars and cameras who are the stockholders in the Japanese whaling companies. My heart would not bleed for the Kremlin either.' He glanced at Ross. Ross raised his eyebrows approvingly. 'Thank you for your interest, both of you. Will you excuse us now, we must get back to the party.'

He took his leave of them and walked up to Henry Thorogood. The commander said, 'Great news, I'm afraid. Max has arrived. Heard we were here and flew down this afternoon.'

'Oh Christ,' Justin said.

'He's with Miss Robinson. On the foredeck. Talking.'

He was astonished to find Max so good-humoured. He had expected him tense and resentful and looking for trouble, or frostily polite at best. But when Max saw Justin he gave him a bright smile and started making his way to him through the guests. He looked tanned and handsome and well, in white slacks, shoes, and shirt, and a tie and a blazer. Katherine was following him, and she looked normal. Then she turned towards the bar. Justin came up to him and took his hand. 'Hello, Max. This is a surprise.'

'Well,' Max said, looking around at the guests, particularly the women, 'I heard you were in Acapulco, so I thought I'd jump on a plane this afternoon and come and see the old ship. It was really lucky to arrive in the middle of a party.' He looked back at Justin. 'I take it I'm welcome?' But he said it pleasantly.

'Of course, Max, you're welcome any time. Aren't you getting a drink?'

'Katie's getting me one.' He eyed the women appreciatively again. He was a little fatter, and maybe a little thinner on top, than last time, but Max wore extraordinarily well considering the way he lived. Justin admired the man's clothes. He always managed to look impeccably casual. Max turned back to Justin. 'Katie – she's quite a girl, isn't she?' He lit a cigarette, blew out the smoke, and said, 'I came at my own expense, not the company's, by the way. I thought I'd take a few days' vacation, since you guys were here.'

'Sure,' Justin said, 'why not?' He thought, *A few days' vacation – thank God for that.*

'And to discuss one or two things with you,' he said lightly. 'Business.'

'Sure,' Justin said. 'We can talk about it now, if you like, we sail tomorrow. Where're you staying?'

Max said slowly, 'Right here. In the guest cabin. You've got empty bunks all over the place, everybody's got their own cabin now.' He looked at him hard. 'I take it I'm welcome. I *am* still a member of the Oceanics board, even if in name only. *And* a substantial stockholder. Though not,' he added, 'fifty-one per cent.'

Justin thought, *Here we go, good old Max.* He said, 'I presumed you meant you'd stay ashore, because we're sailing tomorrow.'

Max looked at him and Justin knew that all the friendliness had been an act.

'Sure. You're going to Baja California for the greys. We all know that. You've made enough noise about it.' He said, 'I'm coming with you for a few days. Love to see the old Baja again. Assuming I'm welcome, of course.'

Justin understood now, and his reaction was to take no more crap. He was about to say, 'No you're not welcome, Max,' but he cut it back. He had to know what Max was up to. And maybe diplomacy was still the best way to handle it.

'How will you get back to Acapulco from Baja? There's no air service.'

Katherine came up with Max's drink and handed it to him. 'Thank you, sweetheart,' he said. He gave her his charming smile, and she smiled back, then gave Justin a glance.

Max seemed about to say something to Katherine, then he said airily, 'Get back to Acapulco from Baja? I've hired a helicopter, to come and fetch me, I just have to buzz them on the radio when I want them. Surprisingly cheap, considering. Besides,' he said, 'why not, it's my vacation.'

Justin thought, *Oh Christ. That helicopter is going to come when I say so, not Max. If I can't get rid of him tomorrow morning.*

'Really? Which operator is that?'

Max shrugged. 'Private outfit, friend of mine. Well,' he said looking at Katherine and then Justin, then sweeping a hand around the ship, 'Nice life you have. Like the old days, even. I thought Oceanics didn't throw parties any more.'

'We always have a party at the end of a job if we're near port. Good publicity.'

Max said, eyebrows up, 'End of a job? Last job you finished

was the humpbacks off Bermuda four weeks ago. Didn't you have one there?'

Katherine said crisply, 'I told you on the phone we weren't stopping at Bermuda.'

'So you did. I didn't—' he was going to say 'believe you' and changed it to 'I was very surprised. Why didn't you, Justin?'

All right, Justin thought, *maybe this is all it's about, the guy feels he was snubbed.*

'We decided to skip Bermuda and get on south, we'd had enough of those waters.'

Max said brightly. 'Spent a lot of time in the water, did you? I imagined you spent most of it elsewhere.'

Justin felt a flash of anger but he snapped it under control. Katherine was furious. She flashed at Max, 'As a matter of fact we did.'

'Did what?'

'We did a lot of good work, Max,' Justin said. 'How long do you intend to stay aboard?'

'*Intend*, indeed? Oh, a week or two. Maybe three, I've got plenty of vacation accumulated – and I *am* the boss of Communications, I believe? But,' he gestured at Katherine, 'it must be nice, you two working together, very nice.'

'It is,' Katherine retorted. 'Very nice. Excuse me—'

'Don't go, Katie,' Justin said sharply. He wanted to say to Max: 'Oceanics is the ultimate boss of Communications, buster, and don't you forget it.'

'No, don't go,' Max said. 'We've all just got together again.' Justin was thinking fast through his anger. He was going to get rid of Max even if he had to fire him – and maybe that was the answer. And right now it wouldn't be hard to bring himself to do it.

'You say you have some business to discuss,' he said. 'I'd like to discuss it now. In my office.'

Max shook his head and swallowed a mouthful of bourbon.

'I'm far too tired. Rather complicated too.' He was enjoying himself. 'Account books,' he said. 'The auditors are working on Oceanics' books at the moment and there're a few things we don't understand.'

Justin was taken aback. 'The *account* books?'

Katherine demanded, 'What's wrong with them?'

'Oh, nothing *wrong*! Just things that we find surprising.' He looked at Justin. 'I was going to say *sinister*, but, of course, that's quite the wrong word. But something that the auditor and I,' he gave a little puzzled frown, 'found *inexplicable*. That's the word. And particularly I, as a stockholder.'

'Oceanics' accounts are an open book. If you have a gripe you can bring it up at the annual meeting in April.'

Max pretended surprise. 'I thought you said we could discuss it right now in your cabin? And as for the annual meeting,' he cocked his head and wagged a finger, 'you're wrong there. I've taken legal advice, you see. A stockholder can approach the company with his gripes at any time. Particularly about the account books.' He gave Justin a wide charming smile. 'And now if you'll excuse me I think I'll circulate a bit. It's quite a treat for me to be back aboard. And I'm also tired.' He dropped his hand on Justin's shoulder heavily, then patted Katherine on the hip. 'See you later, my dear.'

He was gone through the crowd, beaming appreciatively at the ladies.

Katherine stared at Justin. 'What the hell was all that about?'

'Bastard,' he said. 'He knows something.'

'What? What can he possibly know? You haven't been cooking the books to cover the costs of this Antarctic operation or I'd have noticed it.'

'No,' Justin said. 'The books are wide open. The only things that are on them are the new silver-zinc batteries for the submarine and the six electrically heated aquasuits. And some radio equipment. All of which can be innocently explained. The explosives I paid for myself. And the Japanese air tickets.' He pulled out a cigarette and stuck it in his mouth angrily. 'What the hell's he up to?'

She asked, 'How can he come to Baja California? We're leaving as soon as we get there. How're you going to get rid of him?'

'I'll get rid of him all right. Even if I have to tie him hand and foot and shove him into our own helicopter and fly him back to

Acapulco. Even if I have to fire him. Which won't be so hard,' he added. 'Just let him make one scene.' He pulled on his cigarette. 'But I've got to find out what he's up to.' He was thinking aloud. 'I can't just shove him off until I know what he's doing, I can't sail off to the Antarctic with that guy suspecting anything and just aching to stick a knife in my back. In all our backs. And we all end up in a Russian salt mine for life. Or dead.'

'What're you going to do?'

'What did he say to you when you were outside with him?'

'He was perfectly civilized. He asked me to come back to Los Angeles. He said he'd come to try to sort something out with me. And so on. And I heaved a sigh of relief, he was being so nice about it. I very nicely said no. No way. But nicely, and he seemed to accept it. Then he starts on us in here.'

'Does he know about us?'

'He didn't mention it. Nor did I.'

He thought. 'Maybe he just wants more time to work on you.' Then he shook his head. 'He's trying to shake me up. And he doesn't want to get off this ship tomorrow. That means he's not going to show his cards until after we sail. He won't have a show-down with me in the morning. Not until he knows I can't kick him off. And I *can't* kick him off – I can't turn him loose until I know what the hell he's up to. We can't set off on this operation with that guy knowing anything. Too much is at stake. And that means we'll have to take the bastard at least to Baja California.'

'God,' she said. 'God.'

'Jesus,' he said softly. 'Why did this have to happen now?'

'Maybe it's just resentment.'

He took a big angry breath. *What can the man possibly know? How? Maybe all he does want is another chance to work on Katherine. And maybe it is just resentment.*

'We've got to find out about that helicopter. So we can make sure they come to fetch him. Tomorrow first thing, Ross must go ashore and make inquiries.'

'Yes.'

He looked around for Commander Henry Thorogood. He saw Ross. He said to Katherine, 'Ask Ross to meet me in my cabin in a few minutes. You too. I'll go and look for the Admiral, they better know about this. Maybe they've got a few bright ideas about how I tackle Max in the morning.'

'How do you think you're going to do it?'

'Diplomatically,' he said.

After he had gone she stood still a moment, alone in the crowd, feeling the nervous tension in her chest and also something like nausea. It was not because she was afraid of Max. She was afraid of everything that lay ahead and, beyond that, dismayed, and Max brought it all home to her.

fourteen

The party finished at three a.m. and by that time Max Hagen had drunk a great deal of bourbon. At nine o'clock the next morning, Justin knocked on his door. He got no answer. The door was locked. Max appeared at eleven o'clock, smartly dressed and well groomed but complaining of a hangover. Justin invited him into his office. He said straightaway, 'Whatever the trouble is between us, Max, I want us to bury the hatchet.'

Max smiled. 'I agree.'

Justin was so surprised he wanted to shake his hand like a schoolboy. He said feelingly, 'Good. Great. Now what was the other problem, about the accounts?'

Max lit a cigarette and uncrossed his legs, and made up his mind. 'It's nothing much,' he said. 'It's nothing that can't wait. I'm upset about those new silver-zinc batteries for the submarine. Why was that expense necessary? The lead-acid batteries are quite good enough for our purposes.'

Justin heaved an inward sigh of relief. 'The silver-zinc are well worth it, Max. They give us well over twice the submerged time before we have to surface and recharge. Which is always a damned nuisance, particularly when we film migratory animals like whales and dolphins. And their life is twice as long. And when they're finished the silver is worth a lot. They're a good buy.'

Max's eyes were hooded. 'Well, it's done now,' he said. 'But the lead-acid were really good enough. At the annual meeting I'm going to have a gripe and propose that the dividend appropriation account be adjusted.'

Justin nodded. He was waiting for Max to ask about the new aquasuits and radio equipment. He didn't. He just sat there. Casually Justin asked, 'So? How long will you be with us?'

'Only a few days. I'd like to take a look at the Baja, that's all. A few dives. And a rest.' Resentment appeared briefly on his face. 'I miss the ship life.'

Justin understood that. If he were cut off from it he would probably die, he thought. He said, 'Sure.' He felt a little embarrassed but he wanted to say it, to bury the hatchet completely. 'I'm sorry it had to work out like that, Max.'

Max looked at him. 'Since we're being frank – I couldn't work under you. Take orders from you. Since we're being frank – you're not good enough to give me orders.'

Justin nodded politely, understanding how the man felt. Max was one of the best underwater cameramen in the business and he was fifteen years his senior and had taught him a great deal of what he knew.

'You got the company out of debt,' Max went on, and there was more bitterness in his voice. 'Big deal. Anybody could have done that with the luck you had, the film subjects we were making. And firing half the staff. And being a slave-driver.' Justin thought, *Here we go again*. But he admired the man's honesty, and it helped to get it off his chest. He wasn't going to argue. 'And with the magic name Magnus.' Max grunted. 'Sure, you've done some good things; I'm not saying you haven't. I'm just saying that I also know this business inside out and I'm the best underwater cameraman – and director, probably – that you'll find. And I was with the Old Man from the beginning almost, when you were a kid. And you're not good enough to dictate to me.'

'Fine,' Justin said. 'Fair enough. I respect your opinion. Is it too early for a drink?'

Max refused, holding up a hand. 'But,' he slapped his knees and stood up to go, 'I'm not making myself miserable about it. At least I'm my own boss up there in L.A.'

Justin got up too. 'You're doing a very good job,' he said.

'Sure I am. And I enjoy it. But I like to come to the old ship occasionally for a few dives.'

Justin thought, *If the guy's acting, he's a damn sight better actor than I gave him credit for.* There was just one other matter to straighten out between them. He went to his refrigerator and got out two beers. 'Have a drink, Max?' he said.

'All right,' he said grudgingly. 'Gin.' He went to the liquor cabinet and got it himself.

Justin decided to move a step further. He wasn't looking forward to this, but it was best to make it clear right now. Max would make an unpleasant scene if he found out later. And maybe it would also make him leave now. 'Max?' Max turned to him. 'I understand something of your feelings for Katherine.' Max stiffened. 'I feel for you, because she's a wonderful person. I'm sorry if this hurts you, but it's fairest for all of us for you to be told. Katherine and I have developed a very close relationship now.'

Max had his drink poised in front of his mouth, staring at him, and Justin saw the emotion flash across his face. Then he blinked and his face was a mask.

'I thought so.' He took a slow sip of his drink, staring Justin in the eye. 'I goddamn well thought as much.'

'I'm sorry, Max.'

'Jesus,' Max said. He put down his drink. His eyes were cold. 'If there's one thing I'd never do it's take away my friend's girl.'

Justin said quietly, 'I don't think she was your girl at the time, Max. Or, if she was, that I took her away from you. She left of her own accord.'

'Don't give opinions on things you know nothing about. You weren't there, and she damned well would have been my girl if you hadn't pulled her back here.'

112

Justin said, 'I'm sorry, Max.'

Max looked at him a long, hard moment, then turned and walked out of the cabin.

At noon they sailed. Max Hagen was in his cabin.

fifteen

In Baja California, on the west coast of Mexico, there are many lagoons, blue, tentacled, meandering deep into the rolling sand dunes, connecting each other. Some are narrow and very shallow, and some are very deep and many miles wide, winding on and on. There are many secret places, and a good sailor can get lost. In the Mexican winter the great grey whales come down from the Arctic to the warm lagoons of Baja California to give birth and to mate.

Then the vast winding lagoons are full of their wallowing and spouting. Amorous bulls mill about a coy amorous cow, trying to push each other out of the way and rub themselves against her winningly and leap upon her irresistibly. Finally she chooses one, after a long chase, and she rolls over onto her side. The lucky bull rolls onto his side too, and they embrace belly to belly, hugging each other with their flippers.

Along the shorelines are the nursery coves, where the pregnant cows go to give birth. Each cow has her midwife to help her push the baby whale up to the surface to take his first breath, for he has no air in his lungs yet to make him float naturally; and to help her teach him to swim properly, prodding him along. In the wintertime the lagoons of Baja California are alive with happy whales, and it was to these lagoons that the American whalemen used to come to do their slaughter.

The whaling boats rowed up stealthily on the great animals, the harpooners standing in the bows with their long barbed harpoons on high, the stout ropes coiled in the bottom of the boats.

Then the harpooners hurled the first barbs, throwing more harpoons as the shocked animals fought and thrashed. A wounded whale would sound and drag the long line and whaleboat behind it, all across the lagoon, until the whale was exhausted, until it could fight no more. Then it would be stabbed and stabbed to death.

And the whalemen rowed into the nursery coves, because the calves were frisky and would come gambolling towards the boat to play with it and could be easily harpooned. The mother of the wounded calf would always come charging after the whaleboat, and it was easy to harpoon the mother also. And then her helper would come charging up, and it was easy to harpoon her as well.

The blue lagoons were red with the blood. Every winter it was the same, until there were almost no whales left and they were not worth hunting anymore. Then the nations gave official protection to the grey whale.

The *Jubilee* lay at anchor off Scammon Lagoon, waiting for the high tide. Deep inside the lagoon, out of sight around a long-cornered tentacle, was a small Mexican fishing village. Justin, Ross, and Spider rode slowly in a Zephyr across the lagoon to visit the village, to pay their respects to the elders. This was part of the alibi, to show themselves, to explain themselves. It was important. Thereafter the screamingly important thing was to get rid of Max.

Justin sat hunched, thinking, his eyes screwed up against the wind and glare. The past three days had been peculiar and difficult and very confusing. For three days Max had shown little of himself. He had slept late, missed a lot of meals, and done most of his drinking alone, either in his cabin or lying in a deck chair on the flying bridge, above the wheelhouse. He had been coldly polite to Justin, but sometimes had given him a smile in passing. Sometimes, again, at meals, he had been full of affability and questions about the progress of the whale film so far, and optimistic about it. He had praised the quality of the footage he had seen, congratulated them at different times on the quality of their camera work, was reasonably critical here and there, and advised on technique. At meals, when he had addressed Justin on technical matters, he had seemed normal. Justin would respond and Max would reply in turn. Then, the next time, Max would ignore him.

The odd thing was, Justin really liked Max Hagen. Max had been his friend a long time, his whole boyhood and beyond, and had taught him a great deal. Max was good company when he wanted to be, and under the Old Man's regime, he had always been so, and Max and Justin had been wild as hell together.

At times Justin thought he understood: it was all about Katherine. Max was trying to handle it, the disappointment and resentment, and it had to be admitted that he was not doing badly. He was a fool to have exposed himself to the pain by coming aboard, and more so for staying when he had had the truth confirmed, but one could not blame him for that too much. Coming here had been his last chance at Katherine and, in a way, a courageous attempt; staying was probably just his pride. When he thought about it calmly, Justin was reassured. But the man was getting on his nerves, and the situation had got on his nerves. Why did this have to happen now?

'Don't trust him,' Katherine had said. 'He's moody as hell, anything could set him off. Especially with the amount he's drinking. He's quite capable of taking it into his head to stick around just to upset you. Or me. Remember he thinks he should be the boss – this is *his* ship. You know what I think he's doing?'

'What?'

'He's playing a game. He's enjoying getting on your nerves. He's wearing you down until you lose your temper. And explode.'

'For what? For God's sake.'

'You stole his ship. *And* his girl. To make you do something dumb like punch him. Then he'll take a good swipe at you.'

'A good swipe from Max would be very effective. He grew up the hard way.'

'He's as strong as an ox. And very proud of it. He'd love to have a go at you.'

'He's got me to the point where I'd love to have a go at him. What worries me is the atmosphere on the ship.'

'Oh God,' she said, 'it's electric.'

'We all need peace and team spirit now. And to get down to work and get this goddamn business over with.'

There was strain. He could feel it in himself and he was sure he could see it in most of the others; the strain of knowing they were about to set off on a highly illegal and dangerous operation. After all, they were all amateurs at crime. There was a tendency to think about it too much and to want to talk about it, and they could not with Max around. Max was an irritant. They wanted Max to get the hell out, they wanted to get on with the job. Riding in the Zephyr now to the fishing village, Justin noted that Ross's usually earnest good-natured face was tight, grim. So, he noticed, was Craig's. Even happy-go-lucky devil-may-care Craig, who had had himself a ball for forty-eight glorious hours in Acapulco with a thirty-year-old divorced platinum blonde he had picked up on the beach. Looking at him, Justin felt another pang of anxiety. Jesus, he wasn't even twenty. Maybe he shouldn't have let the kid in on this thing. He was responsible for him. If something happened to him. . . . Then he dismissed the thought again. It wasn't a question of age or personal relationship, it was a question of duty. Craig had as much duty and responsibility as anybody. Nature and the oceans had given him a damn good life and would continue to do so. If the kid was old enough to dive among man-eating sharks, he was old enough to do his duty. Justin leaned out and touched his brother's shoulder. Craig came out of his brood, then smiled. 'All right?' Justin asked.

'All right.'

Ross looked over. 'When we get rid of that bastard, we'll be all right.'

'Tomorrow. He'll have a couple of dives today. If he doesn't want to go tomorrow, I'll order him to go.'

'He's not a bad guy,' Craig said.

'He's a snake in the grass,' Ross said.

Justin said, 'Max is all right as long as nobody treads on his toes.'

'He's a screwed-up Scorpio,' Ross said.

The Zephyr was gliding over the placid lagoon. The *Jubilee* was out of sight, around the point. The sun was beating down on

116

the yellow sand dunes that rolled on and on. All along the hot shorelines were the dark green mangroves. It was an ideal location for an alibi. There were countless lagoons stretching up on the coast, all uninhabited. Once the *Jubilee* entered those lagoons, only a diligent search by helicopter would be able to affirm that they were not in there anymore. That was why he wanted to show himself to the only villagers in the huge area, so that if it ever became necessary the villagers could testify that they had entered the lagoons.

It was magnificent, wild, remote water. Justin looked at Spider Webb and smiled. Young Spider was probably the only crew member who was not tense at all. He just could not wait. He was looking around at shorelines as he steered, a gleam in his eye. This was Spider's kind of country. Along with the Himalayas, the Andes, the Sahara Desert, the Zambezi Valley, and similar places. Spider would have liked to be parachuted in here by himself with just a knife and a snorkel and be told to survive; he would live like Robinson Crusoe, feeding himself off the water and the land. Like a bushman. Max Hagen's hang-ups would not bother Spider; one word from Justin and Spider would just sling Max over the side and get on with the job of fucking up the Russian whalemen. Justin nudged him. 'All right, Spider?'

'Beautiful.' Spider nodded at the lagoons. 'Beautiful, man.'

'Wait till you see the Antarctic.'

'Oh *yeah*,' Spider said.

It took another hour to reach the village, and they spent an hour there. When they were halfway back Katherine called them on the two-way radio.

'I thought I'd better warn you. Max is sitting in your office, evidently waiting for your return. Over.'

'What the hell does he want? Has he been diving? Over.'

'No. I asked him what he wanted, he just said "Business". Over.'

'Why the hell hasn't he been diving? That's what he wanted to do. Over.'

'I don't know,' she said. 'I don't know what he's been doing. I've just found him in there.'

sixteen

Justin did not feign surprise as he entered the office.

'What can I do for you, Max?' He walked straight to his desk, sat down on the corner, folded his arms, and glared at him.

Max sat in the armchair, legs crossed, smoking. He said, 'I would like Katherine present.'

Justin turned and pressed her intercom switch. 'Katie, come to the office, please.'

He looked at Max's drink and kept himself from saying, 'I'm glad you made yourself at home, Max.' He sat there on the desk with his arms folded, waiting. The door opened and Katherine came in. She looked at both of them questioningly. Justin gestured her to the sofa. He looked at Max. Max's face was blank, but he was enjoying himself.

He said to Katherine. 'So you're in on it too?'

She frowned. Justin felt his anger rise. 'I don't know what you're referring to, Max,' she said.

Max looked at Katherine. 'So he wants you because you speak Russian.'

Justin was astounded – and furious. He said, 'Will you come to the point? We don't know what you're talking about!'

Max said to Katherine, 'I assume you know that they blew up the Japanese whalers a couple of months ago. I assume you realize that going with them now to sabotage the Russians also makes you an accomplice to the Japanese crime? I believe it's called an accessory after the fact.'

Katherine was staring at him. Justin kept his voice grimly level. 'Will you for Chrissake cut out the theatricals and come to the point! This is my office and company time.'

Max looked at him for the first time, a hint of triumph on his face. 'Sabotaging foreign whaling fleets is not company business. Nor a justifiable company expense. It all figures, Justin.'

'Then figure it! If that's what you're sitting here to do.'

Max smiled thinly. He knew he had shaken him and he was in no hurry. 'I knew you were up to something,' he said, 'and you're a fool. You thought I wanted a few days vacation on the *Jubilee* with you guys after Acapulco? All I wanted was a chance to nose around the ship. I know this ship like the back of my hand, remember.'

'Out with it!' Justin snapped. 'So we know what the hell you're talking about.'

He was over the shock of it now. He was just outraged at the man's demeanour and furious at being found out. He kept his face straight, but his mind was racing. What the hell was he going to do about it? Maybe he could still bluff his way out. Max got up and walked across the cabin to the porthole. He glanced out of the porthole a moment, then turned to Justin. 'I'll omit the more arguable points. Like your obvious effort to avoid me at Bermuda. And your indecent haste to pull out of New York so I couldn't spend any time aboard there. And your dragging Katherine back from Los Angeles the moment the Old Man died and you had full legal control of Oceanics and could start your dirty work—'

'Omit them, then,' Justin interrupted, 'because they're nonsense.'

'And we won't bother to argue about the fact that even in the Old Man's day you were always swearing that one day you were going to blow up the fucking whalers unless they stopped hunting.'

'And you believed me,' Justin said. 'Will you for Christ's sake tell what points you *are* going to make? So we can get this idiotic conversation over with and get on with our work.'

Max began to pace the cabin. 'Which brings me to another point. *What* work? What are you doing in Baja California in November? The grey whales don't arrive until well into December, over a month from now. You're here long before you need to be. Why? Why aren't you doing a spot of coral-reef filming in the Caribbean? You know you need more footage for *Disappearing Reefs*. Or why aren't you in the Galapagos?' He looked over at Katherine. She was trying to appear bored, but her face was tense and her heart was hammering. 'Because you want to establish an alibi! Tell the world you're in Baja California, disappear into the lagoons and nobody would know whether you're there or not.' He cocked his eyebrows. 'You aren't staying here waiting for the greys to arrive in December. Because what else happens in December?'

'You tell me.'

'In December the Russian whaling fleet arrives at the Antarctic.'

Justin stood up from the edge of his desk. 'So does Christmas come in December.' He walked around to the back of the desk and picked up some papers. 'If that's all you've got to say will you please leave now? I've got work to do.'

Max smiled, standing there in his white slacks and slim-fitting white shirt, which showed his tanned biceps and chest. 'No, that is not all I have to say by a long shot. I haven't come to the most important evidence.'

'Then *come* to it.'

Max kept his smile, with effort. He wasn't going to let Justin out-talk him this time, especially in front of Katherine. He said, 'You replaced those perfectly good lead-acid batteries in the submarine with those silver-zincs. And that expensive radio equipment—'

Justin decided to get angry. He slammed his hand down on the desk. 'Jesus Christ! I'm listening to this theoretical crap despite the fact that you came into my office uninvited and despite the fact that you've been damned objectionable ever since you've been aboard only because you're a good friend of mine – or used to be! As managing director of Communications and as a stockholder of Oceanics, you're entitled to have your beefs and get things off your chest. But you've been making highly libellous statements without one jot of justification and I've gotten damned tired of your objectionable manner. Everyone of these so-called points you so theatrically mention has got a perfectly innocent explanation. Now will you kindly wrap it up and leave me alone and go back to California or Timbuktu for the rest of your vacation!'

Max had listened with a display of rapt attention. 'Then give me an innocent explanation for this piece of evidence. In your cunningly disguised wall safe you have a number of interesting, incriminating things.'

Jesus Christ, the bastard knew the combination for the wall safe! Not even Craig knew the combination, only he and Katherine. Justin slammed his hand flat on the desk.

'Christ, the audacity of you! How dare you go through my private safe!' He wanted to leap the desk and grab the bastard by his shirt-front.

Max grinned at him, delighted to have made him lose his temper. 'You didn't know I knew the combination? Oh yes, you see the Old Man and I were very close. He trusted me with almost everything – unlike his successor.'

'He didn't trust you enough to make you managing director or majority stockholder. And you're not going to be managing director of Communications much longer. I want your resignation on my desk in ten minutes or I'm going to fire you.'

Max cut in. 'No you're not. In fact both Oceanics and Communications are going to be run much more as I say in future. Because in that safe—'

'I know very well what's in that safe and there's a perfectly innocent explanation for that too. That's not going to be my reason for firing you, it's your damn impertinence in opening it and your general manner and insubordination—'

Max threw back his head and laughed. 'Insubordination! I taught you everything you know, kid. And at least I'm subordinate to the laws of the United States of America.' Max cut his grin and glowered at Justin. 'Possession of a forged passport is another crime.' He pointed at the picture behind which the wall safe was installed. 'And in that safe are twelve forged passports. One for each member of your crew. In false names. Even for Katherine. And thirty-six thousand dollars' worth of American Express traveller's cheques in their false names. Three thousand dollars each. What is it? Extrahazardous-duty pay? But that's the least of it! What I found particularly interesting is that *your* forged passport – and Ross's and Steve's . . .' he paused portentously, 'each have Japanese immigration stamps. For the day before the Jap whalers were blown up! And,' he held up his finger, 'exit stamps the day of the explosion. How do you explain that innocently, my friend?'

Justin knew what he had to do now. He could handle every

point Max had made, including the forged passports and the other things in that safe: he could simply destroy them when it suited him and deny they ever existed. He was prepared to deny that this very conversation ever took place and to testify under oath that Max was a raving lunatic. There was almost nothing that Justin would not do to achieve what he had set out to do. What he wanted now was to know how much the bastard knew and what he proposed doing about it. He said, 'Carry on, Max.'

Max paced back to the porthole. 'But that's not all that's in the safe, is it?' He looked back at Justin. 'There're also about a hundred photographs of the Russian factory ship, the *Slava*. Taken in some harbour – I figure it must be Cape Town. Taken from sea level and also from the air, presumably a helicopter. And what else do we find? In your forged passport is an immigration stamp for South Africa for last November – Cape Town, in fact.'

Katherine was shaken. Her face was white. She did not know what to say to help. She felt sick.

Justin leaned against his desk, towards Max. 'Anything else?' It didn't matter any more. It was clear what he had to do right now about Max: Max could not get off this ship while they stuck their necks out down in the Antarctic. There was only one other alternative and that was to convert Max. He had nothing to lose either way. Max put his hands behind his back and stood there looking at Justin.

'From all these things it is obvious what you plan to do. There's only one piece of evidence missing and I'm sure quite I'd find it if I had the chance.' He smiled. 'Somewhere on this ship there is an arsenal of sabotage weapons. Probably limpet mines and marine explosives. Maybe even torpedoes. There're plenty of places you could hide them, but I know this ship as well as you do. But so many places are locked. Like the helicopter and the sub holds.'

He shook his head at Justin regretfully, parentally, for Katherine's benefit, and went back to the point. 'It's obvious what you're going to do. You're going to the Antarctic, just like you always swore you would, to blow up the Russian whalers.'

seventeen

Justin stood behind his desk, very angry, almost shaking. He was determined not to lose his temper, but, good God, the bastard infuriated him.

'You know damned well why we're doing this, Max! Because whales are facing extinction. And this is the only way left to stop those bastards.' He looked him straight in the eye. 'What is our business about? And what is our role in the world? Our business is the beauty of the world!' Max opened his mouth to retort, but Justin cut in. 'Our job in this life is to make people *aware* of the beauty of the world. To make them conserve it. Conservation, Max, that's our job in this world. Not just making money, Max—'

Max interrupted, 'Don't tell me my job—'

'Like hell you know or you wouldn't be against us! These are the most magnificent creatures this world has ever known. With magnificent brains maybe even better than man's – creatures that have a language. They can make more sounds than any other creatures, including birds. Brains so highly developed they can tell the emotional state of each other with their sonar echoes. Talk. Distinguish each other. Navigate. Locate food. All at the same moment, for Chrissake! No other brain we know about can do all that. Brains that have taken fifty million years to evolve. Jesus, Max!'

He caught his breath. 'And the kindest, most gentle, most good-natured creatures this dog-eat-dog world has ever known. Creatures that can kill us with one swat of their tails but that let us ride on their backs, and roll and frolic with us, and love to play with man. God, God! You've seen them, Max. With hearts as big as all outdoors.' He spread his hands angrily, incredulously, then shouted, 'And what has man done to them, Max?' Max started to speak, but Justin shouted, 'You don't seem to know and so I'm telling you! For the last goddamn time! Because for all your expertise, it still hasn't sunk in.'

He paused, then said, 'And how do they kill them, Max? Like

we slaughter cattle in the abattoirs? Cleanly, humanely? Do they kill them like game rangers cull herds of wild animals? Do they kill them like civilized people put down horses and cats and dogs?' He glared at Max with contempt. 'No, we kill them *slowly*. Because there is no other way to kill an animal so massive, Max, but slow-slow-slowly.' He let the words hang.

'Imagine killing a horse, Max. Imagine this is the way we kill horses: by shooting it with an arrow from a heavy truck. And the arrowhead explodes inside the horse's guts and blows half his guts to bits. But, of course, this doesn't kill the horse. It doesn't kill the horse because the arrow's pretty small compared to the size of the horse. And the weight of the explosives in the arrowhead is only enough to blow *half* his guts to bits! And now this horse begins to drag us *and* the heavy truck through the streets, Max. By the arrow that is buried in its shattered guts. With all the butchers riding in the truck. The horse drags us through the streets by its guts, and all the time it is bucking in agony. And then it falls down exhausted, spewing blood all over the place, then it picks itself up, agonized, crazy out of its mind. And tries to gallop off in another direction, dragging the big heavy truck even though the truck has its brakes on. And it falls down again, screaming and whinnying and kicking its legs, blood pumping all over the street, but still it struggles up and tries to run some more. And there's a big winch attached to the truck, see, and it's dragging the horse in closer and closer, and all the time the horse is going crazy with panic, and it tries to run harder and harder, but, of course, it's getting weaker and weaker, and it's in terrible agony and terror. . . .

'But this doesn't kill the horse for a long time. It probably doesn't kill it for at least an hour. Maybe it's two hours. Three. Four. And all that time there's the screaming and the agony and the terror and the blood. . . .' He went on, his voice lower. 'Finally it dies. When the blood spews out of its nostrils.

'How do we stop people killing horses like that, Max?' He waited a moment, then shouted it: 'By God, it's the only way left to stop the bastards – that's why I'm doing it. Because everything else has been tried and failed – that's why. When the rest of the whaling nations were *reducing* their whaling fleets! When they were holding emergency international conferences to try to *reduce* the numbers of whales being killed! When they were trying to make regulations so that whales were not shot before they had had a chance to reproduce themselves! When they were desperately trying to create whale-breeding sanctuaries and shorter Antarctic whaling seasons to try to protect whales from extinction! What were those Russian and Japanese bastards doing?'

'I know!' Max shouted.

'They vetoed all these proposals at the International Whaling Commission. When the scientific committee produced evidence that blue whales do not reach sexual maturity until eighty-four feet in length, those bastards argued that there was such a creature as a pigmy blue whale that only grew up to seventy feet in length! When blue whales had been almost butchered out of existence, they vetoed the proposal to protect them for even one goddamn breeding season. They vetoed the proposal to extend protection to the finback whale. They vetoed every proposal to put a moratorium on whaling to give them a chance to breed up again.'

He glared at Max furiously, blue eyes bright, then said softly, savagely, 'And why? Because it costs a lot of money to convert highly specialized whaling factory ships into oil tankers and fishing boats, you see! Oh God, yes, it costs *money*, Max! It would cost the fat Japanese stockholders money to change from whaling to commercial shipping. And it would cost the poor Russian government money too, wouldn't it? And we know what a solemn matter money is in Russia. My God, the poor Russian government has enough expenses running its salt mines and political prisons and its nuclear navy and building up its massive army and all those expensive international ballistic missiles. Shit no, the additional expense of converting their whaling fleets to ordinary commercial uses would be a bit too much for the Kremlin to worry about until it absolutely *had* to! Until it squeezed every last drop of whale oil out of the oceans, until there are no more whales left to kill!'

He was now in the middle of the cabin. His mouth was dry and his voice hoarse. 'So Kill! Kill! Kill! Kill! Kill! While we can still find whales to kill. And when the last one is dead, *then* we'll convert our ships.'

Max just stood there. Justin was almost enjoying himself now. He said softly, 'You *know*, Max. You know like most of the world knows, but do you *feel* it? *Do you care?* . . . Oh sure you care, like the United States cares when it finally bans the imports of whaling products into America. And says factories must stop pouring chemicals into our rivers and seas and killing all the fish and water life. They care when it's too late. When there's so much chemical in the oceans that fish become poisonous and sea-birds can't breed any more. You care in theory, Max. Like isn't it terrible that the Nazis killed six million Jews. And isn't it terrible that all the oceans of the world are covered in a film of oil because fucking oil tankers clean out their tanks at sea to save money . . .

'Money! That's what it's all about, Max, money money money! Rape the earth and it's okay as long as it makes money. Nobody interferes with the big establishments because they're making the money, and because they have the money they have the power. Power to pressure the government to let them keep on pumping their chemicals into the oceans and poisoning the fish. Why? Because they're making money, Max!' He rasped, 'Money rules this world, Max. Not feelings! Not democracy!

'When did the International Whaling Commission give protection to the humpback? When they had been so badly butchered that whalers couldn't *find* any more to kill! Fortunately there were just sufficient numbers surviving for them to breed up again, but what about the blue whale? Oh no, the blue whale was far too valuable! The American government finally bans the importation of whale products, yes, when the whaling companies are going broke anyway; but does it ban the importation of all Japanese and Russian products? Like it banned Cuban and Chinese products? Does it hell! Why? Because it would be too bad for business! For money-making! So let the slaughter go on.' He waved his hand. 'Let the Russians and Japanese go on slaughtering until the last one is dead! And we'll just shake our heads and say isn't it awful. And go straight on buying Japanese radios and T-shirts and watches and cameras and petfood for our fucking cats.' He pointed at Max. 'That's how much the world cares. Is that as much as you care, Max?

'That's *exactly* how much the Old Man cared, Max! What did *he* do? With all *his* power and prestige? When he went on television promoting his books and films he managed to say a few words about how terrible whaling is and how it should stop. He even managed to squeeze a few pages about it into some of his books. He once even had his ghostwriters write a whole magazine article about it – for which he got paid ten thousand bucks. And he paid for a few advertisements that prominently carried his name. But did he use his enormous clout and prestige?'

Max said, 'You're being unfair!'

'The hell I am! Sure he was a grand old man, Max, but did he use his grandness? He was the Grand Old Man of the Sea whose name was a household word. Even the president of the United States called him a grand American institution. He wielded enormous clout and prestige. And what did he do with it? He made *money*! Off the sea! But did he use his prestige and his money to protect the sea he made his money off of? The hell he did! Did he put back into the sea a fair return for what he'd got out of it? The hell he did! He *exploited* the sea—'

Max retorted, 'I won't hear any more against him. He did a hell of a lot for conservation. And you were always shooting your mouth off at him, trying to tell him his job.'

'I spoke my mind to him,' Justin snapped, 'about our moral and human duty. I told him he was becoming overcommercial. Speaking one's mind to one's business partner is not being mean. And my father was far too self-opinionated to suffer from so-called meanness. He was a bull-headed old man who knew exactly what he wanted. Did he ever serve on a committee – Save-the-Whale or any other? Did he ever take the time off his glamorous schedules to attend public rallies and join boycott campaigns of Russian and Japanese products to help the Save-the-Whale Campaign? Did he ever join any of those pickets outside the Russian and Japanese embassies for Save-the-Whale? Did he ever go picket the annual meetings of the International Whaling Commission? He did not! Ross and I did, Max, at our own expense. Every year. He didn't even offer to let Magnus Oceanics pay our air tickets.'

He looked at Max, disgusted. 'And all the time he was making his fortune out of being the Grand Old Man. Why didn't he do as I suggested, namely go down to the Antarctic and film the whole horror of it? The horrors of the hunts and the terrible death struggles and the sea full of blood and all the gore and carnage on the factory ships, hundred-foot animals being torn apart! And show it on every television set and in every movie house all over the world in forty-eight languages. And send the royalties to Save-the-Whale or the World Wildlife Fund.'

Max came back at him. 'How could we have made that movie? The Russians wouldn't have allowed us anywhere near their fleet.'

'Bullshit, Max! We've got fast speedboats. The *Jubilee* can do thirty knots. We've got telescopic lenses. We've got the helicopter. And the submarine. By international law they can't stop us coming close enough to film them with our telescopic lenses, or from the helicopter. What can they do, shoot us out of the sky with an anti-aircraft gun? Bullshit! If we can film man-eating sharks a hundred feet down we could have filmed the whaling fleets. We could have buzzed over them with our helicopter.'

Max said, 'Why don't *you* make that movie now then – instead of this crazy sabotage?'

'Because now it's too late for that. By the time the movie was made and released and had any effect it'd be too late, the last whales would be over the brink of extinction! You've got to understand it's too late for propaganda. This is our last resort. The Old Man should have made that film. If he had, maybe we wouldn't have to do this now.

'So what do you recommend, Max? Just give up, shall we? And let the industrialists pour their fucking chemicals into the rivers and seas and kill all the marine life? And let the oil tankers go on pumping their dirty oil out onto the high seas until the oceans are all smothered and can't reoxygenate themselves and then all the oceans will just die?'

Max shouted, 'I know as much about the goddam oceans as you do!'

Justin shouted back, 'Then why the hell aren't you worried sick about it?'

'I am worried!'

Still shouting, Justin asked, 'Then when are you going to do something effective about it? When it's too late? When the last whale is dead? When the oceans are dead? Yes.' He dropped his voice and said slowly, 'Because your kind never does anything about it, Max. Because they don't care *enough* to do the only obvious thing that will work to stop those butchers. You care more for money. So we'll just shake our heads and say isn't it terrible that there's nothing we can do, and just let the goddamn moneymakers kill the world in front of our eyes.'

Max said, 'I'm not saying we should do nothing.'

'What, Max? What do *you* suggest we do, Max? What *can* we do, except say isn't it awful and just give up, because persuasion doesn't work very well. Well, I'm telling you, Max. *I'm* not giving up! Because very obviously something *can* be done about it!' He stopped, then almost whispered, 'And I'm going to do it, Max. . . . And, I have a good clear conscience about it. Because it's morally right! *Right* to save a miraculous creation! Right to stop savage cruelty! Right by the laws of humanity! Right by the laws of nature! What legal right have *they* got to destroy a magnificent part of nature, which belongs to the whole world? Whales belong to the earth. To *everybody*. Not just to them. What right do those bastards have? None! They're fucking outlaws!'

There was a silence. Then Max spoke. 'You forget one small law. International law!' His voice rose. 'I'm talking for a change, Justin! . . . The law of the sea, and you goddamn know it very well. And the law of the sea is the freedom of the seas, and *that* law says that *any* country can exploit the seas, because high seas are free.' He glared at him. 'Therefore, the Russians and Japs are *not* being illegal at all! And you know it very well!' He looked at him triumphantly.

Justin took a big angry breath. 'International fucking law! That's not *law*, it's a bunch of essays written by some ancient Romans and Dutchmen! Nobody applies it except when it damned well suits them. Do the tankers when they clean their oil tanks in mid-ocean? The tuna fishermen who net dolphin? The industrialists who pump their poisons into the sea and sky? The automobile manufacturers who kill the air with exhaust gases? The sky and the air are international too, aren't they? And we only *breathe* the stuff! We're only utterly dependent upon it for our lives!'

He waved his arm at Max. 'Don't let's be bothered about international law, Max. Nobody else is. It's international lawlessness! It's the law of the jungle! Might is right! I have not the slightest conscience about international law. Any more than international law has about the poor whales! It's the laws of nature that make us right. The laws of common humanity and decency give us the right to attack those bastards – the right and the *duty*! The duty, Max! . . . To save the most marvellous animal from extinction! And Magnus Oceanics in particular has got that duty. We've got the ship, the submarine, the helicopter, the money. The know-how. The power. Yes, the power! Just like these big fat industrialists have got the power because of their wealth, so have we. And we're going to use our power. Magnus Oceanics has made a fortune out of the oceans for thirty years. The seas have given us all a good life – look at us. Look at this terrific ship! We've got more contracts and money now than we know what to do with. We've got power! And I know what we're going to do with it.' He thrust his finger at Max. 'We're going to put some of it back where it came from. As is our natural God-given duty. To mankind. To nature. And this lovely ship is going to do a bit of dirty work for a change! And our swell little submarine. And our playboy helicopter. . . .' His eyes were hard. 'We're going down to the ice, Max, whether you like it or not. And sink that fucking Russian ship *right* to the bottom of the sea!'

Max now stood in the middle of the cabin. 'Are you?' he said. 'You're crazy, Magnus, you're a goddamn fanatic. You'll never get away with it.'

'I will,' Justin said quietly.

'Jesus,' Max shook his head at him. 'Jesus Christ. You risk the whole of Magnus Oceanics. Everything we've built up for years.'

130

Katherine closed her eyes and she felt the cold fear in her chest again.

Max said, 'You'll kill people. You realize that? *Kill people!* And yourselves. . . .'

'No, we won't,' Justin said. 'We have a very efficient plan, believe me. Especially to ensure that *nobody* gets killed – not one person. . . .'

'That's what every terrorist says. They don't intend to kill, only to blow up the train or the airplane or the embassy, not the people inside.'

'We are not terrorists,' Justin said. 'The opposite! Our purpose is to save the whales and the people involved!'

'Yes? And anything can happen . . . *anything* can go wrong!' Max turned and started for the door.

Justin said, 'One moment, Max!'

Max stopped at the door and looked back. Justin said, 'I'm not going to argue with you any more. But you've found out about me. Now I must find out about you.'

'Meaning?'

'Meaning that I'm not letting you off this ship because you'd sabotage my operation.'

Max stared, incredulously. 'Keep me prisoner?'

'Meaning,' Justin said, 'that I have to take you with us. Either as a participant . . . or, as you say, a prisoner.'

Max looked astonished. Justin thought it extraordinary that the man hadn't foreseen that Justin would have to do this.

Max half laughed. 'You're crazy. It's a joke.'

'I'm deadly serious. What the hell did you expect me to do, resign in embarrassment?' He was almost calm again – deadly, reckless calm – and he wanted to win Max over now. 'Max, I'm going to do it. As surely as the sun will rise in the east. And I'm not going to let you or anybody imperil the job. I'm sorry you found out. And I'm sorry about all the things that have come between us. Right now I've had a gutful of you, but you're my friend from way back. You're an important person in the company, and in Communications. I excluded you from this operation because I knew you would not support it. And now you know about it. Okay.' He spread his hands. 'I'll tell you first what I *want* to happen. I want you to join us, Max. The alternative of keeping you under control is very distasteful. Now I ask you to think about your options realistically. First, you can't dissuade me, Max. . . . Two, how can you stop me?' He paused. 'Realistically? Can you sabotage the ship so that it has to put into a port for lengthy repairs? No. First of all, you own fifteen per cent of the shares in this company and you would be injuring yourself; second, you won't be let near anything.'

Max said, 'Don't do me the added insult of imagining that my own financial loss would influence me.'

'I apologize. Or you could try to sabotage the submarine. Or the helicopter.' He shook his head. 'No, Max. Both are safely locked in their holds. Or maybe you could try to radio the Russians to warn them. Or the American authorities for that matter. No. The radio room is occupied all the time. You will not get near it, I assure you. You will have no opportunity to do any of those things, whether you join us or whether I lock you up. In both cases you will be watched like a hawk. An enormous amount is at stake. Nature. Our crew. Magnus Oceanics.'

Max tried to smile. 'And what do you think you're going to do with me when you get back from this operation? *If* you get back.'

'I'll cross that bridge when I come to it. But I don't like your chances of blowing our alibi.' He pointed to the porthole. 'Those are very big lagoons out there. And there'll be twelve credible witnesses from the *Jubilee* to say that we were there all the time and that you're crazy. Perjury is the least of my worries. And . . . you'll lose a very good job if you report us. *And* your Oceanics shares won't be worth a damn. What are your shares worth now? Nearly half a million? . . . But only with Magnus Oceanics functioning under my leadership. Without me, without all of us, Oceanics is worth the value of the ship and a few secondhand movie cameras and snorkels.'

Max turned to Katherine. 'Do you realize you could go to prison for life? If you don't get killed.'

'I realize everything, Max.' She did not look at him.

Justin walked behind his desk and slid the panelling on the

bulkhead back, exposing the safe. He turned the dial and swung open the little door. The passports, photographs, and traveller's cheques were gone. He looked at Max.

'Spare us the indignity of forcing you to tell me where they are.'

Max just glowered at him.

Justin picked up the general intercom microphone and flicked it on. 'Ross? And Spider? Come to the office, please.'

Max said, 'They're in my suitcase.'

'Thank you.' He looked at him. 'Well, Max?' There was a knock on the door. 'Come in,' he called.

Ross came in, followed by Spider.

'Ross,' Justin said, 'please go to Max's cabin and bring his suit-case. Then search the whole cabin thoroughly for any weapons, listening devices, radio transmitters, and so on.'

Max said, 'Save your time. I didn't come prepared for this.'

'Spider,' Justin said, 'you and Steve and Black Bob will guard Mister Hagen twenty-four hours a day, eight-hour watches, until I tell you to stop. Starting with you. Got that?'

Ross looked intrigued. Spider looked astonished. 'Sure,' he said. 'What do I do?'

'You stop him doing anything to sabotage our operation. Including trying to escape over the side or putting messages in bottles or arsenic in our soup. Okay? Can you wait for him out in the wardroom?'

Ross and Spider went out.

'Well, Max?' Justin said. 'Are you in? Or do I lock you up as well? I want you to join us, Max, you're a good man to have.' He looked straight at him. 'Now, for the last time. In? Or locked up?'

Max had clenched his hands at his sides to stop them shaking. He shot a glance at Katherine, then looked back angrily at Justin.

'In!' he snapped. 'Satisfied?'

He flung open the door and slammed it behind him.

Katherine sat rigid, ashen, staring at nothing, the cold feeling in her stomach. Justin stood at his desk. He said, 'Katie?'

She turned her head slowly and looked at him, but he could see the fear in her eyes.

'Katie,' he said sharply, 'are you having doubts?'

She looked at him a long moment, then she breathed deep. 'Will you really not kill anybody? Do you really believe you can do that?'

He looked at her steadily.

'Yes.'

Her eyes were intense. Then she blinked slowly and sighed. She turned her head away.

part four

That year, in the South Pacific Ocean, the great blue whale gave birth to her calf. He was twenty feet long when he was born and he slipped out of her belly very quickly and easily, tail first, downwards into the sea, without a breath in his floppy body, and without knowing how to get air into his lungs but knowing that he had to get some. His mother did not have any other females to attend her, and the male blue whale who was her mate did not naturally understand what to do in these circumstances, although he knew very well what was happening and he felt very good and happy about it. The cow twisted her great body around desperately and she got her head under her calf and shoved him up to the surface and into the blinding sunshine. He took his first gasping blowing breath, then he wallowed on the top of the sea, with his mother underneath him keeping him afloat and making her encouraging mother noises to him, and the bull whale milled and swam around and around them.

For six hours they stayed in the same place on the ocean, huffing and puffing and wallowing and slopping and milling and splashing, teaching the baby whale how to breathe and how to use his flukes and his flippers and his great floppy body. After six hours he had learned how to do these things and he could almost swim properly already, and he took his first drink of milk. He naturally knew where to go on his mother's massive body; he went flopping down her long grooved belly, nudging her, looking for the teats, wallowing and splashing. And she rolled onto her side and humped her flank out of the water because he would not yet be good at getting his mouth around her teats without swallowing salt water. He lifted his snout out of the water and pressed it against her, and she contracted her mammary muscles and squirted the milk in a big jet into his open mouth. That night they slept in the same place on the ocean, the cow and the bull side by side with the calf between them, three blowholes sighing and puffing.

For six months the blue whale cow and her mate and her calf swam and migrated down through the Pacific, playing and wallowing, and the calf suckled two hundred gallons of milk a day, and he gained ten pounds in weight every hour, two hundred and forty pounds every day, because the milk was extraordinarily nutritious and because he had to expend so little energy dealing with the force of gravity, formed as he was in such a way that the sea supported his weight. In six months the calf was forty-five feet long, more than half the length and weight of his mother already, and he could swim almost as far and fast as she. Through the Southern Hemisphere's autumn and winter the three great animals stayed in the South Pacific, and the bull and the cow mated again, and she was pregnant again. Then came the spring and the call that only whales can hear, that soon it will be summer at the Antarctic and ice will melt and the seas will be unlocked and full of the fat plankton that whales love to eat. Now the calf had enough blubber on his body to withstand the cold down there, and they set off on their long journey to the ice.

eighteen

The *Jubilee* steamed south in the Humboldt Current, which comes up off the Antarctic West Wind Drift and flows up the long jagged coastline of South America. It is a major route of the great whales, heading to and from the Antarctic in the southern spring and fall. For two days there had been heavy winds and high waves, but today the sun was shining brightly out of a clear blue sky and the *Jubilee* rolled only slightly on a smoothly undulating sea.

The *Jubilee*'s appearance had changed. Her dark blue hull was nearly entirely repainted white. Black Bob, Craig, Ross, and Spider were hanging over the side in bos'n's chairs, slapping white paint down to the waterline. Hi-fi Bob was tending their ropes. Justin Magnus was in a bos'n's chair slung over the bows, carefully painting on a new name, *Sea Queen*, in both English letters and Japanese characters. Hanging on bos'n's chairs, side by side, three feet above the cold, dark blue rushing water of the Humboldt, solemnly slapping white paint, Craig Magnus and Black Bob were singing spirituals and anything else that came into their heads. They came to the end of 'Ole Man River' and just kept on slapping white paint, and then Black Bob said, '*White* – everything's gotta be white. Why we gotta have a white ship, why can't we have a black ship?'

Craig slapped paint. 'Ever heard of a black iceberg? That's why we're painting this ship white, so it looks white, like an iceberg, see?'

Black Bob painted moodily. 'Everything's *white*,' he said. 'It's a white weddin'. If the bride's a virgin. An' even if she ain't.'

Craig pondered this point. 'Do you want a black wedding for virgins, like a funeral?'

Black Bob slapped white paint. 'An' white lies,' he complained. 'A lie's a lie, ain't it?'

'There's white sharks,' Craig pointed out helpfully. 'And Moby Dick was white. He was a bad bastard.'

'Where I come from,' Bob said, 'everything was black. Black

black black, man. Especially the future.' He started to sing: 'Goin' home . . . goin' home. . . . I'm a goin' home. . . .'

He stopped singing and Craig was disappointed. He liked singing. 'Carry on,' he said.

'Nope.' Bob shook his head. 'I don' wanna think about that black place. I wanna think of the sunshine. I wanna think of the sea, an' all the nice clean things in this world. That's why I left that terrible place.' He shook his head, slapping paint. 'Birmingham, Alabama, yessir. Black, man, my part of it, just like it sounds.'

Craig liked to hear Black Bob talk. 'Tell me about Death Row,' he said.

Bob shook his head. 'Don' wanna even think about it. That street was so bad even the cops didn' wanna think about it either – they wouldn' go into it. Prostitutes, thieves, killers, pimps, you name it, we had it. Those people were your friends an' relatives. Only Jesus Christ and God himself could clean that place up.'

'Why didn't they?'

'They will, They will, brother,' Bob mused. 'That's where I met Them, large as life.' He added, 'Cured me of my asthma, didn't They?'

'Where did you see Them?'

'In the Evangelist Church,' Bob said simply. 'Large as life.'

'What were They doing?'

Bob sat slumped in his bos'n's chair and smiled at the white paint. 'They were just *there*, man. . . .'

Craig was impressed despite himself. 'I mean, were They smiling or what?'

Bob sighed at his paint-job, the blue, clean sea rushing by just under his feet. 'They were just . . . *joyous*,' he said, 'And so was I . . . .'

'Both of Them, or just the one?'

'Just Jesus,' Bob said. 'But it's all the same thing, isn't it? Just Jesus is good enough for me.'

'What colour was He?'

Bob knew when Craig Magnus was teasing him and when he wasn't. In fact, he nursed a secret ambition to convert Craig

138

Magnus one day. 'No colour.' He added, 'Not even white. He was just *there*.'

'What did He do?' Craig asked.

Bob slumped in his chair, feet and paintbrush dangling. His voice came out deep brown resonant: ' "Robert Clark get out of this Sodom and Gomorrah! Get out of these terrible streets with their pimps and whores an' murderers an' thieves an' drunkards an' that moonshine factory underneath your bedroom window an' all those lost souls fightin' and stabbin' in the street an' all them crooks an' false prophets. Go away, Robert Clark, to where the sunshine is an' the air is clean an' help God's creatures by fightin' the Anti-Christ! . . ." An' I cried, "Where must I go Lord?" An' the Lord said to me, "Go to California, Robert, an' I'll show you how to fight the Anti-Christ!" ' Black Bob thought for a moment. 'An' I went. An' He showed me, didn't He?'

'How?' Craig said.

Bob turned and looked at him. 'He introduced me to you, didn' He? So I could join Magnus Oceanics. An',' Bob added, 'he cured me of my asthma.'

Up forward on the bridge David Cartwright called by megaphone to Justin, who was over the bows painting the new name. 'Mister Magnus? Ship ahoy, starboard bow. Not heading this way.'

Justin turned in his bos'n's chair and looked at the horizon. He could not see anything. Then he could just make out a small black shape. He looked at his watch. Then he put the lid on his paint pot, swung up out of the bos'n's chair, reached up to the hand rails, and heaved himself back aboard. He untied his lifeline and called to Hi-fi Bob, 'Let's take a break. Call the boys up for coffee.'

He walked across the foredeck, then climbed to the bridge. 'Where?' He took the binoculars from David Cartwright.

Cartwright pointed, then clasped his skinny musician's hands in front of him. 'Whalers, I think.' They were. They were nearly twelve miles away. And one of them seemed to be chasing. He watched through his binoculars, then he said, 'Yes, you bastards. You'll be the next to go.'

They were whalers of the Chilean-Japanese company that

operated from a shore-based factory in Chile. Chile did not belong to the International Whaling Commission, Japan did; to get around the commission's regulations the Japanese had formed a subsidiary company with the Chileans, which hunted all year round in the Pacific and particularly in the Humboldt, shooting anything that moved. Cartwright said, 'How'll you do it?'

Justin held the binoculars out to him.

'Change course. Five miles over to east. Just in case the bastards swing over this way.'

'Five miles eastward,' Cartwright said.

'How?' Justin said. 'Blow up their shore factories, that's how. Get in there somehow and blow their factories to Kingdom Come. No use killing whales if you haven't got a factory to process them, is it?' He turned and walked angrily into the wheelhouse. 'And the South Africans will be next. I'll blow up their shore base at Durban. And then the Australians; I'll blow up their shore base too. So help me God!'

He walked into the radio room behind the bridge. Katherine was sitting hunched over the radio, earphones on, a big Russian dictionary open in front of her. He put his hand on her shoulder and she looked up. He smiled. 'Hello, comrade. Coffee break for the workers.'

She pulled off her earphones.

'Radio Tashkent,' she said. 'It's Greek to me. They've got terrible accents.'

He said, 'Not many whalemen come from the Balkans. All North Sea types. Come and have some coffee.'

She got up and straightened her jeans. She brushed her hair as she walked. 'Had Radio Vladivostok a little while ago. I think all the Siberian radio announcers are bears.'

Commander Henry Thorogood looked up from the coffee pot. 'Is Russia still the land of milk and honey?'

'Milk and honey. Joyous workers everywhere gratefully fulfilling production targets ahead of schedule. The United States is starving, workers dying in the streets.'

The commander laughed and handed her a cup of coffee.

'Not all the time. In their news broadcasts pretty much, yes.

Every time a comparison is made. The roaring success of communism, the wicked failures of the West.'

Justin thought she looked tired. They were all under strain. L. C. Singleton came in from the galley with a tray of sandwiches. White flecks on his face. He had also been over the side, painting. He patted Justin on the shoulder as he passed.

'Hello, L.C.'

The commander said to Katherine, 'How did a young Boston lady come to learn Russian, anyway?'

Spider, Ross, and Black Bob came in. They all had white paint spots all over them. 'Enter the Picassos,' Ross said.

'I thought I might make a career in the United Nations,' Katherine said. 'Or the Foreign Service. Or something.' She added, 'Dad was in the Foreign Service and we spent a few years in Moscow when I was a kid. He insisted I keep the language up when we left.'

Justin said, 'She thought two hundred million Russians can't be all wrong. There's a spot on your forehead you haven't painted white, Bob.'

'Yeah,' Black Bob said. 'Keepin' that bit for later.'

'Then,' Katherine said to the commander, 'I got a passion for publishing the work of exiled Russians. At Random House I tried to get an editorial monopoly on Russian writers.' She added, 'I'd taken Russian as one of my majors at college, of course.'

Hi-fi Bob came in scowling. He picked up the pot and sloshed coffee into four mugs. 'Now I'm a goddamn waiter,' he said.

'Where're the others?' Justin said.

'Putting up framework for the new funnel,' Hi-fi Bob said. 'Sugar, whether they like it or not!' He thumped a spoonful into each mug.

'Take 'em a sandwich each,' L.C. said. 'I didn't make all those sandwiches for nothing.'

'I haven't got enough hands!' Hi-fi said. 'That's my trouble, I only got two hands, see?'

L.C. shouted after him, 'Try to paint *and* cook at the same time.' Bob Matthews stumped out with the mugs. Justin picked up four sandwiches and followed him. He climbed up behind the bridge, where the funnel was going up. Steve, Spider, Victor, and Max were welding pieces of piping together. The piping was bent into a cylindrical frame the same size as the *Jubilee*'s own funnel, tall and slim. The frame would be fastened to the deck behind the real funnel, then sheathed in tin and painted. It would give the *Jubilee* a very different silhouette. Max was standing by, watching Steve and Victor welding. Hi-fi Bob banged the mugs down on the deck. 'All sugared,' he barked. 'One spoon.'

Justin said, 'Sandwiches.'

Victor straightened up creakily and put his wrists to the small of his back. He gave Justin his craggy smile. Steve was dressed only in shorts. He was not heavily built but his body was very tanned and hard and lean, and his arms were blue with tattoos.

Max nodded at the frame and said, 'It won't hold. Not in a storm.'

Victor said quietly, 'She'll hold, with stays. She'll be belted to the deck well.'

'The stays won't matter,' Justin said. 'The funnel's just for cosmetic effect, to give us a deceptive profile.'

'She won't hold in those winds around the Horn,' Max said quietly, 'stays or no stays.'

Justin didn't look at Max. He was trying to interpret the man's tone. It was ambiguous. It could have been provocative, disparaging, or it could have been a sulky attempt at helpfulness. He had been like that ever since they left Baja California. He had done everything asked of him with the same manner. He had even turned out for Justin's exhausting get-fit exercises three times a day, even though only the five of them who were actually going to board the *Slava* were required to do so. He knew that Max was drinking nearly a bottle of bourbon a day, but he coped with the exercises well. He was in remarkably good condition. Apart from a flabbiness on his gut and thighs, he was formidable, muscled. Justin wanted to believe Max was trying to make a helpful comment now, he wanted to encourage any sign of co-operation from the guy. He said, 'Maybe we better make two, one as a reserve, to erect in a hurry. Victor? How about we make two, one as a spare?'

'Sure,' Victor said. 'But she'll hold.'

'Excuse me,' Max said. He picked up his coffee and walked off. He climbed down the ladder. Justin looked at Steve.

'Well?'

'Search me,' he said in his soft voice. 'He does what he's told. No more, no less.'

'Was he being helpful just now?'

'First thing he's said all morning. Except "Why the hell you doing this?"'

Victor ran his hands through his hair. 'Don't worry about him.'

'Worry about him? If nothing else, he's bad for morale.'

'He can't do anything else,' Steve said. 'Except give me the shits.'

Morale was good enough. Justin kept a sharp eye and ear open for the mood of the ship, and he was reasonably satisfied. But apart from the commander, they were all amateurs at this kind of thing. There was tension.

Lying in his arms, the night before, Katherine had said, 'Oh yes, there's tension all right.'

She sighed, and he felt her tension. 'But that's to be expected,' he said. 'Nobody's done anything like this before. How're you?' He was worried about her. It was late, the hour after love-making, everybody except the night watch was in his bunk, supposed to be asleep. There was a big moon out there shining silver on the vast sea, the *Jubilee* ploughing evenly on into it at twenty knots. He stroked Katherine's long smooth back.

She thought and then spoke, and her voice was strained. 'Now it's really happening. What we've been talking about. Thinking about. We got used to the idea, that we were going to do it – hardened, I guess. Even I did. It seemed a long way ahead.' Her eyes were closed. 'Then when Bermuda was finished, the reality began to come back. This was it. It was really going to start happening soon. Soon. And gradually, or maybe not so gradually, the reality, of the danger I guess – yes. The fear of what could happen, it starts presenting itself, more and more. You shut it out. You carry on with your work, and you're going to go ahead and do the job anyway because you're committed, and so is everybody else, they're relying on you, there's no question of chickening out, because not only is what you're doing right and good but also you're committed to the others. You can't break down now and let them down, for God's sake. It's a question of honour.' She opened her eyes and looked at him. 'I won't let you down. But I wish to God it would hurry up and be over with. That's how I feel. I guess that's how most of us are feeling.'

He trailed his fingertips along her eyebrow. 'I have no fear that you'll let me down.' He was worried about her nerves.

She shook her head. 'I'll just scream occasionally.'

He laughed. 'Scream at me. In here. Not on the bridge. Okay?'

'Okay.' She smiled at him. 'You nearly made me scream just now. But that was something else.' She got up onto her elbow. 'My Russian's okay,' she said, 'but the accents worry me like hell. I've got all the nautical terms now. But I'm also worried about the slang.'

'As long as you can decipher where they are, that's all. You haven't got to get through the Lenin Naval Academy. Shall we have a drink?'

'You've got to be up in six hours to do your damned exercises.'

'I'm all right,' he said.

He got up and walked through to the office naked. He mixed her a martini and got himself a Budweiser from the refrigerator. He sat down cross-legged opposite her on the bed. She looked at him in the glow of the lamplight, then stretched out her hand and ran the back of her finger across his chest. The drink was making her feel better.

'Oh yes.' She smiled. 'You're all right, Magnus. And those eyes!'

'You're the one with the eyes,' he said. He was relieved she was cheering up.

She sipped her martini.

'Everybody's okay.' She said it to persuade herself. 'You've got a good bunch of guys working on this thing. All the way down to L.C. and Victor. Ross is great. And the commander, God, he's a tower of strength.'

'Solid oak,' Justin said.

'He inspires such a sense of . . . dependability. What I find so surprising somehow is that he's such an upright gentleman, God save the Queen and the Geneva Convention and all that, so how come he's doing something illegal like this?'

He wanted to amuse her. 'Because there's a job to be done, chaps, and by God we'll do it! We'll show those jolly Ruskies they can't kill all the whales, chaps! England this day expects every man to do his duty! And his duty is to Magnus Oceanics and the policies of Magnus Oceanics. Of which, as an English gentleman and captain of this ship, he approves. He *approves* of us, you see? He loves the sea, he believes in conservation. And because he approves he'll go down with the ship if necessary. Saluting and singing "Rule Britannia". As simple as that. It's his *duty*.'

'Yes, that's him, I guess.' She twirled the stem of her glass. 'In a different way Dave Cartwright inspires the same sort of confidence. He's also utterly dependable. He's got about as much worldliness and sense of humour as a young curate, but somehow that's part of his dependability. He's so bookish . . . so *pure*, somehow. You sort of feel that with Mister Cartwright on our side we must be right.'

It was good sitting here together in the middle of the night, naked, having a drink, talking. The lamplight shone on her skin and hair, and her breasts and hips were milky white. She said pensively, 'Spider also inspires confidence.'

'Spider,' he said. 'Yes.'

'Oh yes, Spider. He's so . . , tough and ingenious. You feel nothing *physical* is impossible for him. You feel that if nobody else can find his way out of the jungles, Spider will. Spider can run from Athens to Sparta. *He* hasn't got any tension about this operation.'

Justin said, 'It's not all fun for Spider. He takes our work very seriously.'

'Oh yes.' She thought for a moment. 'In a different way, you're like Spider. If you can't do it, nobody can. If you're doing it, it must be possible, you'll find a way. You're sort of . . .' she closed her eyes, thinking, 'indestructible.' She looked at him. 'I think that's the feeling you inspire.'

He smiled. 'I hope I'm indestructible.' Then he wished he had not said that.

She lay back and closed her eyes. 'Oh God, so do I.'

He wanted to talk her away from that mood. But he thought it a bad idea to get into a discussion, at that hour. He decided to let it go. She opened her eyes and looked at him. 'The pure idealist, Justin Magnus.' God, she wished she shared his utter certainty. 'How's *he* feeling?'

'We're all tense, Katie. I guess I'm even more tense than I realize. But it's to be expected. Morale is good.'

'Okay. But let's get this thing over with.'

He said, 'It soon will be. Like clockwork.'

'What are we going to do about Max?'

He pulled slowly on his cigarette. 'I don't know yet. He's behaving well enough at the moment. At the first sign of trouble I'll lock him up. We'll see tomorrow when the rehearsals start.'

nineteen

A large map of the Antarctic was taped to one oak-panelled bulkhead of the wardroom. To another was taped the plans of the *Slava*. A sketch of the *Slava*, with each important feature labelled in Justin's handwriting, was drawn on a blackboard standing on an easel. On the long mess table was a slide projector, for showing the photographs of the *Slava* that he had taken at Cape Town. The carpet of the wardroom was covered with boxes, crates, and wrapping. They were all there, except David Cartwright and Victor. They sat around the table. Justin tapped the bulkhead.

'These plans of the *Slava* will remain up, here, until we get to the ice. Then they will be destroyed. Just in case anything goes wrong and we are ever boarded. So make sure you know the plans. Where each and everybody has to go. Know them blindfolded. Backwards. Forwards. In your sleep.'

Hi-fi Bob Matthews muttered, 'Who can sleep?'

'I know you all know the plan already. But this is a recap. Any questions, any worries, anything you don't understand, for Chrissake bring it up now. No matter how stupid you think they may be. Anything you want to hear again. Even if we've got to say it a dozen times. It doesn't matter. Just so long as everybody is clear.'

Nobody said anything. Justin looked around at them, then said, 'And the first thing to be very clear is that the purpose of this operation is to sink the fucking *Slava* without killing anybody. Not one single Russian. And not one of ourselves either.'

He returned to the table.

'Everybody in the boarding party is going to be armed to the teeth with pistols, submachine guns, and riot guns. And by the time we get down to the ice, you're all going to know how to use them. But . . . the real purpose of the pistols and submachine guns is *intimidation*.' He paused. 'To get those Russians under control and to get them off that ship into their lifeboats before we blow the thing up.' He looked at them sternly. 'And anybody who uses his weapons, except to make a noise, will only do so in self-defence. Only if he damned well *has* to.'

Nobody said anything. They were all staring at nothing. 'Remember,' he said, 'ninety per cent of those deck labourers on the *Slava* are women. We are *not* terrorists. We are *not* shipjackers. And we certainly are *not* womankillers. All we want to do is get everybody safely off that ship and then sink the thing so it will never hunt again.'

On the map of the Antarctic the land was pure white and the sea around it was different pale shades of blue. The sea all the way around the white land mass was divided into sectors labelled I, II, III, IV, V, and VI. These were the official demarcations of the International Whaling Commission. Justin got up from the table, walked over to the map, and pointed to a long white peninsula sticking up northwards towards the southernmost tip of South America.

'Sector one. Drake's Passage, off Graham Land. This is the most popular whaling area, where there're most whales these days. What there are left. Sectors two to six have been almost completely shot out.' He touched the map. 'That's where we'll find the bastards. Somewhere around Drake's Passage. We're lucky here, because Drake's Passage is a natural bottleneck between Graham Land and South America, as you see, and that will make it easier for us to find them.'

Bob Matthews said, 'And for them to see us.'

Justin pointed to the northern tip of Graham Land; there were many islands all the way up the long snow-white peninsula.

'The *Jubilee* will anchor here, in the first instance. In the bay of this island. You can't see it very well on this map, but according to the charts it's ideal. There's a point here we can anchor and nobody can see us from the open sea – only if they come right into the bay, which they have no reason to do. Because they are not suspecting any danger, they won't be looking for anybody. If they *do* see us on their radar, we'll just look like an iceberg on their screens.'

Hi-fi Bob said, 'And if they see us visually?'

Justin answered patiently, 'We're a white ship called the *Sea Queen* from Nagasaki. With two funnels. And we're oceanographers.'

Nobody said anything. He went on. 'First, we hole up in this bay out of sight. And locate the Russian fleet. They won't be too hard to find. That big factory ship and twenty catchers all around about Drake's Passage and Graham Land. We'll find them,' he said, 'with radio. Katherine will find them for us, she'll tune into their radio and sooner or later the fleet will give their navigational position. Once we know where they are, we use the helicopter. To locate them visually. Flying at ten thousand feet where they can't hear us – right, Ross?'

Ross said, businesslike, 'At ten thousand feet they can't hear us. And they can hardly see us, except with binoculars. And then only if they're looking up in the sky for us. And there's no reason why they should be looking up at the sky.'

Justin said, 'Radar. Explain that briefly.'

'Well. They won't see me on their radar either, at that height. Because their radar is beaming out horizontally, over the sea, looking for icebergs and its own fleet and so forth. Not up into the sky.' He looked at Justin inquiringly.

Justin looked at Hi-fi Bob. 'Right, Bob?'

'Yeah,' Bob said, 'that's more or less right.'

'Is it right or not, Hi-fi?' Steve asked him.

'Right,' Bob snapped back, pink and freckled. 'I said so, didn't I? Want me to give it to you in writing?'

Justin smiled. They were all grinning except Bob, and Max was not grinning either. Max reclined in his chair, arms firmly folded, expressionless.

'Ross pinpoints them in his helicopter and tells us how spread out they are, how much iceberg cover there is, the whole general picture. Takes aerial photographs. Then the *Jubilee* can move out of its hiding in the bay and follow them, get close as possible, hiding among the icebergs. We can stay just over their radar horizon, about twenty-five miles away from them, and they won't see us on their radar screens. Anyway, if we stay among the icebergs, they will block us out of the Russian's radar. So. The *Jubilee* follows the fleet. All the time Katherine is tuning in to their radio to get their positions and movements, and Ross goes up in the helicopter to give us a bird's-eye picture.' He nodded at them. 'Easy. We'll find them all right. . . .' He added, 'It doesn't matter how long it takes.'

Justin walked back to the table and leaned on it.

'Then,' he said, 'we've got to find some of their dead whales. That won't be too hard either. After they've killed a whale, they stick a hollow spear in it, pump it full of air, and leave it floating for a towing boat to get and drag off to the factory ship for processing. It radios the factory ship to tell it where the whale is. The factory ship could be fifty, sixty miles away—'

'Or it could be five miles away,' Bob Matthews interrupted.

'In that case,' Justin said, 'those particular whales will be no good to us. We'll leave them alone. We've got to find whales fifty miles or so from the factory, to give us sufficient time. We'll find some suitable whales okay. If it takes us a whole month, we'll find them.'

He looked around the table. 'Katherine will tune into their catchers' radio calls. They'll be telling the *Slava* where they've left their dead whales so the towing boats can find them – we'll be able to pinpoint them easy enough. It's just a question of time for us, to find the right whales in the right location for our purposes. I don't care how long it takes to find them, even if we have to stay there all summer.'

'Except,' Steve said, 'that the longer we spend down there looking, the greater the chances of them spotting us.'

'Not if we're careful. Because once we've located the factory ship with the helicopter, the *Jubilee* could go back into hiding. Somewhere among these numerous islands here.' Justin moved back to the map and pointed to both sides of Graham Land. 'Or here. Or among the icebergs. Remember, all these parts that look like open sea are chockablock full of icebergs to hide among.'

'Oh, dandy,' Hi-fi Bob said.

'Commander?' Justin turned towards Henry Thorogood.

Commander Thorogood nodded. 'Oh, yes. I'll just need a bit of time to choose my spot. But certainly. That's a huge area and there's plenty of natural, er, cover.'

'Why didn't we just rename her the *Titanic*?' Hi-fi Bob said.

'Oh shut up!' L.C. yelled.

'All I need is enough time,' Henry said. 'And of course, ideally, we need an area that gives the *Jubilee* a good opportunity to get steaming away for South America as soon as we have found the whales we need – and successfully implanted the explosives in them.'

Justin picked up an aluminium cylinder, and held it up for them to see. It was six inches in diameter and fifteen inches long.

'Courtesy of the quartermaster's stores of an unnamed South American republic. For a fee. Its tradename is Submarex. Made by I.C.I.' He patted it. 'Standard submarine blasting gelatin, the

150

best there is. Used for ocean oil drilling, general underwater demolition work, et cetera. Very high velocity detonation underwater. In case anybody's interested,' he consulted the manufacturer's label, 'it's ninety-one per cent nitroglycerin, seven per cent nitrocellulose, plus two per cent barium sulphate.'

Craig said, 'Sounds terrific. I've never done a blow-job before.'

They all burst out laughing again. Katherine was blushing. Justin waited, then went on.

'Each canister is twenty-five pounds. If we manage to charge six whales, each should have two canisters. Fifty pounds. Commander?'

'That'll do it,' the Englishman said. 'Three hundred pounds of that stuff, that'll make a lovely bang.'

'But,' Justin said, 'if we only manage to find *less* than six whales, we load each with three canisters. Seventy-five pounds each. We've got twenty-four canisters, enough for twelve whales. We'll be delighted if we manage to find six whales. We'll be satisfied with three.' He paused, then continued. 'In any event, we charge the whales with the required amount of explosives. And, of course, with detonators.'

He picked up a small metal box from the table and held it up. It was about two inches by three inches.

'The electronic detonators. Also courtesy of the friendly quartermaster's stores. A very simple but effective device, standard equipment in all remote-control explosions. We used identical ones in Vietnam. The detonator is to be implanted in the last canister inside the whale. Here's your actual detonator cap.' He tapped the little cylinder protruding from the box. 'Inside the box is a battery and a switch and a tiny, simple radio receiver. From the submarine we send this little radio receiver a signal on a pre-established wave band. The receiver then activates the switch, which turns on the little battery. Which sends an electrical current through this little detonator, which is set into the final canister of explosive. And boom.' He looked at them cheerfully. 'All right?'

Nobody spoke.

He picked up another metal box. 'And at the same time as we plant the explosives we also plant one of these into each whale, too.'

He held it up. It was a black metal cube, half the size of a shoebox.

'This is a radio transmitter. The transmitter sends out a constant signal that we in the submarine pick up on our radio receiver. Each of these little transmitters is sending out a different signal on a different predetermined wave band, which has a range of about two miles.' He put the box down on the table again.

'So. Having fixed up our whales, we in the submarine proceed as fast as we can towards the factory. And there we wait. Meanwhile the Russian towing boats are towing our whales to the factory ship. They are placed in tow behind the factory's slipway. Of course, there will probably be other whales in tow behind the factory at the same time. But we in the submarine will know when *our* explosive whales have arrived – by their radio signals.'

Max spoke for the first time. He sat there, arms folded, eyes hooded. 'And if those radio transmitters don't work?'

Justin was pleased that Max was participating.

'They'll work. They're the best there is. And,' he added, 'it's Hi-fi Bob's job to make sure they damned well do work.' He looked at Hi-fi. 'Right, Bob?'

Bob Matthews shoved his glasses up his nose, then admitted grudgingly, 'They'll work.'

Justin looked at Max almost expectantly, hoping he'd participate further. Max just reclined there, arms folded. Everybody looked at him, waiting. Then Justin went on.

'Meanwhile, we in the submarine – the boarding party – are in position.' He looked at the commander.

'Yes.' Commander Thorogood cleared his throat. 'About one thousand yards off on the factory's beam. Submerged, of course. Just our periscope and radio aerial sticking up. One thousand yards is a safe distance for us, in my opinion.'

'As soon as we know our explosive whales are in position behind the factory's slipway,' Justin said, 'we detonate them electronically. With our radio. When we do – boom!' He clapped his hands once. 'An enormous explosion. The percussion through the water wrecks the factory's rudders. And, with a bit of luck, wrecks the propellers as well.'

They were all quiet, absolutely attentive.

'And,' he said, 'shocks the living shit out of the bastards.'

For the second time Max spoke. He took a big, bored breath and said, to nobody in particular, 'Are the Russian whalers armed?'

'Certain officers will certainly have pistols,' Justin answered. 'And there may be a number of automatic rifles locked away. But that's all. For mutiny purposes. But they'd certainly be locked away, not readily accessible.'

'And if your explosion doesn't wreck the rudders?'

Justin was again keen to encourage Max. 'It will, Max. Commander?'

Henry Thorogood nodded. 'It will, over that short distance. You've got a minimum of two-hundred-and-twenty-odd pounds of Submarex going off all at once. Oh, yes. It will wreck the propellers as well. I'm sure of it. Used to knock Jerry's rudders out with less than that.'

'Okay, Max?' Justin said.

Max shrugged and said nothing.

'And if for some reason it doesn't explode, or if for some reason, say, one of the whales doesn't explode because of some radio defect . . .' Justin glanced at Bob Matthews and he scowled back, 'then at the very least we will still have a tremendous explosion right slap bang behind that factory, which will certainly make them stop their engines to investigate.'

He paused. 'That,' he said emphatically, 'is the real purpose of the exercise. *Make them stop.* So the submarine can get safely underneath their keel. So we can stick those limpet mines on.'

Nobody said anything. Katherine was staring at him.

'Then,' he said, 'while the confusion and commotion is all going on at the *Slava*'s stern, the submarine takes us up to the bows. It surfaces. And we board. . . . To capture the bridge. And make sure every single person gets off into their lifeboats. We are *not* going to take a single life.'

There was a silence. Everybody was staring at nothing. Then

Max said with a kind of idle curiosity, 'Why are you going to board them and capture it? Why don't you just stick the limpet mines on, go away a couple of miles, then radio them that the mines are going to go off and tell them to abandon ship?'

Justin was getting tired of Max. But while there was hope he did not want to knock him back.

'Because,' he said, 'we are going to make absolutely certain that nobody goes down with the ship. Nobody.' He glared at Max, without meaning to. 'We are not going to kill anybody. I won't have it on my conscience that I stuck bombs on a crowded ship and just left them to it. I want everybody off that ship *before* the limpet mines go off. Because although the mines would take about an hour to sink the ship after they've exploded, anything could happen. Boilers could burst. Engineers could be trapped in the engine room. In the bilges, trying to repair the damage. People in sick bay. People injured in the panic. Women locked in the john. The captain may take it into his head to go down with his ship in true-blue naval tradition. Besides,' he held up his finger, 'they may not believe there really *are* limpet mines planted on their keel. It's rather an unlikely thing to happen, isn't it, down at the Antarctic? Or they may decide to send divers over the side to investigate, to try to pull them off. Or they may wait until the mines explode before they do anything and then there's terrible panic—'

Max came out of his boredom and said, 'There's going to be a damn sight more panic when you guys go aboard and start waving your submachine guns around!'

Justin said, 'There are over five hundred people on that goddamn ship, Max.' He tapped his own chest. 'And I personally am going to make one hundred per cent sure I do everything in my power to get them off.'

Max said, with a wisp of a smile, 'And if you don't?'

'We will.'

'How? . . . How are you brave guys going to capture this ship?'

Everybody was watching the two of them.

Justin spoke. 'We're coming to that. But to answer your question in a word: with tear gas.'

'I'm agog with anticipation. But tell me one thing. The *Slava* is a modern ship. It will have all kinds of watertight doors to seal off flooded areas and keep the ship afloat. Have you considered this?'

'I have.'

'And what are you going to do about that little problem?'

'The tear gas will stop them closing a lot of the watertight doors. But once we have captured the ship we will place additional explosives down in the factory deck below the waterline.' Max was appearing to listen to him with rapt attention. 'Furthermore, we are going to throw these explosives down the vat holes on the deck, down into the whale-oil vats.'

He picked one off the table and held it up for them to see. He said to Max, 'Thermal time bombs. Encased in asbestos to resist extreme heat until the timing device detonates them.'

'*Thermal* bombs? . . . In the whale-oil vats? What the hell for, pray? *They* don't help sink the ship!'

Justin said, 'Because I want to blow that killer factory machinery to Kingdom Come. Because I want that whale oil blowing sky-high! Because I want great sheets of flame from their terrible product whooshing up into the sky for the whole damned lot of them to see! For the whole goddamn world to see! So every other whaling ship in the world will remember it.'

Max looked at him incredulously. 'For the *theatrical* effect?'

'The reason we are boarding the ship is twofold: to place those additional explosives to make sure that no watertight doors stop that ship sinking and, most important of all, to make sure everybody is off that ship before the explosives go off!'

'You're crazy,' Max said. He looked around the table at all of them. 'You're all stark raving crazy!'

Justin cut in quietly, 'Then get out.'

Max crashed his hand on the table and scrambled up, redfaced. 'I will!' He turned and knocked over his chair and strode for the door, looked at Katherine hatefully, and punched his finger at her, 'And you're craziest of all!'

twenty

Everything was brand new, straight out of the boxes. The five of them lined up on the foredeck of the *Jubilee* under the blazing Pacific sun, to try all of it out. In front of each was his new Dolphin thermalsuit, electrically heated, the battery hanging from a belt around the waist. Each wore a canvas tracksuit, like overalls, tailormade, with many pouches. Under the tracksuits they wore the latest development in bulletproof vests. On their feet were new running shoes.

Stuffed into the pouches of the tracksuits were two dozen small tear gas grenades and two dozen smoke grenades. Around his waist each man wore a big canvas belt: from the belt hung a holster containing a .38 pistol, and the belt itself contained one hundred bullets. Across one shoulder was slung a standard police antipersonnel tear gas gun, also capable of firing smoke canisters. In their hands they carried small Expers Riot Guns, a double-barrelled weapon; one barrel fired conventional bullets on single-shot or repeat, and the other fired antipersonnel rubber bullets, for riot control. The rubber bullets would knock a man down but would not pierce his body.

From the heavy canvas belt around their waists hung spiked running shoes and sixteen pouches, eight packed with rubber-bullet ammunition clips, eight with conventional ammunition clips. Also from their waists hung a policeman's rubber truncheon, four pairs of handcuffs, a large sheathed knife, a waterproof flashlight, and a pair of diver's flippers. Sewn into the tracksuits at the side of the chest was a small two-way radio. The radio had a tiny earphone that could be plugged into the ear and receive sound without wires. Dangling around their necks hung gas masks; into the gas masks were built a transmitting microphone; another transmitting microphone was sewn to the front of the tracksuit, near the collar. On their hands they wore insulated nylon gloves.

On the deck were five large canvas bags, each contained a large supply of rubber and conventional ammunition clips, and smoke and tear gas canisters. There was another canvas case, containing a strong two-way radio. There were three megaphones. Justin studied his men, sweating in the sunshine.

'You all look great. Stick on your gas masks, and switch your radios to receive.'

Most of the rest of the crew were up on the bridgewing watching, except Katherine. She was at her station in the radio room. They all wrestled on their gas masks and switched on their radios.

Justin said into his gas mask transmitter, 'Do you all read me? Over.'

They came in in a ragged chorus, 'Yes. Over.'

Justin switched to transmission again and said to Katherine, 'Jonah calling One. Do you read me? Over.'

Out of sight, in the radio room on the *Jubilee*, Katherine answered, 'Loud and clear. Over.'

Justin said into his gas mask, to Ross, hovering in his helicopter ten miles away, 'Jonah to Two. Have you read everything so far? Over.'

Ross said, 'Loud and clear, Justin. Over.'

'Jonah's the name, please, everybody. Justin's a bit close to home, just in case some bright Russian finds our wave band.' He went on, 'Jonah to Three. Have you read us so far? Over.'

From five miles away, from the sub just beneath the surface of the sea, came Hi-fi Bob Matthews's voice, 'Yeah, I read ya! Of course all this equipment works, I told you it would, didn't I?' He added, 'Over.'

Justin smiled. 'Do you mind if we just test it out, Bob? The boys would just like to sort of satisfy themselves, you know, on account of it's all brand-new and rather different equipment than they're used to, and their lives depend on it. Okay? Over.'

Hi-fi came back, 'I know the stuff works, don't I? I chose it and tested it for you, didn't I? And it's hot as hell down here in this sub in my wet suit. Why've *I* got to wear a wet suit in the submarine? Once I get into this submarine down there I'm staying *put*, pal. When I said I'd come, nobody said anything about going for swims in the Antarctic!' Bob added, 'Over.'

'Absolutely, Bob.' Justin went on. 'Everybody must of course keep their radios switched in to receive, unless they want to transmit something. So I, or anybody, can talk to One, that is to Katherine on the *Jubilee*; or to Two, that's Ross in the helicopter; or to Three, that's Henry in the submarine, and, of course, Bob. And you can all hear. And any of you can transmit information to the rest of us. If you take your gas masks off you can still use them for radio purposes simply by lifting the mouthpiece and talking into it, like this.'

He demonstrated.

'To recap – the most important radio messages are going to be as follows: firstly, among the five of us on the *Slava*. Telling each other what's happening, where help's needed, et cetera. Next, from the *Jubilee* to the five of us. Katherine will be tuned in to what the rest of the Russian ships are saying among themselves, any counterattacks, et cetera, and L.C. will be helping her to transmit such warnings to us. Thirdly, and most important, my call to Ross. To tell him to come and airlift us off the *Slava* after we've got all the Russians evacuated into their lifeboats and planted our additional bombs.

'Any questions? Before we go on to the next thing? Over.'

It was a beautiful helicopter, the Bell JetRanger. Cruising speed one hundred miles an hour, maximum one hundred and fifty. Range five hundred miles normally. With the additional tanks he'd had fitted, nine hundred miles. Ceiling, twenty thousand feet; it could hover at thirteen thousand. The landing gear was also fitted with pop-out inflatable floats for landing on water. The craft was designed to carry the pilot and four passengers and for heavy transport work. Justin wanted to get only one more man in. But at the important time, everybody would be scrambling and throwing themselves into the helicopter any way they could manage, on top of each other. So the doors had been taken off, the back passenger seat and the luggage rack had been taken out, and the floor covered with polystyrene as protection against the cold. Bob Matthews had fitted an extra set of earphones and microphones for the extra man. The helicopter had been repainted sky blue.

It was a lovely little submarine, too. She was built by the North American Electrical Corporation, mainly for use in offshore oil-drilling operations. She was designed to be 'air-transportable, for global deployment'. Length overall, twenty-seven feet; weight, four thousand pounds; crew, two, plus three divers. Eleven viewports plus periscope. Two hatches: one in the little tower, the other aft, a lock-in–lock-out hatch for divers' use underwater. This hatch opened downwards into the sea and, because of the air pressure in the submarine, the water did not flood in upwards; the divers could simply climb in and out of the open hatch, at considerable depths. She had two exterior manipulator arms, designed to take rock samples or lift machinery underwater. There were numerous external lights and closed-circuit television cameras to enable the crew to see what was going on outside the submarine.

Her speed was five knots cruising, maximum ten knots. She had three motors, all of them external to the hull, each ten horse-power, each motor mounted on a pod and capable of being rotated in different directions, thus giving exceptional hover and current control. Her power came from four main silver-zinc batteries (normally only two) plus an auxiliary, giving double the normal range. The batteries could be recharged by a two-horsepower diesel generator. Oxygen life support: six cylinders, giving three hundred and sixty man hours; carbon dioxide removal by three baralyme canisters, each with its own motor-driven blower. She could dive to two thousand feet.

Justin had stripped her of all her unnecessary weight: her heavy manipulator arms, totalling five hundred pounds alone; her four exterior equipment pods; her anchor and recovery buoy. She was designed to carry only five men. Justin was going to cram seven into her.

Stripped down, the submarine could easily cope with the extra men aboard. But inside, it was a very tight fit indeed. The interior consisted of two spheres: the main control cabin, seven feet in diameter, and the aft divers' cabin, which was six feet in diameter. They were connected by a crawling tunnel two feet in diameter. Above the control cabin was the tiny tower, containing the main hatch. The interior of these two cabins could be stripped of nothing. In fact two things had to be added: a bank of radio equipment and a small chemical lavatory.

'Oh terrific!' Bob Matthews said. 'That's what I like when I take a crap: privacy!'

'If you don't like it, see your union representative,' Justin said. 'And tell them you've been blowing up Russians.'

'This is what I call crappy conditions,' Hi-fi Bob said.

'I'm hoping nobody wants to use it. If only because anybody clambering around trying to go to the crapper will upset the submarine's trim. So for God's sake, on the big day everybody go to the crapper *before* the action starts.'

Steve said, 'To hell with the submarine's trim – it's the efficiency of my gas mask I'm worried about.'

They were all laughing. They climbed down into the submarine, to their assigned places.

Justin looked around the control cabin. He was standing at the periscope. Commander Thorogood was seated at his controls, Bob Matthews was at his radio bank. Steve and Spider were sitting on the tiny deck, holding their knees. Justin crouched down and peered through the passage into the aft chamber at Craig and Black Bob. They had all the spare bags of ammunition and the other radios with them. They all were in their gear, fully armed. 'Everybody comfortable?' Justin asked.

'Oh, sure,' Steve said.

'These are your positions. Every time the same place. Sorry it's so crowded but it's the best we can do. On the big day we're going to be like this for hours. If necessary, someone can stretch out in the connecting passage.' He looked around, then reached up into the tower and pulled the watertight hatch down and heaved the handles around to seal it. It was hot.

'Right,' he said to the commander. 'Periscope depth.'

twenty-one

The sun shone bright on the dark blue Humboldt Current, the air was sunny South Pacific warm. The *Jubilee* steamed south, rolling slightly in the undulating sea. She was a completely white ship now, and she had two tall white funnels. From even a short distance, the second funnel looked very real. Justin had considered rigging a second false mast aft, made of light aluminium, to increase the difference in the ship's profile, but it would interfere with the opening of the submarine hatch and with the helicopter pad. He had considered the old trick of rigging a tin foil curtain between two masts to give the ship a deceptive appearance on a radar screen, but he had abandoned the idea. Hi-fi Bob Matthews explained it to Katherine as he did a routine check of the radio equipment.

'What a crackpot idea that was. All it would do is increase our size as an echo on a Russian radar screen. Big deal.'

'It would make us look like a bigger ship than we really are, wouldn't it?' she asked. She was only talking to unwind. It helped. Her nerves were tight and she was sick of listening to Radio Moscow. Bad-tempered Bob Matthews was another person who gave her a sense of confidence. He was an expert; he was a very experienced seaman, and a born pessimist and complainer. If a man as pessimistic as Hi-fi Bob Matthews was in on the operation, it must be all right.

'That's right. Who wants to look like a bigger ship? The trick is not to be seen at *all*. And the whole idea is to look like an iceberg if we're spotted on their radar screen – that's the clue to our success on this goddamn operation. Icebergs. You understand how a radar setup works, don't you?'

'Yes . . . I think so.'

'You either understand radar or you don't,' Bob said. 'And it's very important to this operation.'

She got up from her chair and followed him out into the wheelhouse to the radar screen. Bob pointed a screwdriver upwards.

'Outside up there are our radar antennae, that disc that goes round and round. You know what that's doing, don't you?'

'Yes,' she said, 'it's sending out sound waves like a radio and receiving back the echoes.'

'Much more complicated than that. Now get this straight or you'll never understand.' He waved his screwdriver at her and said in a starchy professional tone, 'An *active* radar system, namely that disc of ours up there, pulses out very high-frequency radio waves in all directions as it turns around. When these radio waves strike an object, like another ship or an iceberg, or even big clouds, they bounce back as an echo. These echoes come all the way back to our radar system up there, which receives them and reflects them down onto our radar screen here,' he indicated, 'like a television screen.'

'Yes,' she said, trying to look interested and thinking her earlier answer had said just that.

'But the echo shows up on the radar screen only as a dull ragged light. You can more or less tell the size of the object that reflected it, but not much more – only that it's something. In the Antarctic it may be a ship or an iceberg, right?'

'Right.'

'And we *hope*,' Bob said, 'that the Russians are going to think we're an iceberg, if they see us on their radar screens. So what's the point of looking like a bigger iceberg, with all those icebergs around?'

She had to try hard to keep a straight face. 'He's abandoned the idea,' she said. 'It was just an idea because he was thinking of rigging the second mast down aft.'

'Crackpot,' Bob said, 'like all this business of repainting the whole ship white and that second funnel. If the Russians chase us we depend on our superior speed to get away, and if they catch us it doesn't make any difference how many funnels we got, we all end up in the Siberia salt mines.'

'The paint job and the funnels are to deceive any shipping we meet on the way. If we're chased, we're assuming we'll get away.'

Bob snorted and got back to the subject she couldn't argue

with him about. 'We're relying on icebergs,' he said, 'to give us cover. Because the Russian radar can't see us *through* icebergs, do you understand that?'

'Yes, I think I do.'

Glaring at her through his thick glasses, he said, 'The radar radio wave bounces back as an echo off the first object it strikes. Say it's an iceberg. Therefore, if we are *behind* that iceberg, and it's a big one, no radio wave strikes us and we don't show up on their radar screen. Right?'

'Oh, yes,' she said, 'I knew that.'

'Do you know what "beyond the radar horizon" means?' Bob went on. He was enjoying the sound of his own voice.

'No,' she said obligingly.

'That's most important to understand in this operation. It means *as far as we can see*. The human eye can only see as far as the horizon, right? Over the horizon the curvature of the earth dips away, and you can't see what's there. The higher up you go the farther you can see, right?'

'Right.'

'So if you're standing up on top of this wheelhouse where our radar is, you can see about twenty-two miles. That means your horizon is now twenty-two miles. Anything beyond that, beyond the horizon, our radar cannot reach. So we don't get any echoes back. Anything beyond that point is said to be "beyond the radar horizon". Got it? Most ships our size have roughly the same radar horizon.'

'Got it.'

'Now, we can make our radar work *passively*, which means making it work as a *recording* device, something like a radio, that picks up the Microwaves of another ship's radar and translates them onto our screen with an audible ping. So that tells us there is a ship within twenty-some miles using its radar. For convenience, we call it "passive radar". Right?'

'Gotcha.'

'What's its importance to us?' He shoved his spectacles up his nose and squinted at her through his thick lenses.

She said, 'If we hear any pings from our passive radar, it tells us that we're within twenty-two miles of a Russian vessel that is using radar – even though we can't see it on our radar because icebergs are in the way.'

'Right,' Bob said, somewhat reluctantly. 'And what do we do then?'

'Turn around and run away. Sail over his radar horizon,' she said.

'Or,' Bob said, 'make sure we can hide behind some good solid icebergs. Because if we don't, he's likely to see us on his *active* radar screen—'

Suddenly there was a sharp crack crack crack of pistol fire, then the cacophonous staccato of half a dozen pistols firing all at once. She jerked and closed her eyes and stood there rigidly.

'Firing practice,' Bob Matthews said. 'Go on, my dear,' he added with unprecedented warmth, 'go back to your radio, you're doing fine. Would you like a cup of cocoa?'

'No thanks, Bob.' She walked back into the radio room and sat down. Bob came in too. 'Thanks for explaining all that to me,' she said.

She put on her earphones, switched on the radio, and tried to listen hard. Hi-fi Bob stood behind her. Then he put his gnarled hand gently on her shoulder. 'It's all right,' he said gruffly, gently. 'He knows what he's doing. I wouldn't be here if he didn't. Nobody's going to get killed.'

She put her hand up to her shoulder and squeezed his fingers once. He turned and stomped out of the room.

She sat there, eyes still closed. Then she took two big long breaths, to steady herself. But the spine-chilling, staccato cracking of the pistol fire was still shattering the air. She took another deep breath and pulled herself together.

She swivelled her chair and got up and walked to the bank of closed-circuit television sets. She flicked on the switch that read Aft, then she returned to her chair and looked at the television screen.

There they were. She could see only their backs as they stood in a row in their tracksuits, facing the stern. Propped up against the stern rail were the five big sandbags that they had loaded in Baja California. Pinned on each sandbag were the cardboard targets, riddled with holes. They stood, firing together. Through the porthole she could hear the cracking. Then they stopped. They all walked aft to the sandbags and examined their targets.

She could see them, as in a silent movie, talking, comparing targets, Justin, Steve, Spider, Black Bob, Craig. Ross and the commander also came into the screen to look, then Victor. Then L.C. entered the screen to look too. Max was not there. They bunched together, and there were some smiles. Justin looked at each target, saying things. Then they talked a bit, the light wind blowing their hair. Then they all turned and walked back towards the camera. She tried to study Justin's face as he walked into the screen and she felt a deep twinge. There was the man she loved. Then he turned his back to the camera.

They each picked up another weapon. It was the Expers anti-personnel riot gun that fired rubber bullets But it fired them with the crash of a baseball hurled at close range, and a rubber bullet would send a man flying a long way and put him out of action, even more than a pitched baseball would. This, she knew, was the weapon they were principally relying on; and for its effectiveness she prayed.

Suspended at man-height from one of the submarine-hatch davits was another sandbag, about the size of a man's torso, and dangling from the bottom of it were two pieces of timber the length of a man's legs. She saw Justin raise his Expers riot gun to his shoulder, then she heard the thud of the report and the sandbag wrenched and twisted on its suspension, then swung back and forth. Then Spider was firing, another thud and the sandbag wrenched again. Then Steve. She got up and switched off the closed-circuit television. She returned to her radio and sat down.

She sat there, staring at her machine without seeing it. Then she clenched her fists on her knees and closed her eyes and prayed.

Dear God, please not the guns, please keep the real guns out of it, please don't let them have to resort to guns.

The prayer came out in a rush.

And please please please God, rid me of this terrible sense of foreboding. . . .

She sat there a long moment with her fists bunched and her eyes shut tight. Then she opened her eyes. She put her earphones back on her head, picked up her pencil, and started listening to Radio Moscow again.

Every early morning and every evening he made them do the physical exercises on the afterdeck, then, straight afterwards, the firing practice so that they became accustomed to using their weapons while panting and exerted and sweating. He was satisfied with their marksmanship. The exercises were basically for their legs and arms and shoulders, for violent bursts of exertion, as in hand-to-hand fighting and scrambling up and down ropes and ladders. The exercises included karate. Both Ross and Spider knew it well and taught them all the basic falls. In addition, now, he had everybody on a scientific health diet and vitamin pills to beef them up: they might have to fight for a long time, after many cramped tense hours without food. They all complained loudly about the food and the exercises; they had all been in good shape anyway. But after ten days an additional glow of health and fitness was on them as they relaxed around the wardroom in the evening.

After the exercises came the rehearsals, every day down the long ragged coast of Chile. Every day he had them get out the sub and helicopter and made them practise, over and over and over again. And every evening, at the end of the long day, after their health meal, sitting around the long wardroom table with the tired glow of a lot of exercise, they rehearsed their Russian. Katherine sat at the head of the table; in front of each of them were the stencilled sheets of phrases she and Justin had prepared. Each man alone, and then all together, they recited the Russian words, until they had them perfect, except for their accents.

This ship is captured.

This ship is captured. It is about to blow up and sink.

This ship is captured. Limpet mines have been placed under the keel and these will blow up and sink the ship in sixty, fifty, forty, thirty, twenty, ten, nine, eight, seven, five, four, three, two, one minutes.

Put on your lifejackets and oilskins and proceed immediately to your lifeboat stations. This ship is about to blow up and sink.

You must proceed immediately to your lifeboat stations in an orderly manner and abandon ship under the directions of your coxswain. Any resistance will be met by force.

Your captain and others are our hostages. They will only be released when you are in your lifeboats in the water.

Do not be afraid. You will not be harmed if you proceed to your lifeboat stations immediately and abandon ship in an orderly manner under the directions of your coxswain. Your catching fleet and your tanker will be summoned by radio to pick you up safely. But any resistance will be met by force.

This ship is fully under our control. It is heavily mined and nothing can save her. Proceed immediately to your lifeboat stations.

Outside the wardroom windows a waning moon shone less and less brightly each night on the vast black sea. The *Jubilee* ploughed evenly south into the Humboldt Current, and out there it was getting colder now.

twenty-two

The days went like that.

She looked for work. She was all right when she was with him, when she was working, when she was talking to somebody about anything at all, but not when she was doing nothing or listening to that radio. Her head reeled with Russian; she often dreamed in Russian. She was good enough, she was sure, but then almost every time she tuned in for more practice she encountered words and phrases she either did not catch because of accent or that she did not understand, and then she felt panicky. Everybody was relying on her, she had led them to believe that she was a competent Russian speaker – and here she was missing whole sentences all over the place because she was stumbling over idiotic words and phrases. *She must not let them down!* She had made enormous lists of words extracted from the dictionary, and she had translated great tracts of the *Jubilee*'s navigation manual now. She'd gotten David Cartwright to read into a tape recorder all the sorts of things that navigators and deck officers and radio officers shout back and forth to each other, and would be likely to say to each other hunting whales in the Antarctic; then she had translated them arduously into Russian, then taped herself saying them. She listened to herself rattling off navigational talk in Russian whenever there was nothing worth listening to on the radio. She had made Cartwright explain the meaning of everything to her minutely until she thoroughly understood what she was listening to.

'You're getting very good at navigation, Miss Robinson,' Cartwright said shyly.

'Please call me Katherine.'

'I'm sorry.' Cartwright blushed.

Sitting in the radio room waiting for something worthwhile to listen to, she had edited Justin's book a second time. She had checked over the *Jubilee*'s current accounts, she had brought the library catalogues and indexes right up to date, she had been over the whole ship asking them all if they needed help, she had studied the First Aid Manual from cover to cover and studied the contents of the *Jubilee*'s large medicine chest. She often went down to the galley for coffee. 'Can I help you, L.C.? I'm between broadcasts and going out of my mind.'

'Don't do that, darlin', we need you. How do you feel?' He looked at her.

'Fine.'

'Gets you down, doesn't it – the waiting.'

She said, 'How're you taking it, L.C.?'

L.C. gave her his smile. 'The army cook is too busy sweating and cursing over his stoves to worry about the cannon balls overhead. That's me.' He gave a mock sigh. 'Besides, a woman's work is never done.'

She wondered why he said that, if he wasn't gay. She wanted

to say, 'Are you gay, L.C.? I don't care, you can tell me.' Instead she said, 'How do you think everybody else's taking it?'

L.C. knew how she was feeling. 'Everybody's a bit uptight, Katie. You're not the only one. But don't worry, they're all as tough as nails.'

After a minute she said, 'What do you think is going to happen with Max?'

L.C. gave her a reassuring smile. 'It's a dilemma. But he's behaving pretty well, isn't he? And I have supreme confidence in Justin. He'll handle it. Correctly.'

She wanted to talk about Justin. She needed to talk. She said, 'Was he as wild once upon a time as people sometimes hint?'

L.C. gave her a wary look. 'You don't want to know about that.'

'Go on, it's all right.' She added, 'I've seen him written up in enough gossip columns with different dazzling women.'

'You're the most dazzling of all.' L.C. cocked his head on one side. 'I'm so . . . glad about this,' he said. 'About you two getting together at last. You're so . . . ideal together.'

'Thanks, L.C.'

'I could never understand why it didn't happen long ago.'

'Business was business. And still is.'

L.C. cocked his head again. 'Go on – tell L.C.! Are you going to get married?'

'I don't know.' She said, to change the subject, 'You were saying about Justin?'

'Yes, he was wild. Him and Max together when they hit port? And what a gambler. He always seemed to win. You heard the one about his airplane, didn't you? And how he was bound over to keep the peace. By the judge?'

'No,' she said. 'Nobody tells me anything.'

L.C. shrugged. 'It's all right to tell you, I suppose. You should hear Ross tell it, when he's had a few drinks. Ross can be as funny as hell. You know Ross was his roommate at Stanford at the time – he's got a few stories to tell about Justin.'

'Tell me.'

'Well,' L.C. said, 'Justin won this little two-seater airplane, in some big-time poker game. Anyway, he was . . . courting this girl at some girls' college. Used to fly his airplane over to see her on weekends, it impressed her no end. Anyway, one time they had a fight because of some other girl or something. So Justin tries to climb up her drainpipe, in the dead of night, see? And this girl's dormitory is on the fourth floor. And just as Justin's about to reach her window . . .' he guffawed, 'the drainpipe tears away from the wall!'

She burst out laughing, as much at L.C. as at Justin. They were both laughing.

'But it doesn't come crashing down,' L.C. went on, hardly able to control his mirth, 'just the top comes away, and it's hanging like this, like a top-heavy wheat stalk – with Justin clinging terrified to the top like this. . . . And that's how he was when the house mother saw him and phoned for the police. And all the girls are hanging out of their dormitory windows cheering him – except the house mother and Justin's girl friend, who's screaming abuse at him.'

They leaned against the galley table laughing.

'And Justin splits his trousers!' L.C. screamed. 'And as the police arrive the drainpipe breaks and Justin goes crashing down – *kerpow* into the geraniums. And Justin goes running off through the flowerbeds and across the hockey fields with his ass hanging out of his trousers and a policeman in hot pursuit and all the girls shouting encouragement.'

They were both helplessly laughing.

'Anyway . . .' L.C. sputtered, wiping his eyes with the back of his wrist, 'anyway, Justin makes good his escape, see? To roars of applause. Then . . . the next day . . . Justin's lost some face, I mean his ass hanging out of his trousers and all that. So what does he do?' L.C. raised his bushy eyebrows at her. 'He decides to do stunts in his airplane over the college. He tries to do sky-writing with one of those smoke trails and. . . .' L.C. clutched his stomach and screamed, 'and he's skywriting "Same place tonight, baby!"'

He threw down his bread knife and went into uncontrolled laughter, over the table.

'And what happens? He gets into terrible engine trouble and has to make a forced landing.'

She collapsed back against the bulkhead laughing.

'On the hockey fields. . . . And he makes it under the telephone wires very nicely but a fence tears his wheels off . . .' L.C. thumped the table, 'and the hockey field tears the bottom of his airplane off, *and the grass burns the seat of his trousers off! . . . and they carry him off in a stretcher with a green raw ass!*'

Katherine was clutching herself, laughing. She didn't care how much of the story was true. She felt better.

twenty-three

Steaming south in the Humboldt, they were a long way behind Moscow time. In order to pick up the Moscow evening broadcasts, which offered the widest range of programmes, she had to get up long before dawn. The alarm clock trilled, she woke up deep in the double bed, her naked body touching Justin's; he always stirred with the alarm. She lay still for a few moments, waking up, feeling his body touching hers, letting him go back to sleep before she crept out of bed. Then she carefully got up. She walked naked across the cabin into the bathroom still half-asleep, hair awry. She flicked on the hot shower tap and stood, eyes closed, hugging her breasts, waiting for the water to run hot, then stepped into it. She let it beat down on her head and shoulders for a minute, then she took a deep breath and flicked the tap to cold. She gasped and bore it beating on her until she was cold and thoroughly awake for Radio Moscow.

Commander Henry Thorogood was an early riser too. She was always glad to see him on the bridge, the ship so quiet, ploughing on into the waning darkness. She brought him up tea from the empty galley. 'Ah, thank you, my dear, that's the ticket!'

She found him reassuring in the cold reality of the early morning. Sometimes she got him to talk about his life in the navy.

'Why submarines and not ordinary warships, Henry?' she asked this morning. 'Submarines would give me the heebie-jeebies.'

'One's either a submariner type or one's not. Marvellous life if you're cut out for it. Finest bunch of fellows in the world. One thing you can be sure about in any submarine: every fellow is a first-class chap, right down to the lowest rating. All the biggest bunch of individualists imaginable, maybe even crack-pots – you've almost *got* to be a bit nutty to join submarines, I suppose. But every one of them is a first-class chap and thoroughly reliable. If he's not both those things he's soon posted out of submarines; you can't afford to have an unreliable or unpopular man in a submarine. You can't afford trouble down there. The result? A submarine is always a happy ship. Every-body's friends, the commander down to the lowest rating.' He stroked his beard happily. 'That counts for a great deal in this life. Very similar setup on the *Jubilee*.'

She said, 'What was it like during the war? You were in the minisubs, weren't you? That sounds terrifying.'

'Wonderful life.' He loved talking about those days. 'The old X-craft. Five-man crew. I was only a nineteen-year-old ensign then, of course, about the lowest form of marine life. But what *men* I worked with! Absolute laws unto themselves. The regular navy left us alone. They knew we had to be daredevils. What the X-craft men wanted they usually got – as long as it wasn't more money or less work.' He looked at her. 'Can you imagine? When we went into operation our only cooking facility was a tiny electric stove? And a bowl of soup passed from one man to another could upset the trim of the submarine. That's about all we got to eat, too. And we had to crawl everywhere. And the smell of oil and sweat. No bunks. Oh no, you slept on the deck curled around some piece of machinery. And our job was to sneak into German harbours and stick limpet mines under their battleships and installations.' He began to stroke his beard again. 'Of course the navy didn't interfere with us too much. They were damn grateful to have us.'

She thought, *God, yes.* 'Did you personally swim out of the submarine to stick the limpet mines on?'

'Yes. When I was an ensign.'

'What was that like?'

'All in a day's work.' He glanced at her. He knew why she wanted to know. 'Not much to it really,' he said. 'The more dangerous part is *in* the submarine, entering Jerry's harbour. Usually can't see a thing of course, flying blind. Pitch black, almost always at night. Can't use our sonar much because they'll pick up our pings on their passive. So any moment you could crash into one of their bloody antisub nets. Or even into a wharf or something. Bit unnerving, that part. Got to stick your jolly old periscope up now and again to see where the hell you are, that helps. Anyway, eventually you know where you are and can make out your target lying there, big black shape. And,' he shrugged, 'under you go. Under her keel. When you reckon you're about there, up goes your antennae.'

'What antennae?'

'Three telescopic legs,' the commander said. 'Very simple. You just press a button and up go your three antennae, like those fancy car radio aerials, till they touch the hull of the ship, so you're nestling against her.' He added, 'Justin and I considered fitting the *Jubilee*'s submarine with them, for the *Slava*. But we decided against it because that little sub has such excellent hover control, the three external motors that can rotate in any direction. Wonderful little sub, that, pure luxury compared to those old X-craft.'

'And then?'

'Well, meanwhile your poor unfortunate diver is sitting gloomily in the flooding chamber with his limpet mines, ready to go. The flooding chamber in those old subs was the conning tower, and also the lavatory, by the way. Not like our fancy sub at all, with its aft pressurized lock-in–lock-out setup that doesn't require flooding. Anyway, you lock the diver in the tower, and you open the jolly old tap and in floods the water, into the tower. As soon as it's full, the diver opens the top latch and out he goes with his little bundle of joy – his limpet mines.' He said, 'And that's it. Out he swims. Chooses his spot on the keel. Scrapes it clean of barnacles and seaweed. Clamps on the mines. Sets the timing dial to give the sub time to get the hell out of it. Then swims back into his nice warm flooding chamber. Closes the hatch. Knocks three times to say he's back. They blow the water out of the chamber with compressed air. And bingo! He crawls back into the submarine all wet and horrible, and complaining bitterly. They give him a cup of cocoa.'

It made her own fears seem despicable. She would be sitting safely in her radio room while they were all out there under the *Slava*.

'How long did you do that for?' she asked.

'Most of the war. For a while I was on those two-man torpedoes – you know, you lie on them, or ride on them like a horse. And buzz into Jerry's harbour that way. Same job.' He added, 'Bit more uncomfortable.'

God, she liked him. And it was good to have him aboard. 'And when you got back to England after a job like that?'

He smiled at her, and his seamed plump face gave a flash of boyishness still. 'Gave it a bit of a tonk,' he admitted.

It was not hard to imagine the commander giving it a tonk.

'And after the war?' she said.

He sighed. 'They scrapped the old X-craft, unfortunately. Loved to have stayed on them. No, I went on to nuclear submarines. The big chaps.'

She did not want to go back to the radio yet. 'And when you retired? Why did you come to America?'

'My wife died during the Blitz. Never remarried. Had a widowed sister in Connecticut. Only family I have really. England had rather gone to the dogs under the Labour government, and all that.'

'Justin tells me you bought a small farm.'

'Market gardening. But the damn things wouldn't grow. Tried a few other things. But could never settle down ashore. Once a seaman, always a seaman, you can't expect too much of us.'

'And now? Do you miss the Royal Navy and your submarines?'

'I'm mad keen on Oceanics' work, always have been. Read all the Old Man's books in the navy, and Cousteau's. And the films. That's the world of the future – the oceans. Seventy per cent of the earth's surface. *Seventy per cent*. A treasure-house!

A paradise. And we're ruining it. *Rape*. Instead of all this rampant exploitation we should be farming it. Cherishing it. Developing it.' He shook his head. 'Fish-farming – that's what we should be doing. Scientific breeding of edible fish to stop this rape. Even whale-breeding, for that matter. With scientific breeding and harvesting of whales we could keep the world supplied with meat indefinitely – awful thought though it is, like breeding elephants and horses for slaughter. But it's better than the wholesale reckless butchery the world's been doing.' He glanced at her. 'I'm happy here, with Oceanics. See my days out doing something useful for the world.'

He was so positive, so sure of himself. They all were, in their different ways. She felt ashamed of her fear.

And yet she was afraid. Back in the radio room she took a sheet of paper and wrote in her Gregg shorthand:

What I shall always remember of these days: the terrible noise of the pistols and the submachine guns. Every morning and night he makes them practise, and our ears ring with the noise. And I want to cry out: oh God, why the guns? Oh God, please make them not to have to use the guns. Oh God, take the guns out of it. And, oh God, rid me of this terrible sense of foreboding.

Oh God, tell me that they will not kill anybody. Oh God, make me believe now that it can be done without killing anybody. Oh please God, let me believe it now, tell me now it isn't crazy.

Dear God, I am afraid. A cold numbness descends upon me, that makes my heart hard. I love him so much that sometimes now I almost hate him, for risking himself, for his passionate ideals that now in my fear and love seem crazy, for risking taking himself away from me. Sometimes it seems now that it is almost too painful to love him, I want to fight him fiercely to make him stop what he is doing. And because I cannot overcome him I hate him, I cannot bear to love him. And I want to cry out in a loud voice, 'Oh God, look what he is doing! Make him stop! Make him stop this madness and bring him back to me.'

twenty-four

Max Hagen stalked the ship looking bored and aloof. He caused no trouble. He missed most meals, eating them in his cabin, and that was all right with Justin. He did not want sullenness at the table. Max was still drinking the better part of a bottle of bourbon a day, and that was all right with Justin too. He did not mind if Max drank himself into a stupor every day as long as he kept to himself and did not cause trouble.

They were all sitting around in Justin's office at the end of the day, cleaning their weapons. Looking over at Justin, Ross said, 'What're you going to do about *that* guy?' He jerked his head at the bulkhead.

Justin went to his refrigerator and took out four cans of beer. He said, 'How about getting us three more beers from the bar, Spider?' He snapped off the caps and handed the cans around. 'Day after tomorrow we put into the Straits of Magellan to create our emergency fuel base. It's the first piece of evidence of ourselves that we'll leave, and we'll have to lock him up that day, so he doesn't know where we are. So he can never tell anybody where to look for it, to corroborate his story.'

'Or drug him,' Ross said.

'How about tear gas?' Steve said.

'And on the big day?' Ross asked.

'In the brig,' the commander said. 'Definitely.'

'Lock him up,' Justin said. 'We can't take any chances. While we're off at the wars there'll only be Cartwright, Victor, L.C., and Katie aboard.'

Spider came back with the beer. He handed cans to Ross and Justin. They were frosted cold. The men were sweating in their heavy gear after their evening exercises. Justin took a long swallow, and it went down like a mountain brook. The first beer at the end of the day made his cigarette taste like food.

'What worries me,' Ross said, 'is what the hell he'll do when we get back.'

Justin inhaled deeply. 'I think we've got that one figured out.'

Ross clasped his hands on top of his balding head. 'Yeah, but have we? We're relying on the guy's goodwill.'

The commander said, 'Not entirely, there're very real economic pressures on him.'

Justin picked up his Expers riot gun and began to unscrew it. He said, 'Once it's over, successfully, what has he got to gain by splitting on us? Nothing. First of all, he'd have to prove it, and we'd all laugh him out of court. I for one would have no compunction about committing perjury. Would anybody in the circumstances?'

'Black Bob,' Craig said. 'The Holy Roller.'

'Not me, man,' Black Bob growled. 'I ain't scared of perjury an' I got mah reasons.'

'Cartwright?' Ross said. 'Seriously. He's very religious.'

Justin and the commander both shook their heads.

'If it came to a court, he'd be one of our star witnesses. Can you imagine that guy looking like a saboteur in the witness box? You guys, yeah, you all look like cut-throats, but David Cartwright? And Katherine? And *me*?' He pulled the barrel of the Expers gun through, looking at Ross.

'Max has got nothing to gain anyway, even if he could prove it. First of all he'd ruin Magnus Oceanics. If we all got tied up in a trial, Oceanics would collapse. For one thing we couldn't deliver the films under contract on time, particularly *Whale*, and we'd lose a fortune. And so would Max. His fifteen per cent shares are worth nearly half a million bucks. And he couldn't pick up the pieces. He still couldn't make himself head of the company. And he couldn't write the books, and he'd have a hell of a job getting another expert crew together. And anyway, if Oceanics goes to hell, so does Magnus Communications. And he loses his job. He'd be insane.'

'I sometimes think insanity would be an improvement,' Ross said.

Black Bob said, 'Money talks with that guy. He wouldn't sacrifice his snazzy Hollywood life-style.'

Justin said, 'Max's got his head screwed on pretty tight. He's got a hell of a temper and he's got enormous pride, but he's not stupid.'

'That's it,' Ross said. 'His *pride*. You've hurt his pride. And he'll take his revenge somehow. He could be pretty convincing in court, with what he knows, no matter how many of us protested to the contrary.'

'It's that pride of his that I'm relying on. He'd lose his job . . . everything. And he must keep his pride now too – and he is. He's not locked up now. We're polite to him and he's more or less civil to us. He's been invited to participate and at first he did a little. Now he's opted out. Fine. He's made his stand, he's got his dignity. After it's all over, he's still got his dignity. There's nothing cowardly or undignified in refusing to participate in this operation. As a law-abiding citizen and company official, he disapproves. So be it. And after it's over he's got nothing to gain and everything to lose by spilling the beans.'

'That's the theory,' Ross said. 'I sure hope it's the fact.'

'Got any better suggestions?'

Nobody said anything. Then Steve said in a soft voice, 'I don't like him knowing all the details of our plan.'

'How could we keep them from him? The broad details are obvious. He'd soon put the smaller pieces together. Unless we locked him up in his cabin with earplugs for a month.'

'Which mightn't have been such a bad idea.'

'Or dumped him over the side,' Steve said.

They all smiled.

'Justin is right,' Commander Thorogood said. He tugged at his beard. 'One's got to define one's objective. Which is to pull off this operation and live happily ever after. To do that, under the circumstances, we've got to have Max either as a participant or at least neutral.' He made a small movement with his hand. 'He wouldn't be neutral if we treated him like a prisoner unnecessarily. He's got his pride. And he's a Magnus Oceanics man after all. He's not a *bad* man, not a *wicked* man. He wouldn't be my choice as the boss, but he's served the company well for many years. And will continue to do so, I believe, provided this delicate situation – to use a euphemism – provided it is handled sensibly. Delicately. A bit of psychology, that's all. The man's proud. He's got a great deal to lose. The trick is . . . the *clever* thing to do is to use those two facts to our advantage.' He waved his hand. 'For want of a better word, humour him wherever possible. We need him as a friend as far as possible, not an enemy.'

'Exactly,' Justin said.

Afterwards, when the others had gone back to their cabins to shower and change for supper, Ross stayed behind. He sprawled in Justin's armchair, pensively drinking another can of beer. He said, 'You know something? It's not Max I'm so worried about. I think you're probably right, we can put the screws on him to keep his mouth shut. It's Steve that I'm worried about.'

'Steve?'

'Yeah. I don't mean that he'll rat on us or let us down. I mean the opposite, that he'll overdo it.' He chewed his lip. 'That he'll throw himself into a situation unnecessarily for the sheer hell of it and end up killing somebody. Or himself.'

'Oh, bullshit, champion. Katie's been at me about the same thing, she says he's got a death wish. Have you been talking to Katie about this?'

'As a matter of fact,' Ross said, 'she did mention it to me, but I said forget it, the guy's one hundred per cent reliable. Which he is as a comrade-in-arms. But I don't trust him not to go berserk. I don't mean berserk. . . .' He shifted irritably in his chair. 'I mean *look* for trouble. Christ help any Russian who gets in his way. To tell the truth, I was worried about taking him on the Japanese job, for the same reason. But then I decided it must be okay because there was no opportunity for confrontation, really – it was all underwater. But when we board that *Slava* . . . ?'

'Nonsense. The guy's just a born adventurer. He's a fighter, sure. But there's nothing dumb about Steve. He knows how important it is that we don't hurt anybody. You're thinking of that shark episode.'

Ross shifted in his chair. 'I'm not talking about him provoking trouble. It's if trouble arises. I want you to give him a very strong talking-to before this thing starts. And if you don't, I will.'

'I'll give them all a talking-to.'

'But him especially. Katie's right, I think the guy *has* some kind of a death wish.'

'It's a self-confidence,' Justin said wearily, 'that's all. He's got this belief that he can outwill his animal adversaries. That's all.'

'He didn't outwill that hammerhead shark very well, did he?' Ross retorted. 'That was madness. Or that rhinoceros that gave him those scars. I tell you – you look at his eyes when he gets talking about that sort of thing. I'm a very good judge of character. Don't laugh at me, buddy. Katie's right. Perhaps the guy doesn't know it but he courts death. Get him to tell that rhino story again and watch his eyes.'

Justin grinned at him. 'Old champion. "All the world's mad except me and thee, and even thee's a little mad." '

'I'm serious. Watch that guy. And for God's sake talk to him.'

'Okay, I will. But Steve's fine. And Max will be all right too.'

'All I can say is, make sure you're right.'

He believed he was. He understood Steve. He knew Max. He was satisfied he was right, and satisfied in the good feeling that he was doing what he had to do. Sitting collapsed around the wardroom with his men at the end of the day as they cleaned their weapons, Justin looked at his men and by God he was pleased with them and loved every one of them and was proud of them. They were as good as he could wish for, and in the name of God they couldn't be much better prepared than they were, and at the end of the day he wanted them to be happy.

The next night he let Craig succeed in extracting a promise from him, on behalf of one or two others but mainly on his own behalf, that the good ship *Jubilee* would find time out of its schedule, when it got back to Baja California, to put back into Acapulco for some rest and recreation.

'The most beautiful girls in the world are in Acapulco,' Craig said, 'in the No-tell Hotel Restaurant and Bar.'

'Most beautiful girls in the world,' Steve said, 'are in the Night and Day Bar, Montevideo.'

'I thought you never paid?' Justin said to his brother.

'Yeah,' Craig said, 'I don't. I'm not going to pay for it in the No-tell Hotel, either.'

'Never pays for it,' Black Bob drawled, 'but spends a goddamn fortune gettin' it for nothin'. I seen him.' Black Bob did not approve of fornication. He had had a bit too much to drink. Justin knew the signs: soon Bob would start arguing at them about God, and he knew Craig was about to start baiting him, to make him start.

Ross knew the signs also. He glanced at Justin, then said to Steve, 'I thought you were too embarrassed about your scars ever to get your pants off, Steve.'

'Yeah,' Steve said, going along with the joke, 'I am. I just look at the girls.'

Justin knew what Ross was up to and he waited, amused. Ross said, attempting a casual joviality, which Justin thought the worst bit of acting he'd ever seen, 'And the rhino horn is supposed to be an aphrodisiac! What symbolism! What a conversation piece as you take your pants off—'

Justin almost laughed out loud. Ross pressed on. 'Rhino horn *is* supposed to be an aphrodisiac, isn't it? I mean, that's why the rhino's been hunted so viciously throughout the ages?'

'Right,' Steve said. He looked a bit puzzled because he knew that Ross knew all about this. 'It's *not* an aphrodisiac in fact, that's a myth. But that's why the poachers go after rhino, yeah.'

Justin wanted to say, 'Steve, Ross wants you to tell us again about that rhino so I can see your death-wish eyes, go ahead and oblige him.'

Ross went on: 'They're terribly dangerous animals, aren't they? As tall as a man, I believe. Given to murderous charges at anything that moves. Including the well-intentioned game wardens who wanted to move them to safer game reserves.' He turned to David Cartwright and said in what he imagined was a casual conversational manner, 'Have you heard how Steve got those scars?'

Cartwright looked embarrassed at suddenly being the centre of attention. 'Yes,' he said.

Justin managed to keep a straight face. He said directly to Steve, 'What exactly is your theory? About imposing your will on an animal. How do you do it?'

Ross sat back irritably. 'Relate it to that rhino,' he muttered.

'It's simple,' Steve said. 'It's telepathy. Two people can do it between each other. Try it with somebody you know well. You can put ideas into each other's minds. I believe,' he added, 'the Russians have devoted a lot to developing this.'

Black Bob said, 'Yeah, them Russians. Thought-control. That's bad, man. That's the anti-Christ workin'.'

Ross said impatiently, 'Carry on, Steve.'

'It's the same with animals. I've got a stronger mind than an animal. Therefore I can put a thought in its mind even easier.'

'What kind of thought?' Ross demanded.

Steve looked at him and his blue eyes were confident. 'A simple thought, naturally. Like, "Turn around." Or, "Come out of that bush." Or, "Look at me." Or "Stand still." '

'And you've done this?' Ross asked.

'Many times,' Steve said. 'As a game warden. So I could dart it. To tranquillize it. Or maybe it was a rogue that I had to shoot dead. I've done it on elephants, often. There's a whole herd of elephants over there, I want one to come out of the herd so I can shoot it because it's sick or rogue. And with rhino, many times.'

'And it works?' Justin said. He was studying Steve's eyes.

'Sure,' Steve said. Cartwright and Spider Webb were staring at him, fascinated.

Ross said, 'But it didn't work on that rhino?'

Steve knew he was under cross-examination and he was entirely relaxed. 'Sure it worked. I've translocated hundreds of rhino.'

'And the rhino that got you?'

They were all listening hard, even Black Bob.

'It was the last animal in that particular area. It was terribly rugged wild country. He knew he was the last one. He was wild with fear. I'd been tracking him for three days. And he was rogue. He had two terrible snare wounds from poachers, one rusty old cable right down to the bone in one leg. The other deep into his neck so he could hardly breathe. He was desperate. And he was a born killer anyway. He lay in ambush for me.'

'He took you by surprise?' Ross asked.

'No. I knew he was somewhere near. Close.'

'How?'

'I could feel him.'

'*Feel* him?'

'Sure. I can *feel* an animal's presence, even if I can't see him.'

'How?'

Steve smiled. 'Telepathy. He's waiting for me, to kill me. I get his thoughts. Because I'm receptive.'

Justin was watching him closely. Ross said, 'So why didn't you will him to come out of his ambush?'

Steve said, 'I did. And he came.'

'Did you know *where* he was going to come from?'

'More or less. I could *feel* him somewhere in there on my right-hand side. I knew he wouldn't come from my left.'

'And this was thick jungle?' Spider said.

'Thick bush. All around.'

Ross said, 'What happened? How come he caught you unawares?'

'He didn't catch me unawares. I *willed* him to charge. And he did.'

'And?'

'And,' Steve said, 'I stood my ground to draw his charge, then sidestep him and shoot the dart into his flank. That was my procedure.'

Ross pounced, 'Like a bullfighter. Is that standard hunting procedure?'

'No,' Steve admitted. 'Each hunter has his own method. That's mine.'

'What happened?'

'I slipped. He hooked me as he passed. In the thigh.'

'And?'

'You know what happened,' Steve said. 'He threw me over the trees. And when I crashed down, he charged and got me again. In the other thigh. Threw me over his back. Then I managed to dart him. In the backside. He was confused and ran off.'

Ross sat back, dissatisfied. Justin was watching Steve. The man sat there, supremely calm, his eyes confident and cold-blooded. 'My system works,' he said. 'It's just that I slipped.'

It was very impressive.

Ross went on relentlessly, 'And the shark? Why did you do that?'

Justin felt embarrassed. The man had saved his life. He started to protest, but Steve said, 'Do what?'

'Stand back from the cage door to let Justin go through ahead of you,' Ross said, 'like it was a social occasion.'

Steve said, unembarrassed, 'Because no animal will ever kill me.'

There was complete surprised silence. Steve looked flatly at Ross. Nobody had ever heard him say that. Then Justin said, 'How do you know that?'

Steve turned and looked at him. 'I just know.' He tapped his forehead between his eyebrows. 'In here. With absolute certainty.'

They were all staring at him. Spider was mesmerized. Ross said carefully, 'And how about a man killing you?'

'A man is an animal. Like any other. Worse, in most cases.'

Ross said, 'A man won't kill you?'

'Right,' Steve said.

Ross sat back. He looked at Justin.

Later, alone, he said to him, 'Well? What do you think?'

Justin said, 'That's not a death wish. But it's a dangerous attitude. I'll talk to him.'

They sat around the mess table at night, tired, feeling good, drinking wine, talking, relaxing, unwinding, trying not to talk or think about the operation. But there was no way they were not going to get a godly lecture about it sooner or later from Black Bob. Craig encouraged him, for sport: 'Tell the others why you're here, Bob. If you're so against sin and crime.'

That was all Black Bob needed. 'I'm waging war against the anti-Christ. *That's* not a crime. It's all in the Bible, brother. Isn't it Justin?'

Justin nodded, smiling.

'I thought you didn't believe in God?' Craig demanded of Justin.

'I only agreed it's all in the Bible.'

'The anti-Christ,' Black Bob said, 'shall appear as a saviour to mankind in its troubled times. He will sort the world out. All the nations of the world will look up to him. Then he will claim to be the Christ – he will make himself God on earth. Most everybody will believe him.'

'Meanwhile,' Craig prompted him, 'back at the ranch?'

'Meanwhile . . .' Bob said, 'back at the ranch this gent turns out to be a real tyrant, doesn't he? Real bad man.' He spread his hands at them all and his eyeballs and teeth showed very white. 'And *eevil* and godlessness will reign over the world.'

'When is this going to happen?' Craig asked.

'Soon,' Bob went on. 'We're in very troubled times, ain't we?'

'And who is this gent, the anti-Christ?'

Bob leaned towards him. 'You figure it out.' He waited a dramatic moment, then went on, seeing everybody was waiting for him to figure it out for them. 'The Bible says that before the rising of the anti-Christ, the world will be in big trouble. It is, ain't it? Never been in so much trouble!'

Craig said, 'I thought the world never had it so good.'

'So *bad*, man!' Bob cried, his eyeballs flashing white at him. 'And it's all in the Bible, brother. That's how the world's gonna be before the anti-Christ comes along! Now,' he said, leaning forward, 'what else does it say in the Bible?' He spread his hands again. 'Christ said to his disciples, "Jerusalem shall be destroyed and my people scattered – and then Jerusalem will be rebuilt and my people will come together as a nation." And that's happened hasn't it? Them Romans destroyed Jerusalem. And the State of Israel was formed after World War Two.' He gave them a significant look. 'Now what's the next thing the Bible says is going to happen? It says the northernmost country of Europe, which is Russia, is going to gang up with the Arabs to destroy Israel. An' *that's* happening, ain't it? America's backin' Israel and Russia's backin' the Ayrabs – an' Israel's gonna win that war, it says! An' what's the other thing that's gonna happen?'

'What?' Craig said.

'It says in the Bible, brother,' Bob said, 'that there's gonna come about the European Common Market, with ten member states.'

Justin corrected him mildly. 'It says that out of Europe will emerge a great cow with ten horns.'

'Exactly!' Bob cried. 'An' what's that but the Common Market?'

Craig said, 'I follow. But aren't there nine members of the European Common Market, not ten? Brother.'

'Aha!' Bob pointed his finger at him. 'An' who's applyin' to join? Spain! An' when Spain joins, watch out, brother!'

'And then what happens?' Craig said. 'Who is this anti-Christ?'

'I'm comin' to that,' Bob said. 'Now you figure it out. . . . Who is tryin' to get the most power in this troubled world of ours? An' he's succeedin'!'

'Who?' Craig asked obligingly.

'Look at England. . . . Who's the real big power there?' He raised one hand. 'The trade unions, right? An' who's behind the trade unions? The Communists! Right?' He appealed to Justin. Justin shrugged. 'An' in France an' Italy an' Portugal – all over Europe, who's causin' the trouble?'

'The Communists,' Steve said.

'Right!' Bob cried, encouraged. 'Who's behind the Ayrabs fightin' the Jews? Who wants to overrun Europe? Who wants to overrun Asia? Who's got all their big missiles pointed at America?'

'The Communists!' Steve and Craig chorused.

Bob went on excitedly. 'Right! Now you figure out what Justin said in Acapulco about there not bein' enough resources an' how we're squanderin' them an' abusin' them an' all that shit. I mean it ain't shit, it's for real, what I mean is it's *terrible*. Now what I mean is, what's the solution to this shortage?' Black Bob paused, wide-eyed. 'The solution is control!' He slammed his fist on the table. 'Control! You gotta share it out like a schoolteacher with his kids. You gotta say, "I own every-thin' an' this is how much you gonna' have accordin' to how much you need." Control!' Bob rocked forward and said softly, 'An' how do you get control like *that*? With free enterprise? Or with communism?' He spat out the word.

'With communism!' Craig said.

'With communism,' Bob cried, delighted with the doom of his message. 'With state control! With Big Brother telling you what you can and can't have an' do!' Then his eyes slitted down. 'With communism . . .' he hissed. 'I tell you, brother! Communism is the anti-Christ which is to come! The state of total material godlessness! The state is god! The state giveth an' the state taketh away!'

Steve said, 'I always said them Russians were bad bastards.'

'I'm fightin' the anti-Christ!' Bob cried.

'Jesus,' Steve said. 'Complicated, ain't it?'

'Because after the anti-Christ has ruled a few years,' Bob flared up again, 'the Battle of Armageddon will take place!' He lifted his hands. 'When all the forces of the Lord will fly into mighty combat with all the forces of the anti-Christ. Because who is really this anti-Christ?' He howled at them. 'The devil! Satan! . . . All this international strife, all this man–woman strife. It's all the work of the devil! The Battle of Armageddon is the battle of the End of the World! Which,' he cried, 'the forces of the Lord will win! An' Satan will be killed forever! An' after that we go back to livin' in the Garden of Eden!' He sat back and beamed at them. 'I'm fightin' the anti-Christ!'

twenty-five

And at the end of each day Justin and Katherine would lie together in the bath, hot and deep, the suds covering and revealing their bodies according to the motion of the ship, the water silky and shiny on her strong shoulders and her big white breasts and her long legs, the heat of the water seeping down into his hard glowing body, just lying there together, legs between legs, the lovely feel of her soft back against his chest, the side of her face close to his. When she was with him, close to him, she felt better. He held her slippery breasts, kissed her cheek; talking, just saying nothing, trying not to think, sipping two glasses of cold beer. And washing each other, the sensuous joy of washing the body of your love, he soaping the beautiful lines and curves and clefts of her, she gently lathering his penis and testicles, holding them firmly, gently, sliding the penis against her body, slipping it between her thighs, her buttocks, up against her belly, pressing it between their bodies. Mouths kissing, sucking, loving, the faintest taste of soap, the gentle smell of warm, clean flesh. Sometimes they did make love to each other a little, there in the bath. Her hands sliding over him, feeling him, the sculpture of his body, rejoicing in him, the lines and feel and taste and smell of this man, and she whispered, 'Beautiful. . . . Beautiful big hard cock,' and she rubbed it between her legs as she kissed him.

And always the ritual at the end of the day of dressing for dinner. He loved to watch her dressing. Lounging in the armchair, or on the bed, the good, crisp feeling of clean clothes and the warm gutglow of cold beer, watching her choosing something to wear, brushing her hair, sitting at the dressing table putting on her makeup, the curve of her back. Sometimes when she brushed her hair he lay his head in her lap and felt the softness of her belly against his cheek, and he stroked her hips as she brushed her hair, and then she leaned forward so her hair hung down like a veil around their heads, and she pressed her breasts against his face. And then, often, she would sit and sip her martini and watch him dress and laugh and talk with him.

He thought she was truly beautiful and she had been like this ever since he had known her. He had been apart from her before but now he was truly with her, and he would have her for the rest of his life.

One evening it was different. He was lying on the big double bed, gazing at the overhead, feeling the ship pitching in the rough seas that had kicked up during the night. She came in and lay down beside him, and she put her head on his chest.

'Hello.' He hugged her. 'Hello, sweet Katie.'

She held him very tight. He raised his head and looked at her. 'What?' he said.

Her eyes were troubled. 'Nothing. I just love you, that's all.'

'I love you too,' he said.

After a time she said slowly, 'How can you not believe in God? To me it's so obvious.'

He was not sure where this conversation was going. He could sense her tension. He rolled on his side, facing her. 'I do believe in a god,' he said, 'just not that He's like the Christians say He is.'

'Why?' she demanded.

'Because for one thing it's not much good praying to Him. Because God knows everything. He knows the past, the present, the future. If He knows everything He also knows all His future decisions. And if He knows all His decisions, He can't change His mind – because He even knows whether or not He is going to change His mind. So it's logically impossible to *surprise* God, to disappoint Him, or for Him to hope. Because He knows all the answers. Therefore it's useless to pray for His help or forgiveness, because He knew a billion years ago whether or not He was going to help or forgive or punish. There can be no *if* in God's vocabulary. He can never say, "*If* they're good I'll do so-and-so, but if they're bad I'll do something else." Because He already knows. So it's impossible to *please* or *disappoint* God, or to persuade Him.'

She lay there, eyes closed, teeth clenched. She could argue with his schoolboy agnosticism. She could give as good as she got on that sort of thing. But she did not want to argue. She wanted to scream. She whispered, 'Justin, . . . I *know* God exists. And I *know* the end does not justify the means.'

He lay there a long moment, rigid, his arm still around her. Then he got up onto his elbow and looked down at her. 'What are you trying to say, Katherine? It's a bit late for a metaphysical debate on whether the end can justify the means in our operation. The existence or otherwise of God has nothing to do with what we're going to do.'

She opened her eyes and cried, 'It's not too late, Justin! It's never too late! And it has *everything* to do with God! Because He *does* exist!'

He wanted to say, 'Jesus Christ, now you change your mind!' He held his anger and said grimly, 'I see.' He swung up off the bed, then stood beside it and looked down at her. He knew he should try to reassure her but his nerves were too taut. 'What do you suggest we do, Katherine? Turn back?'

She cried at him, 'Oh, Justin, it's simply wrong. There's no way around it. I can't get away from the fact that the end just cannot justify the means.'

'Who says so?'

'Christian principle says so! Christ said so. I say so!'

'Then why doesn't God do something about the ends Himself? Why doesn't *He* stop all the cruelty and the mess and the pollution the world's gotten into? Why does He make it necessary for poor mere mortals like us to do the dirty work if He's all-powerful and all-knowing? I'll tell you why, Katie. Because He's not like you Christians say He is. It's a myth! Christian principles have got nothing to do with what we're doing! It's a cop-out!'

She shouted, 'What you're saying is a cop-out. A cop-out to be a law unto yourself! To take the law into your own hands! To. . .'

He shouted, 'Oh my God! what law? It's the law of the jungle that those Russian bastards are applying – might is right! And that's the law I'm applying. That's the law I'm going to beat them with. I'm going to beat them at their own goddamn rules.'

'That's barbaric! There is God's law and it's very clear, not only in the Bible but in all the experience of mankind. Nothing but bad comes of choosing evil means to achieve a goal, no matter how worthwhile that goal is.'

'Nothing but bad comes of taking no action when an obvious wrong exists. You certainly can't depend on your Christian god to bestir Himself. If He's all-powerful and all-knowing why doesn't He stop natural disasters? Hurricanes! Droughts! Famine! Plague! It's downright cruel not to. Why doesn't He stop thugs from beating up an old lady? You and I would rush to her assistance, why doesn't God? Why doesn't He stop a child falling down the stairs and breaking its neck? Why doesn't God do those things? When a typhoon strikes Bangladesh and kills thousands of people, innocent babies, why doesn't He save them? Why doesn't He stop mankind from killing each other? Why doesn't He stop man killing whales? He made this wonderful world – why doesn't He stop man from abusing it and polluting it and raping it? A lot of decent people are trying, why doesn't He?' He shook his head at her angrily. 'It's so *unreasonable* of Him not to do so that it's incredible! To believe in Him is contrary to reason and contrary to the evidence!'

'No!' she cried at him. 'He *is* helping! There *is* a new awareness in the world about conservation and humanitarianism, worldwide! And people like you and Cousteau – and all these societies, worldwide! God intended you to educate the world. You're His instrument if you like. But that does not give you carte blanche to do what you like, to be a law unto yourself!'

'Bullshit, Katherine! What about self-defence? What about wars? What about Adolf Hitler? Wouldn't it have been justifiable to assassinate Hitler to save six million Jews from the gas chambers?'

She cried, 'For God's sake, Justin, you cannot equate six million Jews with whales.'

He crashed his hand on the bed, 'You can! That's exactly what you can do. Because the principle is the same. The principle of genocide. Genocide is wicked and indefensible whether it's people that are being killed or other creatures.'

She screamed, 'It's you who's going to kill people, Justin! And yourself!'

Her eyes were fierce with anguish. She glared at him furiously. There was no way left at this moment to communicate with him, no way in the whole wide world except physically; what she wanted to do was shake him and hit him to make him see and understand the horror of what he was doing to her.

He came down on the bed beside her and pushed her over backwards brutally and piled on top of her and kissed her hard. She struggled and bit his lip and shouted into his mouth, 'You bastard, don't you understand that I love you so much that I *hate* you for endangering yourself, for risking our love. For Christ's sake, don't you see what you're doing?'

On the fifteenth day the *Jubilee* turned east and put into a small bay in the deserted Straits of Magellan, on the southern tip of Chile. The bay was steep and rocky with grey-green bushes.

191

Max Hagen had been locked in his cabin so that he did not know where they were nor what they were doing.

On a plateau the helicopter landed an emergency cache of aviation fuel and rations, and they hid it in the brush. There was a sharp wind blowing, and they all wore heavy windbreakers.

Back on the ship Justin gathered the crew and point to the map. 'If worse comes to worst, the helicopter and the *Jubilee* will rendezvous right here.' Then he pointed to a small dot on the map. 'Sixty miles or so from where we are now is this tiny town of Fuente Bulnes. If we can't rendezvous, or if we are being pursued by Russian catchers, for example, it's possible to make your way by road from Fuente Bulnes all the way up South America, clear back to New York.' He smiled. 'It'll take you about two years, but it is quite possible. That's why you've all been issued with three thousand dollars' worth of traveller's cheques and forged passports. . . . But it won't happen. It's just an ultimate emergency measure.' He added, 'I want those traveller's cheques back at the end of this little trip.'

The *Jubilee* steamed back out of the Straits of Magellan, through the hard rocky islands of the south Chilean archipelago, back into the cold South Pacific and the Antarctic West Wind Drift. The air was bright, the sun very cold, and the drift was dark welling blue.

Late that day they saw their first iceberg. It was high and peaked and dazzling white, with sheer white cliffs streaked in blue and green, and everything about it was very clear-cut. The next day they saw many more, the horizon studded with icebergs scattered across the sea, big and small, and the *Jubilee* ploughed evenly on across Drake's Passage towards them, due south, and her steel was ice cold, and everybody was wearing heavy gear now.

part five

At the beginning of that summer the blue whale cow and her calf and her mate arrived at the ice. They saw and heard no other blue whales.

The calf was six months old now, and he was nearly fifty feet long. He had thrived from the tons of milk he had suckled off his mother; and now the hairy baleen plates in his mouth were strong enough for him to eat the plankton, and he had enough blubber on his body to stand the cold of the ice, and he hardly ever suckled off his dam any more. Now he swam through the vast shoals of plankton at the Antarctic, his great mouth open, happily gulping then closing his mouth so the water gushed out of the sides leaving the thousands of shrimps sticking to the hairy baleen plates, which he licked off with his giant tongue that was as big as a small automobile. And the plankton were in great vast pink shoals and the whales were gorging themselves after their long winter fast in the South Pacific, and they put on tons of blubber for the next long winter that was coming.

The calf could swim almost as fast and as long as an adult whale, but he was still only a calf and he still needed looking after. His mother made him stay close by her, and at night he slept beside her, his flank touching hers. He liked to play, twisting and turning and rolling and diving and trying to jump out of the water, and running away from her as fast as his flukes would drive him, so that she had to go after him, making her imperative *come-back-here-immediately* noises, until she overtook him and headed him off; and sometimes she had to discipline him with her flipper or her flukes. His echolocations were frequently telling him that there were other kinds of whales around, the big bull sperms diving down deep after the giant squid, and the finback whales and the humpbacks and the sei and the minke that were feeding off the plankton also, and when he heard or saw these whales he was always swimming off after them to play with them, particularly any calves that were there, chasing each other among the adult whales. In the late afternoons, when they had finished feeding and were feeling frolicsome, his mother and father used to play with him, diving down deep with him and then racing him back up to the surface, breaking it, and then crashing back into the sunset sea, and then diving down again, all the time making their happy playing noises to each other. That is what the blue whale cow and her calf and her mate were doing when the Russian seaman standing in the crow's nest of the hunting boat saw the plumes of their blow.

Under the regulations of the International Whaling Commission, of which Russia was a leading member, the blue whale was a protected species, a measure to which even Russia and Japan had finally agreed, because there were so few left in the whole wide world that there was no financial hardship to the whalemen in not killing them anyway. The gunner-captain of the Russian catcher looked carefully through his binoculars, and he knew by the size and the angle of the blows that they were blue whales. But the whaling was bad this year, and it had been bad for a long time, and he had not killed a whale for three days and his ship's bonus was going to be low, and he pressed the alarm button and he rang up full ahead on the engine-order telegraph and he directed the helmsman to swing fifteen degrees to port.

The bell was ringing and the crew were running to their stations, the engines throbbing harder and harder. The whales' blows had disappeared now, but the captain knew by experience more or less where they would come up and blow again. After four minutes the blows reappeared, the two big sprays and the smaller one, a few points to starboard of the catcher's bow, two miles ahead. The catcher was going almost twenty knots.

When the catcher was half a mile off, the whales became aware of it, and they came surging up to the surface to blow, their heads lifting up out of the sea to look about them, and they saw it simultaneously, the small black-and-white ship bearing down hard and fast towards them with the wave curling up from its bow. Both the bull and cow knew what it was, for both of them had seen such things many times before, but the calf gave a squeak of curiosity and he dived down under his mother and went galloping joyfully towards it.

The calf went galloping towards the catcher to play with it, just as the captain of the catcher knew it would, and the cow gave one terrified shriek of warning and she bucked her tail and went pounding frantically after her calf, and the bull went galloping after both of them, making his *danger danger* noises. But the calf ignored both of them because he wanted to play.

The gunner had run down from the bridge to the big harpoon gun that was mounted on the bows. The calf was only two hundred yards from the catcher now, and the gunner was crouched over his harpoon. The calf was only one hundred yards in front of the catcher when the cow came plunging alongside him, shrieking her frantic *come back* noises, and he heard her. She plunged across the front of him to head him off, to get herself between him and the danger. The calf came up to blow, and the cow came up to blow alongside him, panic-stricken gushing blows. The catcher was only sixty yards behind them now. Now they were fleeing back towards the bull, and the bull swam harder towards them, then plunged around behind them to get between them and the catcher. The catcher was only fifty yards behind them now, bearing down rapidly. The bull blew once to show himself to the catcher. One blow to show himself, then he dashed after his cow and calf making his *run run run* noises to them. Then he swerved away to the left to draw the catcher away from them and he went to the surface to show himself, then he ploughed under and galloped on, all the time making noises to tell his cow to run in the opposite direction. And the seaman in the crow's nest could easily see him just under the sea away to portside, and the cow and the calf straight ahead. The helmsman was beginning to turn the wheel to swing the catcher after the bull, and the gunner shouted to follow the cow and the calf.

It is against the International Whaling Commission's regulations to shoot a cow that has a calf with her, but the regulations were unenforceable anyway, and the gunner was chasing the cow now because he knew very well that the bull would lead him as far away from the cow as possible while she made her escape with her calf, whereas if he chased the cow, the bull would rejoin her to protect her. Thus he would keep all three animals together, and he also knew that after he had shot the cow the bull would still stay with her to try to help her, for whales are very loyal creatures. And then he would shoot the bull too.

The cow ran under the sea beside her calf, making her desperate *run run* noise, and the calf swam as hard and fast as he could. But he could not go as fast as his mother and she had to slow down for him, and the gunner could easily see them, and the catcher pounded after them. The bull was four hundred yards away when he realized the catcher was not following him. He came surging up and his whole head broke the surface, and he saw the catcher churning away from him. He gave a bellow of rage that only whales can hear and he plunged around and charged across the sea after his cow and calf, just as the gunner knew he would. And the cow heard him and her great heart lurched, and she swung towards him, and the calf swerved after her, and the catcher swung after them at full ahead. The cow and the bull went racing under the sea, making their desperate noises to find each other, they came towards each other out of the darkness, then swerved to go on together, the calf between them, and now the catcher was only forty yards behind them.

The bull went sounding deep deep deep down into the icy blackness making his *follow follow follow* noises, and the cow and the calf dived desperately after him. Down, down, down plunged the bull into the blackness where the killers could not follow him. Up on the surface the catcher cut its engines to half ahead. The whales sounded, down to six hundred feet. Then the bull levelled out and he swerved to the south again, and his cow and calf swerved with him, and they galloped for another minute. Then the calf just had to come up to blow. He was desperately tired, and he gave his desperate signals and he drove towards the surface, bucking up towards the air, and the cow and the bull went up after him on either side of him. They went thrusting towards the silver surface way up there, then they broke the surface, three abreast, great animals surging up out of the depths. They blew, and from the crow's nest of the catcher the shout went up, and already the helmsman was swinging the ship around onto them. The ship was still only about fifty yards from them, for the whales had not made any distance in the sounding. The gunner only had to swing his harpoon gun thirty degrees around to port, and there were the three surging blowing hides clear in his sights. He aimed it for the cow, and there was the thud of the cannon, and the big harpoon flew.

Flew swift and vicious in a long, low, terrible arc, great hundred-pound steel shaft with the folded barbs, with the explosives in the nose, and trailing the long, thick, white nylon line like a tail behind it. And for a long moment it looked as if it was going to fly over the whales, their backs were bending to plunge again. Then the harpoon suddenly curved down in its terrible arc, and it hit the bull. Hit him in the side of his back and smashed his ribs. The grenade exploded with a shattering crash inside him and the gunner cursed. Now the cow would run because she had the calf to protect. The great bull staggered under the shattering shock, blown to bits inside, then he wrenched to get away from the terrible blow and flee, he wrenched on the nylon line and the barbs sprang out, hooking into his guts and yanking him back, and he went mad with agony and the terror and gave a scream that only whales could hear.

The bull sounded, thrashing down into the blackness, the terrible harpoon buried deep in his guts, his blood pouring out behind him. Then he turned and went thrashing to the surface to blow, trying to shake and twist out the harpoon. Then the big electric winch on the catcher pulled the nylon tight and he plunged away again, pumping out great clouds of blood. He fought so powerfully that the catcher had to pay out nylon.

The gunner was wrong, the big cow did not flee with her calf, she stuck with her mate. She galloped beside him and ahead of him, making terrified sympathetic *run run run* noises to him, running ahead of him to lead him away from this terrible danger, then galloping desperately back and thrashing around him and shouting her frantic encouraging noises to him, and the calf galloped beside her all the way. And the crew of the Russian catcher was loading a new harpoon into the gun to shoot the cow too, but the gunner could not shoot her until he had the bull dead. The big winch was straining to heave the bull in closer so the gunner could shoot another harpoon into him to kill him quicker, but the bull sounded again and the catcher had to give him line. The cow and the calf swam desperately beside him making their sympathetic noises. The cow knew what had happened to her mate for she had seen it happen many times before, and her big heart was breaking. And the bull went driving back to the surface to blow, then he plunged down again, wrenching and fighting and thrashing and screaming.

For two hours the great bull fought. The water was crimson with his blood, and he towed the catcher across the bloody sea. The gunner ordered that the engines be put in reverse to break the great bull's fight, but still the bull towed the ship across the sea, thrashing and twisting and wrenching, and the cow stayed with him all the way.

It took the bull a long time to die. After a long time the thrashing and wrenching grew weaker. And the cow came up underneath him and tried to shove him up to the surface to breathe. And then she did what whalemen have often seen whales do to each other at such times, she rolled over beside him in his bloody thrashing and lifted her flipper out of the water and brought it down over his thrashing bloody body, trying to pull him back down to safety under the sea, desperately trying to take her mate under her flipper to save him.

For two hours the great whale fought, and all the time the agony and the terror and the blood. Then he went into his death flurry. And the cow knew it was his death, she knew her beautiful mate was dead, she knew that now the catcher was dragging him in and that then the terrible ship would kill her and her calf. All the cow wanted to do was stay milling and swimming around and around her beautiful dead mate and cry out and weep for him, but she also knew she had to get her calf away from this terrible place. She called out to him and she sounded deep deep deep, to swim as far away as possible from this terrible place; the cow sounded making her desperate weeping-out crying-out noises that only whales could hear, and her big heart was breaking.

twenty-six

It was summer at the Antarctic. The sun shone long and low and bright, and in the middle of the long day the sky was ice blue and the sea was deep sparkling blue and the ice was blinding sparkling white. In the lateness of the long day the shafts of setting sun were refracted by the ice into all the colours of the spectrum, slowly moving across the ice, and the flamingo glow of the west was reflected by the icebergs upward also, scarlet golden orange shafts and beams slowly moving across the sky.

There were many icebergs, some as small as houses, some many miles long, floating islands hundreds of feet high, some flat on top, some serrated like mountain ranges, nine times bigger underwater than they were on top. To the south lay the Graham Land Peninsula of the Antarctic mainland, cliffs of ice and iced beaches and many islands, but they could not see it because of the icebergs and the islands that looked like icebergs. Dead ahead of the *Jubilee* lay the entrance to the bay of the biggest island in the South Shetland group.

The *Jubilee* was covered in a fine powdering of snow. Her helicopter rose from the afterdeck and the snow blew away in a fine blast. The helicopter eased four drums of aviation fuel up off the deck, dangling them by a steel cable; then it turned and went chopping away, low over the sparkling sea and through the entrance into the bay, and disappeared around the point.

Justin and Ross surveyed the bay from the helicopter: it was an ideal anchorage for the *Jubilee* to hide in when it became necessary. Around the point she would not be seen from the open sea. The beaches were rocky and bare by the water, then, higher up, snowy. They spotted a good place to hide the drums of fuel, behind a mass of rocks. The helicopter set the drums down onto the beach, and Justin leaped out while it hovered, into the blast from the propellers, hair flapping wildly, and unshackled the cable, and the helicopter moved to one side and touched down. Then Ross got out and the two of them rolled the drums with crowbars against the rocks. Then Ross threw two shovels out. In ten minutes they had covered the drums with snow. Then they went chopping back across the bleak bay, back to the *Jubilee*.

The ship had come within the probable range of the Russian whaling fleet. So Hi-fi Bob Matthews went up to the radio room and began switching slowly through the spectrum of radio waves, to find out which frequency the Russian ships were using among themselves. Within an hour he heard the fleet broadcasting. Then it was only a matter of time, of Katherine listening hard on that frequency, before she heard a Russian navigator radio his ship's position in longitude and latitude to the *Slava*. After that, all they had to do was listen long enough before most of the catchers, at one time or another, and the *Slava* itself, also radioed their positions.

In the radio room they had erected the operations table. It was nine feet by nine feet. It was divided into two-inch squares. The latitudes and longitudes were written in chalk. The table represented over twenty-two thousand square miles of the Weddell Sea – one hundred and fifty miles by one hundred and fifty miles.

On the squares were placed markers, numbered one to twenty, each representing a Russian catcher: there was one big red marker, which represented the *Slava*, the factory ship. Another, the same size, was blue, and that was the *Tretchka*, the Russian fuel tanker. There were three other markers that were not yet placed on the table: a green one represented the *Jubilee*; a yellow, the helicopter; and a black, the submarine. And scattered all over the table were white markers, which indicated the approximate position of known major icebergs. Listening to the Russian radio messages, finding out the ships' positions, and then putting their markers on the table was only a matter of time, like slowly piecing a jigsaw puzzle together. The first day everybody was hanging around the radio room, watching the commander working the table, watching the jigsaw fit together. Katherine sat hunched over the radio, her hands over the earphones, concentrating, frowning, her lips moving, the big Russian dictionary open before her, pad and pencil and tape recorder.

She said aloud to the commander behind her, 'Number Eight,

latitude sixty-nine degrees, thirty-four minutes, longitude west forty-three degrees, twenty-eight minutes, pursuing finback whale due east.'

'Aha!' Henry Thorogood said, delighted. 'The Eight at last! Lat six nine and long forty three heading east.'

He put the marker Eight on the board with a flourish. He loved the operations table. It really took him back to the old days. Everybody loved the operations table that first day; tiptoeing in and out, talking only in whispers, standing around staring at it, smoking too much, willing the Russians to talk, willing Katherine to speak. Nobody talked above a whisper, so as not to disturb the commander and Katherine. The navy man sat at the table, his unplaced markers in front of him like dominoes, itching to get them into position, shifting the markers already in position if she spoke about them.

She said aloud, to nobody in particular, 'Bunkering instructions for tonight. . . . Everybody complaining about no whales.'

Two of the most important markers, coloured pink, were not yet in position. They were the two towing boats. The towing boats were most important to the operation, because it was they who went out to get the dead inflated whales from where they had been cast adrift by the catcher, to tow them back to the factory. The distance that the towing boats were from any known positions of dead whales, and then the distance of those whales from the *Slava*, determined the amount of time Justin Magnus's men had to get by helicopter from the *Jubilee* to the whales, place explosives in them, then get from there to the *Slava* in the submarine. But there were few dead whales for the towing boats to fetch. All the gunners were complaining.

'Yes, you bastards,' Justin said. 'Serves you right.'

But he needed dead whales. And he needed them in the right place at the right time, where he could get to them before the towing boats did.

The other important marker that was not yet in a position on the operations table was the green one, the *Jubilee*. The big red marker of the *Slava* was in position, about the middle of the table, in the Weddell Sea, cruising slowly north, waiting for her catchers to find and kill whales. The *Jubilee* was not yet on the operations table because she was still two hundred miles away from the *Slava*, heading carefully through the icebergs into the Weddell Sea, towards the *Slava*.

It was late that night when the commander placed the green marker of the *Jubilee* on the very western edge of the operations table, and whispered cheers went up.

twenty-seven

From twelve thousand feet up, whirring in the helicopter across the high red sky, the sea way down there was black and only the tips of the highest icebergs were catching the sunset, pink streaks against the blackness. Ross suddenly said over the intercom, 'There, on the port sector.'

And there, way faraway down there, was a pinprick of white light shining on the black iceberg sea. Just a pinprick, and Justin felt his stomach turn over. 'Oh yes!' Ross said over the intercom. 'Keep going?'

'You sure they can't see us?' Way up there, twelve thousand feet high, they were still in the sunset, the helicopter bathed in golden red.

'Not unless they're really looking.'

'Keep going,' he said.

They kept going, high up in the Antarctic sunset, eyes screwed up against the gold red light gleaming into the cockpit, peering down into the blackness below. Then, maybe twenty miles on, they saw another pinprick of light, then another, and then another. Then there were half a dozen, scattered wide across the black sea down among the icebergs. Then there was a big cluster of lights and they said together, 'There she is.'

And there she was, the great *Slava*. Justin looked at her through the vibrating binoculars; she was a glow of floodlit decks, and bridge lights, and portholes, and lights shining down onto the sea around the bitch. And it was as if he could hear her and smell her. Rending hacking chopping fuming rattling stinking, tearing apart the whale flesh way down there. Looking at her, he was glad with all his heart with what he was going to do.

'Can you estimate her position?'

'More or less.'

'Keep going,' Justin said. 'Let's find that tanker. What speed are we doing?'

'A hundred and ten.'

Fifteen minutes later, to the east of the *Slava*, they saw the glow of the lights of the tanker. There were half a dozen pin-pricks of light clustered around her. Those were catchers, waiting to come alongside her to bunker. Justin clicked the radio transmission switch and said, 'Jonah to One. Do you read me? Over.'

Katherine's voice came over the air, 'One to Jonah. Reading you loud and clear. Over.'

'Well, we've found them, all right. . . . The tanker's about twenty-five miles east of the *Slava*, bunkering. I think we've spotted about half the catchers. Just wish we knew which were the towing boats. But we won't get any action from them tonight, they can't hunt in the dark, we won't get much more movement from them till daylight. Anything to report? Over.'

She said, 'No. Just bunkering talk and supplies. The Nine-teen's bringing a man to the *Slava* with a fractured jaw, there was a fight in the messroom, if you're interested. Over.'

Justin grinned.

'Hope it's the gunner.' He went on, 'As far as I can tell, our ops table is more or less accurate, though it will have changed by the morning, of course. We estimate you're a hundred-odd miles from the westmost catchers, so it's safe to use our radar. There are three of them strung out more or less in a line about thirty or forty miles west of the *Slava*, that's about ninety to a hundred from you. Does that agree with the ops table? Over.'

'Stand by,' Katherine said. She was gone a minute, then came back, 'Yes, that's about right. Over.'

'All right. Keep steaming at half ahead due east.' He added,

'And you go to bed now, you've had a hell of a day. We don't need Russian again until daylight, put somebody else on. Got that? Over.'

'Due east, half ahead. When are you coming back? Over.'

'Right now. We'll be on board in about an hour and a half. Get to bed, darling. That's an order,' he added, 'we need you fresh at crack of dawn tomorrow. Got that? Over.'

'Will you wake me when you get in?' She added, 'I won't be asleep anyway, my head's reeling with Russian, I'll be hearing it in my sleep for weeks. Over.'

'Put somebody else on the radio and get to bed.' He said, to shut her up, 'Over and out.'

Ross was grinning at him. 'Great girl,' he said.

'Yes,' Justin said. 'Yes, indeed.'

'Turn back?'

He somehow didn't want to leave the bastards, now he had actually seen them.

'Yes,' he said.

The JetRanger keeled and swung away in the sky.

Ahead, was the orange glow across the sky. It was after midnight as they dropped out of the darkness towards the lights of the *Jubilee.* As they came rocking slowly down, the small floodlights on the aft landing pad switched on. Ross put her down, blowing snow all over the place. He killed the engine and they sat there waiting for the blades to settle. Then Justin scrambled out, leaving Ross to lash down the helicopter. He trotted across the afterdeck towards the bridge companionway. The accommodation door opened and Katherine came out, bundled up in her sheepskin coat. 'Hello,' she said, smiling. He stopped at the bottom of the ladder and it was good to see her.

'I thought I told you to get to sleep.'

She came out and put her arms around his neck. 'How the hell can I sleep with you flying around up there in the middle of the night? I even said my prayers in Russian.'

He kissed her hard and short. 'They haven't got anti-aircraft guns, you know. How about bringing us a couple of drinks up to the radio room?'

He turned and scrambled up the companionway, two steps at a time. He burst into the bridge house and into the radio room behind it. 'Aye-aye, commander!'

Henry Thorogood said, 'Welcome aboard! How was it?'

'Smashing.' Justin smiled at the old Royal Navy face and he thought, *Thank God for you, admiral!* He went to the operations table, rubbing his hands, and looked down at it with satisfaction, hands on hips.

'Beautiful! Everything's going beautifully.' He looked at the commander. 'Do you realize how well everything's gone? That ops table of yours is almost one hundred per cent accurate!'

'Thanks to Miss Robinson,' Henry Thorogood said modestly. He glowed at the table. Katherine came into the room with three cans of beer and three glasses.

'Damn right thanks to Katie!' Justin said. Katherine looked lovely bundled up in her heavy coat and fur boots. But she looked exhausted. 'Listen,' Justin said, 'everything's gone beautifully according to plan. We've found them. We've got their positions. Now all we've got to do is get seventy miles or so closer and wait for them to shoot some whales.'

'Seventy miles?' Katherine said nervously.

'Easy,' Justin said.

He took a gulp of beer. 'There'll be plenty of icebergs for us to hide among. There're icebergs everywhere all the way, like islands, some of them. Tomorrow morning crack of dawn, Ross and I'll go up in the chopper and chart the area for icebergs. And get some aerial photographs.' He looked at her and had to restrain himself from kissing her cheek hard. 'And we'll have the new positions of the fleet as far as possible by daylight. So you can sleep later – because you're going to need it. And you too, Henry. Cartwright can take the bridge. It'll be ten hours at the earliest before we get near enough to start worrying about whales. So take advantage of it. Because when we're in position it could be all stations go non-stop from then on.'

She said, 'What about you getting more sleep? Why should you go up in the helicopter at dawn? Send one of the cameramen.'

The commander said, looking at the table, 'Actually, it

couldn't be better from the point of view of sleep right this moment. Their positions won't change much in the dark, and we're well outside their radar range for at least seven hours. If we steam at ten knots, they won't pick us up on their radar nor hear our radar pings on their passive screens, unless of course one of these three catchers here,' he indicated them on the table, 'takes it into its head to steam towards us in the dark.'

Justin said, 'And even if they do, why should they pay attention to one more echo on their radar screens? They're only interested in the icebergs right in front of them, they're chasing whales, not enemy shipping. Anyway,' he said with finality, 'that's just a chance we'll have to take. It's a minute chance anyway.'

The commander nodded. Justin looked at Katherine, and she smiled reluctantly. 'Katie, you did a great job today.' The smile ripened slightly.

Justin turned to Henry Thorogood. 'Tell Cartwright to carry on. And you hit the sack. Tell Cartwright if he picks up any ship on the radio to wake me.'

'Or me?'

'All right,' Justin said. 'You wake me if you're worried. And tell Cartwright to tell L.C. that everybody gets a big steak and eggs for breakfast. I know they're sick of it, but it may be their last meal for a long time and I want their strength up.'

He did not want to leave the beautiful ops table.

In their cabin he put his arms around her. She felt bulky, bundled in her long sheepskin coat. Her face was warm and soft and she had no makeup on.

'Now stop thinking about it,' he whispered. 'Come to bed.'

She let go of him and undid the knot of her belt, then she slipped the coat off her shoulders; she was naked underneath it. He looked at her, her long full body and it almost took his breath away.

twenty-eight

Three hours after he had shut his eyes he was suddenly wide awake. The sunrise was on its way, a red glow at the porthole. She was asleep beside him, her hair a golden tousle. He lay there a moment, then he got out of bed carefully so as not to wake her.

Outside the silent snowy *Jubilee* was bathed in pink from the icebergs reddened by the dawn. He saw two sets of footprints through the snow, going aft: that was Ross and Craig, gone aloft in the helicopter already. He stood still a moment, breathing deep to try to flush the tension out of his forehead with the cold. Then he clattered up to the bridge.

Commander Thorogood was up there already, he had sent Cartwright to bed. Black Bob was on the wheel. 'I thought you'd be in your bunk, Henry.'

'Good morning.' He looked up from the chart table. 'Don't worry, I got enough, an old man doesn't need as much.'

'All right, Bob?'

Bob took one hand off the wheel and waved at the sea.

'Look at that light, man. Look at them icebergs. I gotta get some pictures.' He had his Leica hanging around his neck.

'Sorry, Bob. No photographs, no souvenirs of this trip.'

'I could say they were taken at the Arctic. Man, I can't waste light and colours like this.'

'Yes you can, Bob. Who's that up in the crow's nest? Do we need him?'

'No,' Henry Thorogood said. 'It's Spider. I told him we didn't need him, but he wants to see the ice.'

'Have you seen any whales?'

'Not yet.'

'That's another thing I got to get photographs of,' Black Bob said.

Justin shook his head. 'Any coffee in this?' He went to the Thermos and lifted it. It was empty. 'I'll make some more. Where are we?' He turned and went into the radio room, to the operations table. Everything was in the same position as last night, except the green marker of the *Jubilee*. It was approximately forty miles closer to the Russians.

Henry Thorogood said, appearing beside him, 'Cartwright got a good fix at sunrise.' He indicated the green marker. 'That's about it.'

Justin stared at it. Their positions would be changing now that daylight was back. He itched to get the table going again. But there was no point in waking up Katherine until the *Jubilee* was at least another couple of hours closer. They could rely on the helicopter till then, until the ship was close enough to the action to be able to do something about it. Justin felt his palms prickle. But he was feeling good.

He turned back out onto the bridge and went to the radar screen.

'Only icebergs,' the commander said.

Only icebergs. The blotchy ragged grey shadows of light showing up every time the needle went slowly around the screen. Icebergs all around them.

'Wonderful cover for us,' Henry Thorogood said. 'If it's like this all the way we should have no difficulty keeping out of sight.'

'Yes.' Everything was going beautifully. But he wanted it to go faster. 'Can't we push her up to fifteen knots?'

Henry Thorogood looked at him doubtfully. 'With all this ice? We're doing very well as it is. In another five hours at this rate — nine o'clock this morning we'll be almost on top of the Russians. Or very warm indeed. If they move towards us, much sooner. Ten knots is fast enough for me in this ice.'

'All right.' *All right*, he thought. *Everything going so well, why risk anything? Katie needs the sleep anyway*. He looked at his watch. 'How long have they been up in the helicopter?'

'Twenty minutes. He'll call us, no point calling him.'

Justin wanted to get that ops table up-to-date. Up-to-the-minute. Those Russians would be on the move right now. Christ, why couldn't he speak Russian?

The commander said, 'Why don't you go below, I'll wake you if anything exciting happens.'

'It's all happening. It's all exciting.' He smiled at him. 'Isn't it?'

'Yes, indeed.'

Justin dropped his hand heavily, affectionately on the older man's shoulder. 'I'll get some more coffee.'

He went down to the empty galley with the Thermos and flicked the electric kettle on. He leaned against the table, waiting for it to boil, arms folded impatiently. His nerves were in pretty good shape, he only wished he had got some more sleep. They all needed more sleep, it was bad to go into this thing uptight from lack of sleep. Tonight they could all be fighting for their lives. When it did happen it was going to go like clockwork. Those bastards weren't really armed and nobody can fight tear gas without a gas mask. The nearest thing they'd have to a gas mask would be a few fire-fighting masks, and the nearest they'd have to arms would be a few pistols and a few automatic rifles. The kettle boiled, he filled two Thermoses. He took one up to the bridge. The other he took with him. He walked aft through the snow to the engine-room door, down to the engine room. As he opened it the noise hit him. There was Victor sitting in his old wicker chair, reading. Justin clattered down the steel steps. 'All right, Vic? Brought you some coffee.'

He looked up over his glasses. 'That's very kind of you. Victor's the name, incidentally. Come into my parlour.'

He got up out of the chair and led the way into his workshop. There was the long gleaming lathe. On the shelves stood his manuals and numerous other books, dominated by the big, fat *Complete Works of Shakespeare* and *Roget's Thesaurus*. Across the other bulkhead was his day bunk, where he took his siestas, in the corner his washbasin with its day toothbrush, hairbrush, and eau de cologne. He indicated a wicker chair with an airy wave of his hand. 'Sit thee down.'

Justin said, 'I must get back to the bridge, just came to say hello, didn't see you yesterday.'

'Yes, well, I was worried about all kinds of engine-room orders toing and froing with all that ice around.' He rubbed a hand over his thick grey-streaked hair, then took two cups off his little tea tray. 'Beautiful out there, isn't it?' he said. 'Really spectacular.'

'Fantastic.' He poured the coffee into the china cups. 'I wish you'd show yourself topside more often, Victor.'

'Yes,' Victor said. 'Well, you know me, I'm comfortable in my shell. And,' he waved his hand self-consciously, 'I have my own thing. I've been writing a sonnet about the icebergs, incidentally.'

'Can I see it?'

'Oh, it's not finished yet.' Victor did two little shuffling steps. 'A lonely iceberg. Drifting inexorably north. To its gradual inexorable death.'

'It sounds very symbolic.'

'Oh, yes. Full of symbolism.'

'Of what exactly?'

Victor laughed and rubbed a palm over the side of his head. 'Oh, you know. Life. Life on this miserable planet of ours,' he said with his eyes twinkling self-consciously under his devil's eyebrows. 'Like this planet of ours, the magnificent iceberg breaks off its mother lode in all its glacial purity. And it plunges off into its independent life, sparkling clean, and the oceans of life corrupt it, wear it down. Erode it, crumble it. Down to nothing.' The twinkle vanished from his face. 'And the mighty beauty of it is gone. And once it is gone, you cannot bring that magnificent iceberg back. Only God can. And I'm pretty sure He won't.'

Justin liked Victor. 'That's great. Write it just like that. I'd like to put it in one of the Magnus books.'

'Oh,' Victor said, 'it's nothing, not publishable at all.'

Justin knew he had to leave that subject alone now. He had to go anyway. 'Will you be coming up for breakfast?' he asked.

'Yes,' Victor said. 'I believe I will.'

Justin was smiling to himself all the way back to the foredeck. He shouted up to the bridge, 'Henry!' The commander appeared on the wing. 'I'm going up to the crow's nest. Shout when Ross calls.'

He clambered up the mast rungs. The steel was ice-cold and

he did not have his gloves on, but the skin on his hands was so dry it did not stick to the metal. As he climbed the view widened around him. It was the same minor thrill each time, of climbing his own ship's mast, the deck way down there. He reached the nest and folded his arms on the rim. 'Hi, Spider. How's it going?'

'Hi, Justin. Okay.'

'What do you think of it?'

'Ah. Until you've seen it you wouldn't believe it. Man, this is *nature*.'

'What do you want to do with it, Spider? You can't run around barefoot down here, making fire by rubbing two sticks together.'

'Just stand here and gawk at it. And say isn't it terrific. And thank Christ man can't come and wreck it here.'

'Don't count on that. Seen any whales yet?'

'No. I've been watching. Seen some seals and penguins.' He looked around. 'Man, this is country. I'd like to build an igloo and live for a year here and study the creatures. Maybe with a sled and a team of those dogs, like the Eskimos. And really explore that mainland over there. I bet there are things there like we never seen – ice formations and things like that. Would I be the first man to do that?'

'Well,' Justin said, 'there've been expeditions and geographical survey teams. And Captain Oates lies somewhere over there, entombed in ice.'

'Who's Captain Oates?' Spider said.

'Captain Oates was a member of Captain Scott's team who slogged it out on foot with dogs and walked to the South Pole. On the return journey it was very bad and Oates was endangering the whole team, slowing them down because he had terrible frostbite and wounds that wouldn't heal. They were on their last legs when they were only eleven miles from their ship. There was a howling blizzard. They were out of fuel and almost out of food. They all had terrible frostbite. Oates knew they wouldn't make it if he stayed with them, he would hold them up. So he just got up and walked out of the tent into the frozen night. Into the Antarctic blizzard. And never came back.'

Spider was looking at him fascinated. 'Just committed suicide like that?'

Justin nodded. 'Brave man. Just went out a way and lay down to freeze to death. Never found him.'

'So his body's still there?'

'Yes. Buried in ice. Completely fresh and intact as the day he died. It'll stay like that till the end of the world. A piece of the Antarctic itself.' He nodded. 'Rather appropriate, in fact. Like a monument to bravery.'

'Gee. . . .' Spider said. 'That was some thing to do.' He thought, then said, 'What I would really like to do some day is to go to Africa. I'd like to live like a native. In the Congo. I've always wanted to go to the Congo. Or a place like the Zambesi Valley. What a name. And *really* get to know all those animals. Their habits and all. And live among them, until they accepted me. Wouldn't that be something?'

'Absolutely great.'

'And take lots of photographs of all those rare animals. I mean really fantastic photographs that you can get only by living with them. Like an elephant-man, or a gazelle-man. Or like a Tarzan with the apes. Know what I mean?' He added, 'Steve's told me about Africa. And all that terrible poaching that's going on there. The rhinos and the elephants. Man, that's terrible, how they trap them and kill them just for their horns and tusks. Man, I'd like to do something about that. Steve says in some countries the rhinos and the elephants have been wiped right out.'

'At the moment,' Justin said, 'there are over one *thousand* species in danger of extinction. Since the time of Christ one vertebrate animal has gone extinct every twenty years. Nowadays the average rate is one *every* year.'

'Yeah . . . I'd like to go to Africa and do something about that. That's terrible. I never seen an elephant, except in the zoo.'

'You *are* doing something about it,' Justin said, 'right now. And one whale is the size of thirty elephants. Maybe you should have been a game warden, Spider.'

'Yeah. I'd love that. Except a game warden is stuck in only one place most of the time. I want to go *everywhere*.' He shook his head. 'Everywhere. If I hear that poaching is bad in this place, go there, then on to the next place where it's bad.'

'And what would you do?'

'If I caught one of those bastards – man, I think I'd shoot him. Like Steve says – shoot the bastards, that's the only way. Because if you take them to court, hell they only get a few months in prison then out they go doing it again, causing all that suffering. That's what I'd like to be I guess – a sort of roving detective-game warden.'

'Well, that's what you're doing now. I think I'll go and get my gloves.'

Spider said, 'Take my gloves if you want to stay up here. I'll go below.'

Spider pulled off the gloves, Justin wriggled his hands into them. His fingers were stiff with cold. Spider climbed out of the little crow's nest and worked around Justin on the ladder. Justin climbed in. 'So long,' Spider said. He swung down the ladder like a monkey.

Justin smiled. Some Spider. Spider *would* shoot those bastard poachers, too. He'd just better not shoot any Russians.

He looked about him. God, it was beautiful. There were icebergs everywhere, all the way to the horizon. It was ideal. If they used their heads the Russians would never spot them. He looked aft at the sunrise behind the *Jubilee*, the wake sparkling red and gold. He looked forward, the bows of the *Jubilee* cutting through this strange, vast, faraway sea, and he loved it, he loved his life. This life, this ship, this work, these men. He looked ahead and faraway between the icebergs he saw a solitary whale blow. He jerked his binoculars up to his eyes and he saw it blow again, and his stomach turned over in excitement. *That was the spout of a blue whale.* A blue whale, but it must be a calf because it was small, and he swung his binoculars looking for the spouts of its parents. He searched, excited, and the little whale blew again, but he saw no other blows. He searched the sea for it to blow again, but it didn't. It had gone between the icebergs, and the sea ahead was empty. He lowered the binoculars and breathed deep.

Somewhere, way over there, beyond the iceberged horizon,

the butcher bastards were. And here he was, right here, about to give it to them. Blow up that butcher ship and sink it to the bottom of the sea.

The telephone in the crow's nest buzzed. 'Good morning!'

He turned around and looked down at the bridge. He could not see her. 'Why aren't you asleep? You've got to be fresh today.'

'Listen, for three years at college I lived on Benzedrine for the last month before examinations. And I'm fitter now than I was then, with all your damned steaks.'

'You're in beautiful condition.'

'You're not so bad yourself, Magnus. The commander and I are starting on the ops table.'

By six o'clock everybody was awake. At seven o'clock L.C. Singleton had the steaks and eggs cooked, whether they were wanted or not. He stood at the end of the wardroom table slapping them out onto plates as the crew came reluctantly to the table.

'Eat,' L.C. commanded. 'An army marches on its stomach!'

'In the Royal Navy,' Henry Thorogood said, 'we were lucky if we got a bowl of soup before an operation.'

L.C. said, 'You're getting beef soup too in the submarine. In Thermoses. You can hear the vitamins snapping at you.'

'Beef soup,' the commander said, 'that's the stuff submariners are made of.'

'How can a man eat steak at seven o'clock in the morning?' Hi-fi Bob said. 'Especially every day for a month?'

'Because you've got to keep your strength up! You could all be in that submarine in three hours, you realize that?'

Bob Matthews turned to Justin. 'This is a serious question. I'm very worried about it. I know you think you've made provision for it but I'm not satisfied. I want you to know I feel damned uncomfortable about it.'

'What?' Justin said.

'What if one of us *really* wants to go to the crapper once we're down there?'

L.C. rolled his eyes. 'Oh you horrid little man!'

'It's a serious question!' Bob protested. 'In those tracksuits? What do we do, roll 'em down to our ankles and climb over everybody? Everybody packed like sardines? *I* say that we shouldn't be eating at *all*, let alone all these steaks. I say we should all be on strong laxatives.'

'*Oh you horrid little man!*' L.C. said again.

Katherine's voice came over the intercom, 'Justin to radio room, please.'

He choked down a mouthful of steak and scrambled out of his chair and bounded up the staircase into the radio room. She was hunched over the radio, Cartwright was at the operations table.

She looked up and said, 'The *Slava*'s turned east, away from us. She's doing ten knots, her radio says. There's some pack ice she's going to go through to break a channel for the Twelve and some others on that side.'

Justin was frustrated.

'Damn! How far east is this pack ice?'

'About fifty miles, the Twelve says.'

'Damn! That's another five hours.'

'How far is the *Slava* from us this moment?' Justin asked Cartwright. He went to the table.

Cartwright used his calipers. 'About ninety miles.'

'Are we still doing twelve knots?'

'Yes.'

'What about these three catchers closest to us on the west here? What are they doing?'

'They haven't said a word yet,' she said.

'How far are they, as best we know?'

'Nearest is. . . .' Cartwright used the calipers. 'Just under forty miles, almost due east of us.'

'Give me Ross,' Justin called to Katherine.

'He's almost back now. One to Two. Stand by. . . .' She handed the transmitter to Justin.

'Two. Where are you? Over.'

Ross's voice came back, 'I'm at ten thousand feet, about twenty miles east of you, I guess. Over.'

'We hear they're moving east, the *Slava*'s going to break through some pack ice about fifty miles east of here. Get over there and report positions as quickly as possible. Particularly the catchers nearest us. Over.'

'Roger. Over.'

'Over and out,' Justin said. He added 'Damn!' He turned to Cartwright. 'Put her up to three-quarters ahead.' He stood a moment, thinking, then he turned and headed back down to the wardroom.

Everybody was looking at him. He said, 'Relax. They're moving east. It'll be another five hours at least before we get anywhere near them.'

'Oh, Jesus,' Hi-fi Bob Matthews said. He spat out a mouthful of steak.

'Eat it!' L.C. shouted at him.

twenty-nine

The whaling fleet was looking for whales, the catchers spread out far and wide and the factory following, cruising over the freezing sea. It was a bad season for the *Slava*, so far. It had been getting worse each year. Next year it would be worse still, and the year thereafter worse than that.

The operations table in the radio room of the *Jubilee* was a mess. The only reliable positions were the red marker of the *Slava* and the green marker of the *Jubilee*, about ninety miles behind her. The catchers were all over the place, searching. They did not report their positions much because they had nothing to report. Katherine sat at the radio listening. The last known positions of the nearest catchers were thirty miles ahead, northeast, east, and southeast. But the *Jubilee* was not getting their pings on her passive radar yet. They were too far away, and there was plenty of ice in between them and her. The *Jubilee* was doing a steady eight knots, only keeping up with most of the fleet. There was no point in catching up until whales were shot.

Katherine said, 'Telegram from Leningrad to Comrade Korsky on the Seventeen, if you're interested. His wife's just given birth to a son.'

'Way to go, Korsky!' Justin said. 'Shall we send him a telegram, too?'

It was early afternoon. Justin was tired and disappointed, but he was still in good spirits. He said aloud, to nobody in particular, 'We've got nothing to complain about. We're right on their tails.'

He had tried to make everybody who was not on watch go back to bed. 'Sleep,' he said to Katherine, 'you've got to sleep.' Katherine said, without turning round from her radio, 'Why don't you go and lie down? You've been up since God-knows-when.'

He didn't say anything. She looked around and said, 'It's after two o'clock. Nine hours of daylight left. If any of them finds a whale it'll be two hours at least before it's dead, before we can go near it.'

He looked at the operations table. For practical purposes it was only the three catchers nearest the *Jubilee* that could help them today by finding and killing whales. All the others were too damn far away. It had to be those three, bringing up the rear. That did not seem likely in the rest of today, with so few whales around. If he thought about it, it seemed like a long shot on any day.

Justin chose not to think about it. He did not care how long it took to wait for three dead whales close enough for the helicopter to get to before the towing boats did. He turned and looked at Katherine. He did not care how long it took, but how long could she sit listening to that radio for twenty hours a day? She was the most important one until the whales were found – he could not very well find the whales without Katie telling him where the Russians had left them. He walked across the radio room to her, then he bent down and kissed her cheek. She was wearing her bulky yellow sweater and her heavy tweed skirt, and he yearned to hold her and touch her. Her eyes looked tired. He said; 'I wish like hell we had another Russian speaker, Katie. You're the one who needs the sleep.'

She looked into his eyes, then smiled. 'I know your kind, Magnus. You just want to get a girl between the sheets!'

'Wouldn't it be nice?'

She murmured, 'Wouldn't it.'

The sun was getting lower. But it would still take many hours to go down. Justin had sent the helicopter up again, to get them a bird's-eye view for the operations table. Craig was with Ross.

Ross's voice came crackling over the radio, from a hundred miles across the sea and ten thousand feet up in the sky, 'Two to One. Our position of the *Slava* seems about right. About ninety to a hundred due east of yours. Steaming slowly. Do you read me? Over.'

'One to Two. Which are the catchers closest to us? Over.'

'Closest catchers are still those shown on the table. The Five, approximately thirty-five miles east-northeast of you. The Eight, approximately thirty miles east of you. The Ten, approximately forty miles east-southeast of you. They're more or less strung out in a line, bringing up the rear, about thirty miles from each other. Over.'

'And the rest of the catchers? Over.'

'They've spread out in a big crescent around the *Slava* all over the place, all of them except the Seventeen are forward of her beam. The Seventeen is about eighty miles, north-northeast of her, abaft her port beam. I've got them all marked on my chart, do you want me to sing them out to you? Over.'

Justin said, 'No. We'll copy it onto the table when you come back. But where're the towing boats? Over.'

Ross said, 'Towing boats are both forward of the *Slava*, about twenty, twenty-five miles. Just going along with the rest of the fleet. Plenty of icebergs. Considerably more spread out, but still plenty of them, and some very big ones. Do you want me to take photographs? Over.'

'Yes. Then if you see nothing new, come home. Over.'

'Roger,' Ross said. 'Over and out.'

Justin stood there, rubbing his chin. Then he said, 'Coffee?'

'Yes, please,' she said.

He walked absently out of the radio room, down the stairs to the wardroom. Only Bob Matthews was there.

'I thought you were in your bunk,' Justin said.

'How can anyone sleep on this ship?'

He went into the galley. He was feeling all right.

An hour later Ross was on his way back in the helicopter. Katherine had left the radio to go below to freshen up. The tape recorder was recording any Russian radio exchanges during her absence. Suddenly there were pings from the *Jubilee*'s passive radar. The commander shouted, 'Mister Magnus!' He snapped off the active radar.

Justin hurried out onto the bridge.

'Passive pings!' the commander said. 'Must be from those three rear catchers – we're overtaking them, we've come within their radar range.'

Justin barked out, 'Slow engines!'

He bounded over to the engine-order telegraph himself and rammed back the handles to dead slow. He looked at the commander and his heart was pounding.

'What are they doing?'

'God knows. They must have slowed right down.'

Justin grabbed the intercom. 'Katherine! Get up to radio, please – quickly!'

He strode back into the radio room and grabbed the microphone. 'One to Two. Where are you, Two? Over.'

Ross's voice came back, 'I'm almost dead over ahead at ten thousand, I'll be down in a few minutes. Over.'

'Stay up there,' Justin ordered. 'Get back to where you can see them. Tell me what those three rear catchers are doing. What everybody's doing. Can you see anything from where you are? Over.'

'Stand by. . . . Not really, too much ice. Over.'

'Get your ass back over there until you can. Over and out.'

'Katie!' he shouted into the intercom.

'Here.' She burst into the radio room a moment later still clutching her hairbrush.

'Find out what the hell's happening – we're overtaking those three rear catchers, we're within their radar range suddenly.'

She flung herself down in her chair, rammed on her earphones.

Justin ran back onto the bridge. 'Do we dare use our radar to look for them?'

'No,' the commander said. 'They'll hear our pings on their passive, even though they may not be able to see us on their active screen through the icebergs. They'll know the direction the pings are coming from, and they know none of their own fleet is behind them.'

'Why the hell should they even have their passive radars on? They're looking for icebergs and whales, not enemy shipping.'

The commander said, 'And if they *do* have them on?'

'I get your point. Okay.'

He looked at the horizon through binoculars, and the lenses were suddenly full of closeup icebergs. But there was plenty of open sea in between. They were lucky with all these icebergs around. Surely the *Jubilee* would not show on any Russian radar screen with all those icebergs around; the ship must be in the radar shadow of a dozen big ones. There was also a lot of ice floe. If they cruised through that stuff they would not show at all on any radar screen; all the Russians would see would be the big blur of the ice-floe echo. There was a big stretch of ice floe about eight miles off her starboard beam, the ice floe stretching on out of sight. *That* was the stuff.

He turned to the commander. 'See that big flat iceberg on our starboard beam, Henry, with all the ice floe in front of it? Head for her, engines quarter ahead.'

'Starboard beam, engines slow ahead.'

Justin went into the radio room. Katherine was clutching her earphones to her head with both hands. He stood over her. She looked up. 'I must have missed it when I was down below – nothing of significance yet.'

'Keep listening, Katie.'

Henry Thorogood came into the doorway. 'Mister Magnus?'

'Yes?' Justin turned and followed him out onto the bridge-wing where nobody could hear them. 'I don't like us hiding in that ice floe over there.' He pointed to the big flat iceberg.

'Why not?'

'Maybe we haven't actually *overtaken* those catchers. Maybe they've turned around and they're heading back this way.'

'My God. You don't mean they've smelled a rat? Like seen the helicopter or got our pings on their passive and they're coming back to investigate?'

The commander said soberly, 'It's a possibility. Unlikely, but a possibility. In any case, I don't like us standing still.'

'We could meet them head on?' Justin asked. 'If we stick around here?'

'Exactly. They may overtake *us*. We're sitting there, and suddenly we see three catchers buzzing around us. And we won't know they're coming until we see them, because we won't be using *our* radar. Or worse,' he added, 'surrounding us. . . . And if they *are* investigating us, the rest of the fleet would be hot on their heels.'

Justin looked at him, mind racing. 'How much time have we got?' Then answered himself, 'One hour at least. We're within their radar range, that makes us about twenty miles apart.' The *Jubilee* was steaming south towards the big flat iceberg now, there were icebergs scattered all the way to the east, where those catchers were, as far as the eye could see. 'We *must* be in the radar shadow of some iceberg or other.'

He turned and went back to the radio room and looked at Katherine. She shook her head at him. He went to the other radio and snapped the transmission switch.

'One to Two. What do you see? Over.'

Ross's voice came crackling back, 'Two to One. Nothing yet. I'm still going there. Over.'

'Get over there, Two. Over and out.'

Justin made up his mind. 'Turn around. Full ahead! Get the hell out of their radar range!'

The commander called to Spider, 'Hard to starboard! Steer two seven zero!'

He rammed up the levers of the engine-order telegraph with a clang, and down in the hot engine room Victor shoved his levers in acknowledgement, and then the throbbing got stronger.

Spider spun the wheel hard over and the ship heeled and the bow began to come around.

Justin stood tensely on the slanting bridgewing, staring astern. He could see nothing but icebergs all the way to the horizon.

He went back in to the passive radar. Their pings were still coming through. He said to the commander, 'Get as many icebergs between them and us as possible.'

He went to the radio room door and said to Katherine, 'Anything?'

She shook her head.

'Nobody's saying anything to anybody at all?'

'No.'

He turned to Henry Thorogood. 'Radio silence? Can this just be a coincidence? A whaling factory ship with twenty catchers and a tanker? Something must be up. They must have smelled a rat.'

'Not necessarily,' the commander said, making an effort to appear calm. 'No fleet talks all the time.'

Justin stared at the sea. 'Jesus . . .' he said. 'Oh Jesus. Get over there, Ross.'

He went back out onto the bridgewing. 'Faster, you bitch,' he whispered to the ship.

She was steaming almost flank speed now, back into the west. He went into the radio room. Katherine again shook her head at him. He was about to speak when, from the bridge, the commander called, 'The pings have stopped! We're outside their radar range again.'

Justin felt a surge of relief. He strode back onto the bridge grinning.

'Or,' the commander said, 'icebergs are finally blocking us out of their radar.'

'Yes.' Justin went to the radio. *Come on, Ross!* He said into the microphone, 'One to Two. What do you see? Over.'

Ross's voice came back above the muffled roar of the helicopter, 'Stand by. Coming into view now.'

Justin held his breath. The commander and Katherine waited with him.

'The three catchers are all heading southwest. . . . The Fourteen, the Five, and the Eight. Do you read me? Over.'

'*South*west? Over.'

'Correct. Over.'

'Jesus. . . .' Justin said without looking up, 'Anything on the passive, commander?'

'No.'

Ross came back and they could hear the change in his voice. 'I see other catchers now. They're heading southwest too. The whole fleet's turning south. Do you read me? Over.'

Justin let out a big sigh. 'Yes.'

He looked at the commander and Katherine. 'The whole fleet's turning south – they're just looking for whales. . . . They're just doing a square sweep of the sea.'

The commander exhaled and Katherine closed her eyes. The radio began chattering and she went back to it. Justin said, 'What do you think, Henry? Keep going hard west for twenty miles? To get well outside their radar range. Then turn south too?'

The day went that way. The Russian whalers steamed south, spread all over the Weddell Sea, looking for whales. But they did not find any. The *Jubilee* followed them, through the icebergs, at a good distance, outside their radar range. Late that night, when the Antarctic sun went down, the whole fleet stopped, for they could not look for whales in the darkness, and the *Jubilee* stopped too, silver in the moonlight.

When the sun came up, the fleet sighted whales. But they were a hundred miles south of the *Slava*, almost two hundred miles south of the *Jubilee*. That day the Russian whaling fleet shot eleven whales, but they were all way south.

The next day, again, there were no whales. Nor the next.

thirty

She was a great black-hulled ship, and her gunnels stood high above the sea. She was mostly all deck, like a tanker riding very high.

In her stern was her slipway, the big sloping tunnel, wide enough for a train, leading down from the deck into the sea. The dead whales were towed from the stern and were dragged up this slipway one at a time, up onto the cutting decks to be butchered. On either side of the slipway, mostly below the waterline, were the engine rooms, where steam turbines drove the two big propellers. Above the engine rooms was crew accommodation, alleyway after alleyway of four-bunk cabins. Above this crew's accommodation were the lifeboat decks and the big funnels.

The bridge was at the other end of the ship, near the bow, overlooking the short open foredeck. On this foredeck there was only one hatchway and no mast. Below the bridge itself, from which the ship was steered, were officers' accommodation and administration offices. Below this were the messrooms and galleys. And below the messrooms up into the bow, was more crew's accommodation. Between the bridge in the bow and the slipway in the stern was the long cutting deck, and below that cutting deck was the vast factory.

On the long cutting deck the great whales were hacked up and torn apart and sawed up by the whalemen and women in their oilskins and rubber thigh boots wielding their slashing flensing knives like scimitars on stout broom handles. They plodded deep in blood, and their oilskins and faces were covered with blood.

Along the sides of this long deck were the vat holes, the big circular openings into which the hunks of whale meat were dropped. The meat crashed down these vat holes into the factory below the deck, into the steel cooking vats, several times higher than a man, where the blubber was cooked to oil, and the mincing machines chopped up the meat for refrigeration. The factory deck was a steel hall of hot steaming vats and grinding machines and masses of pipes and dials, all steely grey and shiny in whale oil fumes, with avenues between them. The steel decks were slippery with oil, and there was a great churning, hissing noise of the machinery, and the air was steamy grey and clinging hot, stinking of rich animal fat like pungent gravy. And the oil fumes belched back up the vat holes into freezing air and over the carnage on the cutting deck, the mountainous corpses being hacked and sawed up and torn apart by the blood-soaked men and women. And the slashing of the flensing knives and the rattle of the winches and the roar of the bone saws and the shouting and the blaring of music from the loudspeakers. The great black-and-white *Slava* steamed through the freezing Antarctic sea, hacking clanking rending grinding, the stench of blood and fumes rising out of her. Her twenty catchers were fanned out far and wide searching for whales, for the distant plumes of whale blows.

For ten days the *Slava* and her fleet steamed round and about through the Weddell Sea in the Antarctic sunshine that lasts twenty hours a day, and the *Jubilee* followed them, just over their horizon, steaming silently white through the towering icebergs and the miles of ice floe. Katherine Robinson hunched over her radio listening, and the little markers shifted on the operations table. The whaling was bad; every day the Russian fleet shot only about ten whales. And they were all too far from the *Jubilee* for the submarine to get to the *Slava* in time.

part six

The blue whale cow and her calf swam through the vast icy blue-black sea, between the icebergs, following the shoals of plankton, feeding, and all the time the cow's heart was breaking for her mate. All the time she was making her high-pitched calling noises, calling for she knew not what, knowing very well that her mate was dead but weeping and mourning and pining and calling for him nonetheless. Sometimes, from very far away, she heard the calls of other whales, but she knew they were whales who were different from her, and she heard no calls of blue whales. The great heartbroken cow kept her calf very close by her, always swimming so she could see him as well as find him with her echolocation, and when he sometimes disappeared she felt the great leap of panic, and she shouted at him to come back at once. And the calf also knew very well the horrible thing that had happened, he knew something of the terrors of the world now, and he always came back to his mother very quickly. The cow wanted to leave these terrible seas and swim away back to the north, to the sunny South Pacific where the killers did not come. But she also knew that in those warm faraway seas there were no krill for her and her calf to feed upon, only down here in the freezing seas, and only once a year when the ice was unlocked. She knew she had to nourish her body and the body of her calf for the long South Pacific winter ahead. She knew that she had to stay, and she swam in circles as much as possible so that her echolocation would sweep the whole sea for the killers, and she tried to stay among the icebergs, but many times she had to follow the shoals into open sea.

She was emerging from a range of icebergs when the Russian seaman in the crow's nest, looking through his binoculars, saw her blow many miles away and he raised the shout. One hour later, after she had run panic-stricken between icebergs and the open sea, making her desperate *run run run* noises to her calf, the gunner had her great surging back in his sights, and there was the thud of the harpoon gun, and the big harpoon flew. The grenade exploded in her insides with a shattering crash and the white nylon line snapped tight and the barbs wrenched in her shattered guts. The cow staggered, then gave a scream, and she plunged and went mad.

Madly diving down into the blackness, blood pouring out of her guts in a long thick cloud, with the calf galloping beside her terrified, then she thrashed back up to the surface, twisting and crashing her great tail trying to get at the nylon line to wrench it out with her mouth. The sea was red with her blood now, and the calf swam through it, around her, crying encouragement and sympathy and horror.

For more than an hour the great cow fought, dragging the catcher across the top of the sea, and then sounding again, then staggering up to the surface again to blow. And each time the catcher pulled her in a little further. After about an hour and a half the cow was very nearly exhausted, and the calf came surging up beside her and rolled on his side and lifted his flipper out of the water and brought it down on top of his mother to try to pull her down under the sea. He tried again and again, desperately thrashing and slapping with his flipper, red and glinting in the sun with her blood, but he could not pull her under. And all the time the catcher was winding her in. Now her thrashes were slow and her flukes slapped weakly on top of the red sea. Then she blew for the last time. It came from her blowhole in a jet of ruby red, the blood spurting up out of her lungs, high and red and sick into the air and raining down. Then she went into her death flurry.

She rolled over and over in the red sea flapping her great flukes in her blood and wrapping the nylon line around her. For a long minute she rolled, then she was still. The catcher winched her in with the nylon line, which was red with blood, and the calf swam and milled around her, lifting his flipper out of the water and slapping it down on top of her to pull her under, and the seaman was loading a new harpoon into the gun.

They hauled the massive dead animal alongside the steel hull. She was longer than the ship that had killed her, lying with her great striped grooved belly upwards and the hole in her side with the steel harpoon sticking out, her tail slopping under the water and her smiling head hanging down and the red nylon wrapped around her. A Russian seaman stood on the low deck of the catcher holding a long hollow lance, the sharp end of which was a nozzle. Attached to the other end of the lance was a long, rubber air hose, which was attached to an air compressor. The seaman plunged the lance into the belly of the blue whale, then leaned on it as it sank through the hide into her guts. He pushed it in deeper, then he signalled, and the rapid doem doem doem of the air compressor started. The air pumped through the hose and into the lance and deep into the great animal's intestines, and her stomach cavity began to fill with air and her thousand feet of intestines began to push apart under the pressure, and the air began to force its way up into her chest and the gigantic guts began to swell.

The crew of the Russian catcher stood along the rails looking down on the great animal they had slain, watching her swell up as the air compressor thumped, watching her calf mill and swim and wallow and blow around his dead mother and nudge against her. The Russian crew knew very well that the cow was a blue whale, and they were excited and talking about her great size and her great value and how much she would increase their bonus, for she was bigger than any finback whale the fleet had shot this season. And it was a well-known fact that a blue whale had double the blubber and flesh of a finback, and some of the crew were saying how they remembered when this kind of whale was all over the Antarctic, in the good old days, which were not so very long back. They were waiting impatiently for the cow to be pumped up full of air so she could be cast adrift and left floating for the towing boats to pick up, for then they could shoot the calf as well, for the calf was half the size of the cow and he was as big as many mature finbacks and easily as big as an average humpback.

The seaman had the new harpoon loaded into the gun and the gunner was standing ready, just waiting for the cow to be bloated and cast off, for he could not shoot the calf while the ship was still hooked up to the dead cow, he could not chase the calf dragging the cow by the air hose. The compressor was going doem, doem, doem and the cow's belly was beginning to swell visibly now. In a few more minutes she would be fully inflated and cast adrift, and still the calf was wallowing splashing around right there, lifting his flipper and slapping it down on his mother. And now the whole crew, even the cook and the engineers were on deck and hanging over the rails and laughing and grinning, watching the cow swell and willing it to hurry up so the ship could swing around and shoot the calf before it took fright and ran away. The compressor was thudding and the belly of the cow was very swollen now, and it was nearly time to shut off their air and cast her adrift.

The gunner shouted and the compressor stopped and the seaman yanked the air hose off the lance and sealed its end. He clipped a radar reflector onto the lance and let it go, and it stuck there like a flagpole in the bloated body of the cow. And up on the bridge the mate rammed the engine-order telegraph aft and the ship surged backwards; the gunner crouched behind his harpoon, waiting for the bows to slide backwards past the dead whale so he could aim for the calf, and now the whole crew was watching excitedly. The ship moved slowly and now the bow was almost level with the head of the dead blue whale, and the gunner had the harpoon swung sideways as far as it would go and in another few seconds he would have the sights trained on the calf, then the bows were almost abreast of the calf. Almost abreast now and the gunner almost had his sights on the calf and his hand was tightening on the trigger, in one more second he could squeeze, he was crouched right down ready, and the calf plunged under in panic and as he went under, the gunner fired. It was almost point-blank range and there was a big thud of the gun and the harpoon flew, and it smashed into the sea just over the calf's back. A groan of disappointment went up.

The calf sounded in panic and swam under the keel of the catcher and past its stern, fleeing panic-stricken, making the desperate *run run run* noises its mother had made. He went galloping flat out under the sea astern of the killer ship and towards the icebergs, and by the time the ship had heaved about he was gone.

The great cow lay floating on top of the icy crimson sea, her bloated belly up and her smiling head hanging down, and the pole with the radar reflector stuck in her, for the towing boats to fetch. Three hours later the calf came back to her. He stayed with her all that day, milling about her and crying and lifting his flipper up over her, trying to pull her down.

thirty-one

For three days the fleet had had good luck. In three days they had killed thirty-six whales. But they had nearly all been killed on the far side of the *Slava*, over a hundred and fifty miles away from the *Jubilee*, and they were no good to Justin Magnus.

There was nothing they could do but wait. And it seemed they had waited and waited. Justin did not mind too much how long he waited, but he was worried about the tension on the others, and he was worried about Katherine. For fifteen days she had been sitting over that radio for almost eighteen hours a day, for fifteen days she had been the nerve centre of the operation. How much longer could she keep it up? He was tempted to retreat into the ice for two days to give her a rest. He stood now at the wardroom table, leaning on the heels of his hands, looking at the enlarged black-and-white aerial photographs of ice and the fleet that he had taken two hours ago from ten thousand feet, and that Hi-fi Bob Matthews had just finished developing. He had cut the photographs and pasted them together so they made a big sheet almost three feet square.

The butcher ship showed as a blurred shape on the black of the freezing sea. Through a magnifying glass he could just make out the tiny blurred shapes of half a dozen whales in tow behind her slipway. And scattered all about her, far and wide, were the icebergs and among them the catchers. It was only eleven o'clock on a beautiful morning and already the catchers had killed seven whales. But again they had all been shot on the far side of the *Slava*, too far from the *Jubilee*.

Justin said, thinking aloud, 'By the law of averages it's got to happen soon. Soon they've got to get some whales on this side of the *Slava*, where we can get to them.'

Max had emerged from his cabin, affected by the suspense along with the rest of them. Justin was looking at the photographs along with Spider, Black Bob, and Commander Thorogood. 'I have a question,' he said. He was sprawled in an armchair. He added, 'For the good of us all.'

'Yes, Max?' Justin said warily without looking up.

'Have you,' Max asked, 'calculated what this operation is costing us?'

Everybody looked at Justin.

'Yes, I have.'

'Because,' Max said to his back, 'I've been calculating. And I reckon it's costing over half a million dollars. Especially with these delays. These daily helicopter flights alone are costing a fortune. And we've been steaming around and around for fourteen days since we got here. In fourteen days we could have crossed the Atlantic twice. New York to Southampton.'

Justin straightened up, leaned his thigh against the table, and looked at Max. He tried to sound reasonable. 'There're two ways of calculating the cost. One is your way, whereby you include the daily cost of everything, including salaries and food and wear and tear on engines and equipment—'

'*And* the cost of new equipment you bought especially for this operation,' Max interrupted.

'New equipment I paid for myself,' Justin said. 'With the exception of the silver-zinc batteries for the submarine, which will be a permanent company asset.' He glared at him. 'The other way to estimate the cost is to *ex*clude salaries and food and wear and tear because we would be paying those salaries and eating that food whether we're sitting on our asses at Baja California waiting for the grey whales, or down here at the ice. *That* is the realistic way of calculating the cost. And calculated that way, it is way way below half a million dollars. It is only the cost of the goddamn fuel. And I'll pay for that myself as well, if you like.'

'I do like,' Max said.

'Done!' Justin said. 'Consider it done.' He turned back to the photograph on the table. For a moment he was shaking inside with rage.

Max said, 'As a stockholder I would also like you to pay the salaries and food bill for the entire time of the operation.'

Ross turned on him, his cherubic face angry. 'Then I for one will gladly sacrifice my salary and pay for my own food!'

'Good!' Max said. 'Very good indeed!' He got up and turned

to stalk out of the wardroom but stopped at the door. 'And you can pay my salary too!' He walked out.

'Jesus,' Ross said.

'Forget it,' Justin said.

The commander said, 'I quite agree. These tensions are bound to arise. Seen it many times. It goes when the action comes.'

'It won't in that guy's case,' Ross said.

Justin sighed. 'The thing is not to get drawn into an argument with him. Like I nearly did. We're all feeling the tension, you're right, Henry.'

'I have a suggestion,' Steve said. 'About our problem with the whales.' His tanned handsome face was completely calm, as it always was unless he was making a joke. He looked at the aerial photograph.

'Nearly all the whales are being shot on the eastern side of the *Slava*. Out there in the open.' He touched the photograph. 'We're sticking on the western side close to Graham Land Peninsula, down here, among the icebergs. Well, why don't we move over to the eastern side, where the action is?'

Justin rubbed his eyes and felt for his cigarettes.

The commander said, 'We've thought about this.'

Justin lit a cigarette and blew out the smoke. 'Henry and I have talked about that. And maybe we'll have to do something like that soon. But there are a number of things against it. Firstly, we'd have to get the *Jubilee* over there. That means we'd have to go the long way round; we'd have to sail right around the outside of the fleet, over their radar horizon, and then circle back down the eastern side. That would take us several days, depending on the iceberg cover. Secondly, the ice is a lot thinner over there, in the open; there's less iceberg cover for us to hide in. Over here on the west side close to the Graham Land Peninsula where we are, we're in excellent cover.'

The commander nodded emphatically.

Justin went on, speaking to Steve, 'Thirdly, over here on the west is the best place from which to make our getaway. We cut up through the icebergs to the northernmost tip of Graham Land and there's every chance we'll be hidden by icebergs all the way. And once we get to the tip of the peninsula, we're only six hundred miles across Drake's Passage to South America, the southern tip of Chile. On the other hand, if we were to go around to the east of the *Slava*, into that open sea over there, our only escape route is straight north till we're clear out of the Weddell Sea, without nearly as much iceberg cover. Then we've got to cut across eastward to get back to Drake's Passage. That's a hell of a lot longer to run if they're chasing us.'

'Right,' Henry Thorogood said. 'And we could be intercepted by catchers in the west. Chaps down here.' He stroked the photograph with his pipestem.

'And there's no reason why whales should not be found on the west side, where we are,' Justin said. 'Whales go all over the place following the krill. It's just our bad luck that most of the hunting's been successful over to the east and not closer to us. It's just a question of biding our time.'

Steve's face was quiet and calm, Spider's was boyishly respectful.

The commander said around his pipe, 'Patience. The cardinal rule of the guerrilla.'

Justin stood staring grimly at the photograph. Patience. He could feel his own impatience, his nerves. And he knew what everybody else's must be like. The waiting, the tension of knowing every dawn that today could be the day and the buildup of waiting, that was the bad part. It was bad for morale, it gave them too much time to worry and doubt. And that bastard Max made it worse. And the very real fear of knowing what they had to do, go storming up on board that ship into God knows what, into five hundred Russians and driving them off the ship and then sinking the damned thing – Christ. Or that's how it could look when your nerves began to go from waiting too long.

'One more day,' he said aloud.

He glanced at Steve. Steve's face was still calm, examining the photograph, his lips compressed. He knew what Steve was thinking, and Spider. And right now it didn't seem such a bad idea – it seemed a fucking good idea at that. Get the thing over with. Get the fucking thing over with one lightning strike from the helicopter, directly onto the *Slava*, at night, shooting off tear gas – to hell with waiting for whales. Yes, and that was the way a lot of people would get killed. And the helicopter shot up.

Ross Evans did most things in a very straightforward way. He confronted a problem, took appropriate advice, made up his mind, then went ahead with no nonsense. This was the way he had studied marine biology, swum for his college, played football, taught high school, got married to Mary, joined Magnus Oceanics, and committed himself to the Antarctic operation.

Ross knocked on Max Hagen's cabin door. 'Come in,' Max called out. Ross walked in and stood there. Max looked up from an armchair, surprised. 'To what do I owe the honour of this visit?'

'May I sit down?'

'I imagine we don't have much to say to each other. This should be brief.'

Ross sat down on the other chair. 'Max, I've come on my own initiative. To find out your intentions. And to try for the last time to get you onto our side.'

Max smiled at him. 'For the last time, huh? Do you mean to say you're here without the permission of the great Justin Magnus?'

'For what my opinion is worth to you, Max, I want you to know that despite the fact there is no love lost between us, I do admire your work. I want to say that.'

'Thanks, pal. What else do you want to say? This is a good book I'm reading.'

Ross felt his anger rise but he controlled it. 'Max?' He looked at him earnestly. 'Join us.'

Max looked back at him and his eyes were hooded. Then he roused himself, leaned forward slowly, and said, 'You're general manager of Magnus Oceanics now, huh? Well, buddy, I had that job *years* ago. Under the Old Man. And it took me a damned long time to get there, and thousands of hours in the water, in every ocean and sea in this world you care to name. You're a kid – and *you* try to advise *me* that I should become an international criminal? A saboteur hoodlum like those long-haired kids who skyjack airplanes and stick up embassies?'

Ross said, 'This is absolutely different.'

Max ignored him. 'You're dead right there's no love lost between us – but why? Not just because of a personality clash, buddy. It's because you guys, youngsters like Justin and you, you think you know everything because you've got a Bachelor of Science in marine biology, therefore you know everything. You're going to change the world. Boy,' he shook his head at him, 'I knew every goddamn thing this business needs to know before you ever went to kindergarten! *And I learned it the hard way! With these two hands!*' He shook them at him.

Ross said, 'This has nothing to do with what we're talking about.'

Max slumped back theatrically. 'I'm here now because I had no choice but to come, your boss gave me little option. I have considered everything. Your motives are good. But I dis-associate myself from your actions completely.' He added, 'With plenty of good reasons.'

Ross glared at him. 'And what do you propose to do when we get back?'

'That's for you smart marine biologists to worry about.'

Ross stood up, still controlling his anger. 'Very well.'

'Yes,' Max said, affecting to return to his book. 'Worry about it.'

Craig Magnus did not worry about Max's silence at all, but he did worry about Max's well-being. Craig liked Max Hagen and he felt sorry for him and felt uncomfortable with strife aboard the *Jubilee*. Craig found Max pacing the afterdeck through the snow, his hands behind his back. 'Hello, Max,' he said.

'Hello, kid.'

'You okay?'

'Oh, dandy.'

'I mean, really?' Craig said.

Max had no quarrel with Craig, never had had. 'I'm getting my three meals a day,' he said gently. 'And I sleep with a clear conscience.' He added, 'How're you?'

'I'm fine. The waiting's getting me down a little.'

Max examined him. Hell, the kid looked just like the Old Man.

And he didn't have a bitchy thought in his head. Max put his hand on his shoulder. 'Craig? Do you fully realize what you've got yourself into?'

Craig did not want to talk about that; in fact, Justin had forbidden him to do so. 'Yes,' he said.

'The whole of Magnus Oceanics can go up in smoke. Everything the Old Man worked for. *And* you could get killed. Or go to prison for life.' He added, 'And Katherine.'

Craig had difficulty resisting Max; he had always known him only as his father's right-hand man. He was like an important romantic uncle to Craig. He said, 'We're going to come out of it all right. Justin's figured out everything exactly.'

'Has he? There are many things in an operation like this that you *can't* figure out in advance. The unexpected happens. Like one of you falls and breaks a leg. Or one of your bombs don't go off. Or the captain happens to be carrying his gun and shoots you in the back. All ships' officers have *some* arms. Or a whaleman hides behind a door and jumps you. Anything can happen, kid. And the whole thing blows up in your face.'

Craig said uneasily, 'It's got to be done, Max. Those are risks we just have to take.' He looked away. 'I don't want to talk about that any more. Let's go and have a drink.'

'I *do* want to talk to you about it, Craig.'

'No use, Max, sorry,' he said. 'How about a drink?'

'No . . .' Max began.

'Okay,' Craig said. 'Guess I better go now. If there's ever anything I can do for you, let me know. Talk or play cards or anything.' He added, 'Come up to the wardroom more, Max.'

Max looked at him, then said softly, 'Nice of you to think of it, kid.'

Craig was embarrassed. 'Okay. So long, Max, I better go now.'

He started back across the deck.

Max called after him, 'Craig?'

Craig stopped and looked back. Max stood there a moment, then said, 'Remember – anything can go wrong. The unexpected *happens*.'

*

Justin was just entering the wardroom for one more look at the big photograph of the whaling fleet when Katherine's voice came over the loudspeaker: 'Justin! Justin to radio room!'

He bounded up the companionway. She was bent over the radio, one hand raised to shut him up, the other scribbling on the pad. He stood waiting, his heart pounding, as she scrawled some figures, then she looked up at him and her eyes were wide and anxious.

'The Twelve's got a finback. There's a whole pod of them – the Twelve's near us, isn't it?'

'Goddamn marvellous!' He was already bounding over to the operations table – and *yes*! the Twelve was only thirty miles from the *Jubilee*. Katherine was saying, 'There's a whole pod, they estimate eight whales and the Seven is steaming over to join the chase. The whales are heading south!' And he was looking, heart pounding, for the Seven and, oh God, yes, the Seven was only ten miles east of the Twelve! The commander, Steve, Spider came hurrying into the radio room. Justin pointed excitedly at the table and said, 'A whole pod of finbacks just here, thirty miles away, the Twelve's onto them, the Seven will be among them in half an hour.'

Katherine was leaning into the radio, both hands clamped over her earphones. She shouted, 'Quiet please!' Then she said, 'The Four . . . yes, the Four's also chasing a finback. There's another pod of finbacks at latitude – oh Christ, I didn't catch it! Another pod.'

They were crowded around the operations table. The Four was only twenty miles south of the Twelve, all three catchers were in a thirty-mile radius of each other just fifty miles east of the *Jubilee*, on the other side of these icebergs. Jesus Christ it couldn't be better!

'I hope to God they hit those whales! Where're those goddamn towing boats?'

'Here and here,' the commander pointed. 'Last known positions, they were fetching whales on the far-east side of the *Slava*, but that was early this morning.'

'Katie, any new information on those towing boats?'

'What?' she turned around frantically, lifting one earphone to hear him.

'The towing boats! Any new information?'

'No.' She scrabbled through her notes. 'Nothing for nearly five hours. Last information at, oh, six fifteen, both heading east to get three whales shot by Seventeen and Six and Fifteen. Want the latitudes and longitudes?'

'No, they're on the table.' He looked at his watch. 'Four hours ago, Ross and I saw them. Three and a half anyway. They must have picked up those whales by now. They'll soon be on their way back to the *Slava*.' He grabbed the calipers and put one point on the *Slava*'s marker and another on the three known positions of the whales that the towing boats were picking up.

'Fifty miles at least,' the commander said. 'It'll still take them five hours at ten knots. Then they've still got to cast them off at the *Slava*. Then get down over here to pick up our whales – that's another thirty miles. Two hours at least. Then get them back to the *Slava* – that's another three hours.'

Justin said, 'Five, two, and three – ten hours, Jesus. It could hardly be better. Ten hours before those towing boats get our whales back to the *Slava*? How much time do we need?' He calculated out loud. 'It'll take the Twelve and those other two catchers at least two hours to kill those whales. If they get into them right away. And it'll take us at least two hours after that to find them and get them full of explosives. Then we've still got to get to the submarine – that'll take another hour. And then get to the *Slava* in the submarine. And the *Slava*'s probably doing three knots – we'll have to chase her. If we board the submarine thirty miles from the *Slava* it'll take us at least four hours to catch up with her. How many hours is that? Seven?'

'Seven hours,' Steve said. 'We're in pretty good shape.'

'Yes we are. If those towing boats are where we estimate they are.'

Ross came into the radio room. 'What's happening?'

'Ross, come here.' Justin grabbed his elbow and pointed at the table. 'It's *all* happening, champion! The Twelve's going after a finback here. The Seven's just over here, also after a fin. Here we are and here's the *Slava*. The Four's here,' he pointed, 'also after a fin. Got the picture?'

'Got it,' Ross said, staring.

'There are two pods of fins. With any luck some of these catchers here, like the Six or the Eight, will come steaming over like crazy to get on the bandwagon.' He shook his elbow. 'Get up there in the helicopter. Take Craig. And what we really want to know is where those fucking towing boats are. Got it? Go.'

'Right,' Ross said. He turned to hurry out of the radio room.

'Ross, come back a second!'

Ross came back.

'What do you think?' Justin said to both him and the commander. 'I say we should steam to about here, this bunch of icebergs.' He pointed at the aerial photograph. 'That'll put us about twenty miles from where the Twelve is now. That'll take us two hours at half ahead.'

'I'll find you,' Ross said.

Justin said to Henry Thorogood, 'Okay? Do you think half ahead's too fast?'

'I was about to say – it'll make us a very conspicuously moving echo on their radar screens.'

'With all the action going on right now, they're not going to pay attention to one more echo.'

'We've done so well,' the commander said. 'For fifteen days we've been snooping through the ice without them picking us up. There's another four hours of daylight left. Any whales they shoot will fight for at least two hours before they kill them, we've got plenty of time.'

'That depends on where the goddamn towing boats are!' Justin looked at him, then said, 'Oh, Jesus Christ.' Then looked at the operations table. 'Okay, we'll be going at slow ahead. That's three or four hours before we reach those icebergs.'

'I'll find you,' Ross said.

'Find those fucking towing boats!'

Katherine's hand clamped over her earphones again.

'Yes?' Justin said.

She sat there, then she turned around and said, 'The Twelve's got a finback.'

And Justin wanted to shout, 'Oh yes! Full ahead!' He turned on Ross, grinning all over his face. 'Get your ass up there and find those fucking towing boats!'

Justin dashed out onto the bridge and grabbed the telegraph and put her back down to slow ahead. He stood there a moment, trembling, and he just wanted to ram her right up to full. He was shaking with good honest fear and eagerness and thank God this is it: *Dear God, make this be it – please, God, make this the day. Please help the Twelve and the Four and the Seven hit those whales.* . . . 'This is it, I think, Spider,' he said.

The commander and Steve came out onto the bridge. Justin spread his hands at them. 'This is it! It could hardly be better. Pray that those bastards hit those whales.'

Katherine called, 'Justin.'

He turned and ran back inside the radio room.

'The Seventeen's chasing whales.'

'Terrific!' He dashed to the operations table. The Seventeen was on the far side of the *Slava*. As far as the table reflected the true position, it was twenty miles south of the *Slava* and he shouted inside, *Oh yes! Oh yes! It couldn't be better because at least one of the towing boats would have to go all that way to get the carcass,* and he wanted to shout a prayer: *Please, God, make them hit those whales!*

He went to the other radio and flicked on the transmitter and said: 'One to Two. Get over to the other side of the *Slava* and give me the position of the Seventeen, repeat, the Seventeen, do you read me? Over.'

Ross's voice came back. 'Yes. Seventeen. I haven't taken off yet.'

'Get your ass up there, champion, and get straight back! This is it! Over.'

'Aye, aye, sir: Over and out.'

He turned back and faced them. Katherine had her back to him, listening into the earphones. Steve was smiling. 'This is it,' he said to Steve. 'If the Seventeen hits a whale and the towing boat goes for it immediately, it's absolutely perfect – it'll give us those extra few hours.'

'But even if they don't we're still in good shape.'

'Just pray that the Seven and Four hit those whales. Who's in the crow's nest?'

'Black Bob. Shall I press the panic button?'

'No.' It seemed he had never been so happy in his life. 'Wait till the Seven and Four score first. We've got a couple of hours yet.'

He looked at Katherine's back, her left hand buried in her hair, her other pressed to her earphones. He walked up to her and put his hand on her neck. She looked up at him with gaunt eyes. He kissed her forehead, then lifted her earphones and whispered, 'You've done great, Katie. *Great*. We could never have done it without you!'

She tried to smile, and the smile was full of fear. He kissed her soft, tired mouth and then her eyelid.

'I love you,' he whispered.

She whispered, 'Oh God. Oh God, take care.'

Thirty minutes later both the Seven and Four had hit finbacks, and the Six and the Nine were steaming flat-out over to join them. The radio was crackling all the time, there seemed to be whales all over the place. Thirty miles away, the sea must be red with blood, giant animals fighting themselves to death. The catchers were reporting the positions of their whales jubilantly; there were little red flags for dead whales pinned onto the operations table. Up in the radio room, everybody crowded silently, tensely around the bulkheads, waiting for Katherine to speak. Justin and the commander stood at the operations table shifting the markers, sticking in the red flags as Katherine called out the whales' positions, the room full of smoke and rapt attention, and waiting. This was what they had been waiting for for a long, long time, but there were no cheers now as the whales were shot.

Ross called in. The two towing boats were still working on the eastern side of the *Slava*, at least eighty miles from the five red flags of the five dead whales shot near the *Jubilee* on the western side. And an audible sigh went up.

Justin took a deep breath and said into the radio transmitter, 'It's perfect, champion. Get back now. Is the iceberg cover still good? Over.'

243

'Could hardly be better. I estimate the *Slava* about ten miles into the open sea from the mass of ice you're in now. We couldn't wish for better. Over.'

'Right. Put all the big ice on your chart. And come back home. Over.'

He turned and looked at them all. Outside it was brilliant sunshine, the middle of the long Antarctic afternoon. It was perfect. They had at least ten hours to work in. He said, 'Right, gentlemen. It's all stations go. We've got approximately one hour before Ross gets back and we can take off. Let's get that submarine and Zephyr in the water. Steak-time in half an hour.'

thirty-two

The *Jubilee* lay quietly, propellers stopped. On the bridge the passive radar had ceased pinging. Thirty miles away to the east, spread out over the blood-stained sea, drifted six massive dead animals with markers stuck in them.

The submarine had left, with only the commander and Bob Matthews in it, and the arms and equipment, slipping off into the icebergs on the surface like a sleek fat lady. The Zephyr was on the water, loaded with explosives and extra aviation fuel for the helicopter. The helicopter was on its pad, refuelled, loaded with explosives. Max Hagen was locked in his cabin.

They stood around the radio room. They were dressed only in their Dolphin thermalsuits. On their faces were the serious looks of very tense men waiting to begin. Even Spider Webb looked serious and tense, his boyish face grim. Justin watched them covertly while he spoke, giving them the last briefing. Only Steve looked relaxed, squinting as he dragged on his cigarette, carnal, half-critical, the man who had faced many a charging lion and elephant. Black Bob was sweating, his skin glistening.

Craig said, trying to make a joke, 'Remember it's the anti-

Christ, Bob,' and Bob just said, 'Yeah, yeah' and looked annoyed for a moment. Craig was leaning casually against the door frame, but Justin could tell he was nervous.

The air was blue with smoke. Justin could feel his own nerves tighten. His palms were sweating, his lips tasted salty, and he had been smoking too much. But they were the last smokes he'd have until this was all over. Oh God, when this was all over. . . .

Katherine sat in her radio chair, swivelled around to face them and listen; she had her legs crossed and she was holding a cigarette. He saw it was trembling very slightly. She was pale. She was watching him, trying to listen to what he was saying, her mind fumbling and darting off into fear, imagining, trying to concentrate constructively on what he was saying and not to imagine it.

Justin said, 'Anybody else's palms sweating?' He wiped them on his thermalsuit. 'Come around the ops table, please.'

They shuffled around it.

There was a smell of rubber fabric.

'There she is.' He pointed to the red marker of the *Slava*. 'And here we are. Approximately fifty-five miles away from her, due west. And here, and here,' he pointed to two markers on the far side of the *Slava*, 'are the approximate positions of the two towing boats. And in those six positions marked with flags, these are our target whales.'

Their eyes were riveted on the table as if they had never seen it before. He said, looking around at them, 'We can congratulate ourselves. Everything is about as perfect as can be. The towing boats are about eighty miles away from our target whales; it'll be five or six hours before they reach them. We'll even have darkness on our side. We have ample time.' He lit a cigarette. 'These four whales here and here and here and over here are the farthest from us.' He turned to Ross. 'Ross – you, me, Steve, and Spider, those are ours because we can go fastest in the helicopter. Let's call them A, B, C, and D.' They nodded, never taking their eyes from the operations table and the markers. 'Meanwhile, Bob and Craig are in the Zephyr zooming flat-out to these two carcasses here and over here. We'll call them E and F.' He pointed to the two nearest. 'Same procedure. Okay?'

They both nodded. Black Bob was glistening. Craig's face was set. 'Yeah,' Craig said.

Justin was feeling better now. For a moment it seemed as if he was just directing them before a filming dive. He rubbed his moist hand through his hair.

'Meanwhile, the commander,' he put the model submarine on the table, 'and Hi-fi Bob are right this moment going at full speed straight in the direction of the *Slava*. For thirty miles. Mostly on the surface, to save the batteries. That'll take them two and a half hours. Now, look at this photo.' He picked up the aerial photograph and pointed to a big white iceberg. 'The *Slava*'s moved now, of course, but this is the iceberg the submarine's going for, to rendezvous with us, the helicopter, and the Zephyr. It's quite distinctive, the biggest around there, flat-topped with a peak on the end. Get your bearings on that iceberg. It's approximately thirty miles due east of here. Craig?' he said, turning towards his brother. 'It's approximately twelve miles southeast of where your second target whale is.' He pointed at the red flag on the operations table with one finger and at the approximate position of the iceberg. 'Right?'

Craig said, 'I've got it on my chart.'

'If you have any difficulty finding us, radio us. We'll come and find you in the helicopter.'

'I won't get lost,' Craig said.

'Don't waste time looking. If you're in doubt, radio straight-away. This isn't a survival test.'

Black Bob said, 'Damn right.'

They all laughed. Justin was pleased. He was feeling much better, almost good. 'As soon as we've got those explosives and transmitters into our allotted whales, that iceberg is where we head for. And if the sub isn't there, which it should be, we wait for it to show up. When it does, everybody except Ross boards it.' He looked around at them. 'And everybody knows where they sit in the sub?'

Everybody nodded. Craig said. 'Hi-fi next to the crapper.' They all laughed again. Katherine was massaging her forehead with her fingertips.

Justin went on. 'At the rendezvous, the sub's batteries may need recharging if it has had to dive. But probably it will have got there on the diesel engines all the way, on the surface. We also refuel the helicopter from the spare tanks that are in the Zephyr.' He paused and looked at them. 'Then,' he said, 'we take off for the *Slava* in the sub.' He paused. 'Any questions, so far?'

There were none. He turned to Ross. 'That leaves you all alone in your helicopter, champion. We deflate the Zephyr and sink it. Right?'

'Right.'

'And then you sit on the water in your nice warm helicopter and think of Mary and wait for instructions. And the best of luck to you.'

'Thanks.'

Justin wanted to put his arms around his shoulders and squeeze him.

'Meanwhile . . .' He turned to Cartwright. 'We will have sent you a radio signal, David. As soon as we set off in the sub. You wait here for the sub, then head towards the South Shetlands. Unless you get a radio message to the contrary.'

'Yes.' Cartwright looked more pale and fragile than Justin had ever seen him, his eyes wide and responsive. Justin felt a rush of affection for the nervous young man, too.

'That message could be that you proceed towards the submarine to meet it on its way back. Or to come pick us up at some point. We hope not, because it will mean that we're in trouble.'

Justin glanced at Katherine. He said for her benefit, 'But this operation is going to go very smoothly. We've got everything on our side, it could hardly be better.'

Nobody said anything.

'Meanwhile, we in the sub proceed to the *Slava*. Again, on the surface as far as possible until we get warm, to save the batteries. And again we're in luck. It will be dark by then. That's very good luck. And it's a calm sea, flat as a pancake.'

He lit another cigarette. His hands were not shaking any more. The cigarette burned his throat. God, he felt like a drink.

'As soon as we've stopped and boarded the *Slava*, the sub dives back under and heads back to the *Jubilee* at full speed, empty, just the commander and Hi-fi Bob in her. As soon as we've got all the Russians off and into their lifeboats, we radio Ross to come and airlift us. Then we zoom back to the *Jubilee*. We head in the opposite direction at first to put them off the track, then swing low over Antarctica. Then do a big curve back to the *Jubilee*. They'll think the *Jubilee*'s over in the east.' He grinned at them. 'Simple.'

They were all staring at the operations table and at nothing. Justin wanted to get this briefing over with now. He decided to cut it short, they all needed to get going. Everybody knew it all anyway. 'And that's it. Any questions?' He smiled. 'It's a bit late for suggestions.'

Black Bob said loudly, 'I've got a suggestion.'

'Yes?'

Craig said, 'Let's all go home!'

They all laughed, except Black Bob and Katherine. Black Bob looked at Justin defiantly. 'My suggestion is we pray.'

There was surprised silence. Then Katherine spoke loudly out of the corner. 'I'll second that.'

'Sure, Bob,' Justin said, 'Will you do it?'

They stood where they were, self-consciously, in the half-darkness. Black Bob closed his eyes and was silent. For a confused moment Justin thought Bob must have meant that they each pray in silence. *Very well*, he thought, *prayer might not be such a bad idea at that.* He closed his eyes and tried to concentrate. *Dear God, if You are there, forgive me for not believing in You. . . . In any event, in the name of love and mercy and decency You owe it to Your creations to help us now.*

Suddenly Black Bob called out in his deep brown voice: 'Ya-ya-ya-ya-ya-ya-ya. . . . Oh Lord, not all these good people have seen Your shining light, but don't hold that against them, Lord, they're all good people. You can take it from me, and today we doin' a good thing, Lord, they all doin' a good thing for You and for the whole world, Lord. Dear Lord, you gave us this beautiful world, an' the mountains an' the oceans an' heavens an'

248

the stars that shine an' the fields an' streams an' the jungles an' all the fowls of the air an' the fish of the sea an' everything that walketh an' creepeth an' crawleth on the face of this beautiful world. You gave us, Lord, didn't You? An' You gave man dominion over everything upon this world, an' behold it was very good. But I'm quite sure, Lord, You never intended man to make a mess of it like this, Lord, did You? An' as You know he sure has, Lord. Well, Lord, I'm goin' to make this prayer brief but what I want to say is what we doin' is *right*, Lord. Some-body's got to do it, Lord, otherwise there just sure ain't goin' to be any more whales an' you didn't make those wonderful animals just to have every last one brutally killed, Lord. So we goin' to stop them doin' that now, Lord, an' that's *good*. An' what I want to pray for on behalf of all of us, Lord, is for Your blessing an' help. Just give us the help, Lord, an' we'll do the job. That's it, Lord. Thank You.'

Black Bob opened his big eyes and looked about. 'That's it,' he said to everybody. 'Amen.'

From the gloom of the radio Katherine said fervently, 'Amen.'

'Amen,' Justin said. 'Thank you, Bob.' Everybody was look-ing down, motionless. Then they shifted and shuffled. 'All right. I'd like to add to what Bob said. We've got a swift submarine. They have not. We've got a helicopter. They have not. We've got sophisticated weapons. They have not. Most important, we've got tear gas and gas masks – they have not. We've got the advantage of surprise. They have not. It is dark. That's a big bonus. Our ship can do thirty knots. Their fastest can only do twenty-two. And,' he said, 'we have right on our side. They do not.'

He looked about him in the smoky room. He said, 'Anybody who thinks he may want to go to the crapper better go now. Meet on the afterdeck in ten minutes.'

They had filed sombrely out of the radio room. She sat in the corner. Cartwright had gone back to the bridge, and L. C. Singleton was at the helm. It was quiet, just the sound of foot-steps padding through the wardroom below. He looked at her as the last of them went down the stairs, and her eyes were tired, frightened, big. She was trying hard to be brave. He looked at her for a moment, then he walked over to her. She watched him coming.

'Hello,' he said. He held out his hand, smiling down at her. She took it.

'Hello. My love.'

He held her hand. 'Come,' he said.

They walked slowly down to his office. She walked upright, independently. He closed the office door behind them. She turned and faced him, and he leaned her gently back against the door. He looked at her.

'I love you,' he said.

She breathed deep and closed her eyes. 'Oh God, be careful,' she said.

He said, 'In twelve hours we'll be back here. Steaming for South America. And we'll get very drunk. And then sleep sleep sleep.'

She nodded.

'And we'll live happily ever after, Katie. Everything's going to be all right.'

'Yes.'

'It will, Katie. This is the beginning of our life. We're going to have a wonderful life, Katie, doing the most important things in the world. We are, my Katie. And we're going to have such fun. And laughter. And in twelve hours when we get back we'll have done one of those most important things, we'll have stopped the killing of whales.'

She whispered, 'I know, my love, I know.'

He kissed her brow. 'It's going to be all right, my love – *it's going to be all right.*'

Her eyes were glistening. 'Please don't think about me. For God's sake just think about yourself and for God's sake be careful.'

He felt his eyes burn. 'I will. I have every intention of coming out of this very much alive.'

Then she came away from the door and clutched him tightly

and she clenched her teeth and shook him. 'Take care, Magnus! The world isn't the only thing that needs you.'

He gave a short choky laugh and kissed her mouth hard and short. 'I need you, too,' he said.

'I'll be there. I'll be up there on that radio listening and praying like a Telex machine.' She kissed him hard. 'Go now, your troops are waiting. Goodbye.'

'So long,' he said. 'So long, darling.'

She kissed him again and he felt her breath tremble. 'Yes, so long.'

Justin unlocked Max's cabin door and opened it. Max looked up from his armchair, surprised, then his face became a mask again. 'Yes?' he said.

'We're going now, Max.'

Max just looked at him.

'I wish I had your blessing, Max,' Justin said.

Max said nothing, just glared at him.

'You are on your honour not to attempt to break out of this cabin. You will be severely dealt with if you do.'

Max said nothing.

'Goodbye, Max.'

Justin closed and locked the door. Then he shot home the four big iron bolts Victor had fitted to the outside of the door. He went out onto the deck.

The Zephyr was on the water, loaded, the big Mercury engine put-putting, Black Bob sternly at the wheel. Craig was on the *Jubilee*'s deck, about to uncleat the painter. Justin said, 'Kid?' Craig straightened up.

Justin stood in front of him. He looked so young. Justin felt his eyes burn.

'Good luck, Craig.'

Craig knew what his brother was thinking. 'We'll be fine,' Craig said. 'All of us. Good luck to you too.'

Justin squeezed his shoulder. 'I'm proud of you, Craig. You should be proud of yourself.' He thought, *He's a damn fine brother and he's growing up.*

Craig grinned, embarrassed. 'I am. Oh, I *am*. I'll be all right. And besides,' he jerked his head at Black Bob, 'I've got Jesus on my side.'

Justin smiled at him. 'Don't knock it, kid. I almost believe we do have Him.'

Craig said quickly, 'I'm not knocking it. Believe me. I'm almost converted.'

Justin shook Craig's shoulder, and he felt himself choking up. 'Go,' he said.

Justin looked for Steve. The helicopter was ready, Ross sat at the controls, Spider was climbing in. 'Steve?' he said. 'Come here a moment.'

Steve looked up, slightly surprised, then walked towards him. His short, lean, powerful body shone in the black rubber thermal-suit. 'Yes?'

'Steve? Remember what I said? Cool it.'

Steve looked at him. Then an amused smile came into his eyes. 'Sure,' he said.

Justin held Steve's arm. 'Just cool it. Let's go.'

Ross was watching them. They turned towards the heli-copter. Spider was squatting in the back on the polystyrene floor, where the passenger seats had been. They all had their thermalsuits switched on, gloves on, flippers already on their feet. Justin and Steve climbed in. In the back were the canisters of explosives and the radios, and the small inflated inner tube with the fisherman's net strung across it. It was going to be freezing without the helicopter doors.

She was on the bridgewing with Cartwright and L.C. Victor stood at his engine-room door. Justin strapped himself into the front passenger seat and put the earphones on his head. Ross started the motor and the rotors began to turn. Katherine stood there with her fur coat collar up around her ears. He smiled at her, and she nodded.

The motor roared and the wind from the rotor blades rushed in at them. Then the helicopter began to rise from the deck and the bridge began to drop slowly below them. Now the *Jubilee* was dropping away down there, the faces on the bridge looking up. The tops of the icebergs were drawing up level with the

252

helicopter, icebergs everywhere, and more and more icebergs, and the *Jubilee* down there.

She lifted up her hand and waved to the helicopter way up there and then she closed her eyes and said fiercely, 'God speed these twelve hours.'

But God did not speed them.

thirty-three

It was freezing, the icy wind blasting into the open helicopter at a hundred miles an hour. The sea was flashing by just ten feet below them, the icebergs towering white canyon walls. They went chopping low over the sea in the radar shadow of the ice. Justin sat hunched in the front seat, binoculars to his eyes. The helicopter banked around the end of an iceberg and there was a big expanse of open sea ahead, icebergs far away. He swept the horizon for ships, and it was clear. They were getting near where the first whale should be. He searched the sea ahead; then he saw it, way ahead, the lonely metal pole sticking up above the water and the sea lapping against the grey striped belly.

'There.' He pointed.

Then they all saw it, the faraway pole with the meshed radar reflector. The helicopter banked and went roaring towards it.

Ross brought the helicopter up to the great dead animal, the wind from the propellers blowing the sea in lapping spikes up over the bloated belly, the smiling head under the water, the tail slopping. It was a male, the great six-foot penis slopping too. Ross brought the helicopter down fifteen feet from it. Justin unclipped his safety strap and yanked off his earphones and pulled his hood up over his head. He swung out of the seat and down onto the float. 'Cut engines,' he shouted. 'Come on, Spider.'

Spider clambered down onto the float beside him, took a breath, pursed his face, and stepped into the icy sea. It closed over him in a smack, then he broke surface gasping. 'Christ!' He rolled over and started swimming towards the whale's chest.

'Tube!' Steve passed Justin the inflated inner tube. He dropped it into the sea beside the float.

'Explosives!' Steve passed him the first twenty-five-pound canister. He took it and dropped it into the tube's net. He placed the next one in carefully. Then the third; he crouched down and set it on top of the other two. The tube was sloshing low in the water now.

'Detonator.' Steve was already passing it to him.

'Radio.' Steve passed it. Justin placed it carefully in the tube.

'Come on, Steve.' He stepped off the float into the sea and the iciness hit him.

Hit him shocking cold in the face, and he broke surface and shook his head gasping. Steve was swinging out of the helicopter cabin, down onto the float. Justin grabbed the edge of the tube and kicked hard and began to tow it towards the massive carcass. Steve jumped off the float into the sea and came splashing after him. He grabbed the tube beside Justin, and they went kicking, shoving, towards the whale, ploughing the heavy tube in front of them. Spider was at the chest already, kicking up against the big hulk, stretching up and thrusting with his cutting tool, which was shaped like a small coal shovel, sharp edges all around. Justin thrashed up against the great hulking carcass, dragging the tube with one hand. He reached for the anus. He rammed his fingers into it, kicking his legs, gasping, and clenching his teeth; he heaved one leg out of the water and threw it, grunting, over the animal's body.

Steve was still in the water holding the tube. 'Give me!' Steve held out the first canister and Justin clutched it tight. He rammed his free hand into the anus, and it was hard and rubbery tight. He rammed his fist into it and wrestled it in. Then he pulled it out and tried to force the end of the canister into the hole. But the anus was too tight. He had expected that the sphincter muscles would have relaxed at death, but they had not. He shoved and shoved, rocking, gasping. Then he grabbed for his knife and plunged it into the anus and sawed a cut two inches deep into one edge of the ring. Then he wrestled the canister into the hole again, and it squeezed through. He leaned down on it with all his weight and it went sliding slowly into the body, his arm following it, right up to his armpit. Inside, the carcass was still warm. 'Next one!' Steve held it out, his legs paddling desperately cold in the water. Justin pressed it in carefully. The third one was the most important. He opened a hole in the bottom of it with the point of his knife. Then he pushed it carefully, heaving it into the anus until only the end was showing. Then Steve passed him up the electronic detonator. He carefully slid the point of it into the hole in the bottom of the canister, gasping.

'Radio!' Spider shouted. He had the hole for it ready.

'Take it to him.'

Steve took the radio out of the tube and swam with one hand up the side of the great dead animal, handing the radio up to Spider. He took it, lifted up the wedge of raw flesh, and pushed the radio into the bloody hole. Only a slim antenna protruded.

Justin wrestled his canister and the detonator deeper into the anus until just six inches of its little aerial was sticking out. He looked at it. It was done. He looked at Spider.

'How're you doing?'

'One minute more.'

Justin shouted at Steve, 'Back to the chopper.'

Steve kicked off the side of the whale and went thrashing back to the helicopter, dragging the tube by the string. Justin held his breath and rolled off the whale's back into the sea with an icy splash. Then he swam down its flank to the chest. 'How you doing?' he gasped to Spider.

'Okay.'

Spider stuck a long barbed spike into the side of the wound and shoved it in and through to pin the flap of hide down over the radio.

'Okay.'

Justin turned around and kicked off for the helicopter.

Steve was pulling up onto the float. He yanked the tube up out of the water and slung it into the cabin. Ross was grinning at them. Steve climbed up into the cabin and slumped back. Spider and Justin came splashing up to the float. 'In,' Justin gasped. He heaved himself up onto the float and climbed into the front seat. Spider was getting in behind.

'Damn well done!' Ross said.

'Well done!' Justin said through chattering teeth. 'Go,' he said to Ross.

The helicopter roared and rose from the water. Justin pulled his red rubber hood off his head and wiped his hands and face and sniffed hard. Then he put on the earphones. He said to Ross, 'How long did we take?'

'Eleven minutes. On the nose.'

Justin sniffed again, then flicked the radio transmission.

'Two to Four. How you doing? Over.'

Craig's voice came back above the roaring of the big Mercury outboard motor. 'Four to Two. We've just spotted the first one. We'll be into it in three minutes. Over.'

'Listen, tell your partner he's probably going to have to cut the whale's anus to get the canisters in. About a two-inch cut, try not to make it obvious. Got that?'

'Got you,' Craig said. 'Over.'

'Keep punching. Over and out.'

He looked at Ross. He was intent, watching the sea. Out of the corner of his eye he saw Justin looking at him and he turned and looked at Justin, then smiled. Justin smiled back, then slapped him on the knee.

'We did it, didn't we, champion?'

'We sure did.'

Justin looked at Spider and Steve. They were sitting there, wet and frozen. Jesus Christ, he loved both of them! He said, 'We did it, didn't we?'

Ross said: 'And you're going to do it again pretty damned soon, you poor bastards.'

Justin flicked the transmission switch again and said, 'Two to One. Do you read me? Over.'

L.C.'s voice came back, 'Yes, I've read it all. Congratulations. Everything okay? Over.'

'Everything's fine.' He added, 'How's your friend? Over.'

'She's fine. She's doing a great job. She's tuned into the enemy's wave band, want to talk to her? Over.'

He did want to talk to her. He wanted to laugh and say, 'Oh God, Katie, I love you and everything's going great.' He said, 'No. Just give her our love. Keep us briefed. How's the sub doing? Over.'

'She's on course,' L.C. said. 'Everything's fine.'

'Keep us briefed. Over and out.'

They were chopping low over the top of the water.

Ten minutes later they found the next whale. When they came back aboard the helicopter, Ross said that Craig had called him, that they had made it with their first whale and they were on their way to the next one.

Justin, Steve, and Spider did their second whale in nine minutes.

It was twenty minutes past nine o'clock when they finished the last whale. Justin came back to the helicopter and worked himself up onto the float, and as he pulled off his hood Ross shouted, 'There's no answer from Craig and Bob! L.C.'s been trying for almost fifteen minutes and there's no answer!'

Justin crouched there on the float. 'Fifteen minutes? Try him again.'

The helicopter sat on the water for ten more minutes, and Ross kept saying, 'Two to Four, Two to Four. Come in. Over.'

But Craig did not come in.

thirty-four

Inside the little black electronic box something clicked as Black Bob sat astride the giant carcass, dripping icy wet, and pushed the detonator into the little hole he had opened in the canister. Craig Magnus had just finished spiking the radio transmitter into the animal's chest, and he had swum back to the Zephyr.

He was just out of the water, belly sliding over the big rubber inflated bows when the electronic detonator clicked and the little electric current shot through the detonator as Black Bob shoved it into the canister, and it exploded.

Exploded with a deafening crack right under Bob Clark's hand, exploded Bob in one terrible ear-splitting blinding blast forty feet high into the Antarctic air with his stomach and chest blown clean out as if he had been gutted, and his neck snapped back broken and his guts and blood flying high and wide with the whale's, and the rest of him hurtling cartwheeling high. The explosion blew the Zephyr clean out of the water, flying spinning high through the air throwing the radio and fuel tanks out as it flew; blew Craig Magnus unconscious, with all the breath smashed out of his body, high through the air in the flying rain of blood and blubber without his knowing what hit him; and blew the massive dead animal's belly and chest and spine away. Black Bob Clark came plummeting out of the air in the flying rain of his own blood and flesh, and crashed back into the black sea.

Craig Magnus came flying down, shocked senseless, and hit the water, and the icy blow of it brought him around. The first thing Craig knew was the desperate choking of the sea in his throat and nostrils, and all his terrified instinct knew was that he was under water and he kicked and thrashed his arms and legs, fighting to get upward. His head broke surface strangling and retching, and he thrashed desperately, dog-paddling, getting his throat clear, his head to stop reeling, and the terrible ringing out of his ears. Then after a long time he got his breath and senses back, and then he looked wildly around and he still did not comprehend what had happened. Then he saw the Zephyr. It was upside down, only half-floating, the big Mercury outboard motor gone, the wooden stern ripped out, splintered. He struck out for it, kicking, and he grabbed the big inflated rubber bows and looked wildly about him for Black Bob.

There was no sign of Bob, and no whale. Craig looked around wild-eyed.

'Bob!' he yelled, and it came out as a croak. 'Bob!'

But there was no Black Bob. There was only that big cloud of scummy blood and shreds of flesh on the surface of the sea.

'Bob!' Craig croaked. But there was no Black Bob Clark any more. He was also sinking slowly, drifting down through the Antarctic sea.

'Bob!' Craig tried to bellow and again it came out as a croak. 'Bob!' Then suddenly the horror of it got through to him. The terrible thing that had happened to his friend Bob, and there in front of his shocked staring eyes were the shreds of flesh floating and the clouds of blood drifting up from below the sea. Then slowly came the inarticulate anger with Black Bob's God who had let this happen to him. For a long time Craig Magnus clung there to the upturned Zephyr sobbing. Then his mind reeled in outrage and he filled his lungs and screwed up his face and he sobbed, 'Why did You let that happen? Why didn't You stop that happening? What's the matter with You? Don't You realize what we're doing? Don't You know what he's like? Didn't You hear him pray on the ship? Jesus Christ, don't You know what we're doing?' And then he burst into tears. He clung to the Zephyr gasping, choking, crying. That is what he was doing when the helicopter came over the black sea between the white icebergs to look for him.

They saw the capsized half-sunken Zephyr in the distance and the solitary figure clinging to it, and no whale and no other figure, and they stared and Justin said, 'Oh God. Oh God. . . .'

thirty-five

They were all shocked, staring, stunned at the terrible thing that had happened. Justin sat hunched in the front seat of the helicopter, glaring ahead, his mind reeling under the grief, trying to race through the emergency. The *Jubilee* came into view around the mass of icebergs, small and white over there; then he could see Cartwright on the bridgewing looking at them. Ross brought the helicopter over the *Jubilee* and then brought her down.

Justin jumped out as the floats touched the deck and ran low under the blades. 'Up to the radio room,' he shouted. Steve was already jumping out and dashing after him. Craig sat in the back of the helicopter for a long moment, then he climbed out heavily, with Spider's help.

Justin burst open the wardroom door and strode down the alleyway to the guest cabin. He turned the key and shot back the bolts and flung the door open. Max looked up from his armchair astonished. Justin commanded, 'Please come up to the radio room.' Max gaped at him. 'At once, please!'

Max got up slowly, and straightened himself.

'Come on, Max!'

'What the hell's all this about?'

'I'll tell you up there. I don't want to repeat myself. We've only got a very short time.'

He walked quickly down the alleyway. Max followed, smoothing his hair. Justin went through the wardroom and ran up the steps into the radio room. Everybody was already there.

Katherine was sitting at the radio, her eyes red with dried crying, face gaunt, Victor was there, his craggy face ashen. Cartwright's thin nervous hands clenching and unclenching themselves. The others stood silently, unmoving. Justin stopped at the top of the stairs and waited for Max to come up. Max entered the radio room and looked around. 'What is this?' he said to Justin. 'A lynching party?'

Justin's face was ashen and his voice shook. 'Black Bob's dead. Got blown up.'

'Dead?' Max stared and the shock came into his handsome eyes. 'How the hell . . . ?'

'Now listen, Max,' Justin said softly, angrily, his voice shaking. He pointed west and his finger trembled. 'Forty miles over there is the *Slava*. Twenty miles over there the submarine is waiting for us with Hi-fi Bob and the commander in it and all our gear. Also lying out there are five dead whales charged to the eyeballs with high explosives. And in three minutes exactly, five of us are going to climb back into the helicopter and go back to that submarine and four of us are going to board the *Slava* and blow the fucking thing up. . . . Now listen, Max – please listen good. There's no time for arguments and there's no time for pleading. . . . Four of us are going to board that ship, Max. We need five. We needed Black Bob to hold the bridge and man the radio – to keep talking to Katie so we know what the Russians are doing. And to call Ross to come in the helicopter.' He paused. 'Now I guess we can make it with four, Max, but with four the whole plan and maybe all our lives are endangered. Now what I've called you up here for is to ask you to come and take Black Bob's place.'

L.C. spoke up hoarsely, 'I'll go.'

Justin did not take his eyes off Max, and Max was staring at him, shaken; Justin said, 'L.C. has already offered to go but with all due respect to him and admiration for his courage, he's in no condition to go; he's not in any shape to go up the nets lugging his gear and he hasn't had any experience with the weapons and he's a diabetic and he has to have his carbo-hydrates and insulin on time. . . .'

Max opened his mouth to speak but Justin cut in, 'Cartwright can't go because he's vital to navigate the ship. Victor can't go because he's needed to run the engine room. Hi-fi can't go because he's needed to man the periscope in the submarine on its way back here. There's only one person who can go, Max, and that's you.'

Katherine said from the corner, 'I can go.'

Justin's eyes flicked at her once, then returned to Max. 'Obviously she can't go – she's needed here to monitor the Russian radio.'

Max said, 'Give it up, Justin. You speak as if it's my fault you're in this jam. I could have told you something like this would happen.'

Justin shouted, 'For Christ's sake stop thinking about fault! If it's anybody's fault it's the manufacturers of the detonator. Or maybe it was Hi-fi's fault for not checking it out properly. Or maybe it's all my fault for trying to save whales from extinction. I don't care who's goddamn fault it is, all I care about are the lives of our men and getting those Russians off that ship without

261

killing any of them and that Black Bob's lying at the bottom of the Antarctic right now blown in half and that guy's life is not going to be sacrificed for nothing!'

Katherine said, 'I can also monitor the Russians from the bridge of the *Slava*.'

'We need you, Max,' Justin said. 'Each and every one of us now needs you. *I* need you. Magnus Oceanics needs you. Even the goddamn *Russians* need you to make sure they get safely off that ship! And goddamnit!' he slammed his hand on the bulkhead, 'nature needs you! To save the world of nature from mankind! And right this red-hot moment you, personally, Max Hagen, are the pivotal point of all those needs.'

Max looked at him, eyes wavering, and then he said flatly, 'And Katherine needs me.' He turned to her and then nodded at Justin. 'To get him back safe and sound. . . .'

She looked at him, then she blinked and said, 'To get them *all* back safe and sound, yes. . . . You will have my undying gratitude and admiration.'

There was dead silence. He looked at her, and she looked back, pleading. They were all fixed on Max. He raised his eyebrows, then said, 'Thanks. I could use the admiration. But gratitude I don't need.'

He looked at Justin hard, then he jerked his head. 'Let's go. Have you got another bulletproof vest?'

Justin slapped him on the back, 'Jesus, you're a good man, Max!'

thirty-six

The long, slow Antarctic sunset was beginning. It gleamed into the helicopter roaring low over the sea and into their eyes. In the back the four of them were hunched tight together, clutching onto the three safety straps, Max in the middle, Craig crouched in front of him. The colour had come back into his face. Now there was just the shock. The whole right side of his body felt bruised from the percussion and his right ear still rang and his head ached. They were all grim, awed.

Justin sat hunched in the front passenger seat and said into the radio, 'Two to Three, Two to Three. Come in. Where are you? Over.'

Hi-fi Bob's voice came crackling back in his earphones, 'Three to Two. We're nearly there, we've got the iceberg. Another ten minutes. Over.'

'Roger. Over and out.'

Justin snapped the switch to receive and sat there, eyes screwed up against the air blast, his lips and nose numb with the cold, sick in his guts with the realization of what had happened. He rubbed his numbed forehead hard to force himself to stop thinking about it. *Stop thinking about it, there's plenty of time to grieve after this – stop thinking about it now.* He said loudly into his intercom mouthpiece, 'All right everybody – there's only one thing to do about Bob and that is to forget about the poor bastard for right now. Put it out of our minds.'

Craig burst out, 'Forget about him? How the hell can we forget about him?'

'That's the way it's got to be, kid! And that's the way he'd want it. Now listen. Max? Can you hear me?'

'Yes,' Max said. He was sitting, eyes shut, hugging his chest with his arms. He did not open his eyes when Justin spoke.

'Listen and I'll tell you what you've got to do. We'll run through the weapons when we're in the submarine. Principally your job is to hold the bridge and any hostages once we've captured it. And to keep in radio contact with Katie. If any Russian manages to storm back to the bridge, you shoot the living shit out of him with tear gas and your riot gun. You only use your real gun as a very last resort. Have you heard all that?'

'Yes. I know the plan.'

'Also, if any catcher is threatening to come close you give him a rake on the bridge with the automatic rifle you'll have. You've got over a mile's range with that thing. Shoot up the water all around him and make plenty of noise shooting up his steelwork. Just don't kill anybody.'

Max didn't say anything, sitting there with his eyes tightly closed.

'Now here's what you've got to do, step by step. And I'll tell you again when we get into the submarine. . . .'

Fifteen minutes later they saw the big iceberg. Ross slowed the helicopter down to fifty miles an hour and the sudden drop in the wind was like a breath of warm air. Justin had the binoculars to his eyes, searching along the sheer iced waterline. When they were about two miles off the iceberg he saw her blue-black against the ice, almost the same colour as the sea, just the small hump of the little tower sticking up and the streamlined deck, just above the water, and he saw a flash once.

'There she is,' he breathed.

thirty-seven

The cliffs of the iceberg rose up behind the submarine, a hundred and fifty feet above them. They could see the different grains and streaks of ice in the cliff faces, and the rough pieces caught the sunset in a thousand tiny sparkling spectrums. The helicopter was moored to the submarine by a single painter. They climbed out of the helicopter and went down into the submarine, one by one, pulled off their thermalsuits and put on their bulletproof vests and then their tracksuits. The commander was standing on the small topside deck, one foot on the helicopter float, his craggy bearded face solemn. Ross still sat behind his controls.

Justin said into the radio transmitter, 'Two to One. Do you read me? Over.' Katie's voice came back straight away, tense; he could imagine her sitting at that radio with L.C., her gold hair messed and her eyes tired. 'Loud and clear. Over.'

'We'll be leaving rendezvous point in about five minutes,' he said, 'sailing on the surface for at least the first hour, probably longer. If we dive it should be to periscope depth only, so we'll keep the radio aerial up and we can keep in radio contact all the way. If we have to dive any deeper and break radio contact we'll try to warn you. Have you got that? Over.'

He heard her breathe deep. 'Got you. Over.'

'We've seen the *Slava* from the helicopter. She's about twenty-five miles almost due west, and there seems to be good iceberg cover for at least fifteen, maybe twenty miles. Any more information about her? And the towing boats? Over.'

'None. She seems to be just slowly cruising. No changes of speed or direction reported.' He could hear her turn a page of her notes. 'The two towing boats must be with her now unloading the other whales. There have been no other whales reported, so they must be leaving shortly to get your target whales. Do you want me to read my notes out? But there doesn't seem to be anything of significance. Over.'

'Not now. When we're under way in the submarine I'll want you to. What about the tanker? Over.'

'Lots of bunkering instructions for the catchers but that's all. Over.'

'All right.' He wanted to keep talking to her, to imagine her sitting there. He said abruptly, 'Over and out.'

He looked at Ross. 'This is it, champion.'

Ross nodded. Then gave him his solemn smile.

Justin turned to the commander. 'Everybody ready down there?'

Henry Thorogood looked down the little tower. 'Yes.'

'All right.' Justin climbed out of the helicopter and stepped over onto the submarine's hull. He swung his leg over the lip of the tower and dropped carefully down into the control cabin. Hi-fi Bob Matthews was sitting at his bank of radio gear, Spider and Steve were sitting on the deck, their backs against the curved bulkhead.

Hi-fi Bob turned around on his stool and scowled at him and shoved his glasses up his nose. 'I just want to say,' he said, 'once and for all, while everybody's together: I checked those detonators as best I could. They're the best there is. But it's almost impossible to open them up to check inside because they're waterproof. I opened up one and everything was perfect. They all have the manufacturer's certificate of perfection.'

Justin said, 'Okay, Bob. Forget it now.'

'I did everything I could, unless I opened every one and wrecked the waterproofing,' he said desperately, and it was the first time anybody had ever heard him plead.

Justin dropped his hand on his shoulder. 'We're not blaming you, Bob. Listen – we've got to forget about Black Bob now until this job's over.'

Craig said loudly, bitterly, from the aft chamber, out of sight, 'The one that you opened up – that was probably the one that blew the poor bastard up!'

Hi-fi Bob shouted, 'It was perfect, I tell you! And I sealed the waterproofing up again properly!'

'Shut up, both of you!' Justin said.

'Then why didn't you open them all up to see if they were perfect if you could seal the waterproofing again?' Craig shouted.

'Shut up, Craig!' Justin hollered. There was silence. Justin frowned at Bob Matthews, then bent down and looked through the connecting tunnel into the aft chamber. Craig was sitting against the aft chamber, his face still red-eyed and swollen. Justin said, 'That's the last word on this subject.' He then straightened up and started to pull off his thermalsuit.

He climbed back up the little tower and out onto the deck. The commander and Ross were talking. Justin's face was still flushed, tense from the scene below.

'What happened down there?' the commander said.

'Craig having a go at Hi-fi. He's very upset. They've shut up now.'

Ross said, 'How's Max behaving?'

'Hasn't said a word. He'll be all right.'

Ross shook his head. 'I hope like hell it's all right to trust him with manning the radio – that's a vital job. I'd rather see him in the front line with you guys where he has to fight for his life.'

'Every job's important, for Christ's sake – it's the best job for him because he hasn't practised with the weapons. And that guy will be as keen to get off that ship as any of us. He doesn't want to get blown up either. Or lugged off to face trial in Moscow.'

'At least this makes Max a full-blooded accomplice,' Ross said. 'He can't squeal on us now.'

'The point hadn't escaped me either,' the commander said.

'Yes,' Justin said. 'Nor me. I admire the guy. This isn't his plan, he doesn't *want* to do it. He's doing it for us.'

'Exactly,' the commander said. 'I'd say he's turned up trumps.'

'Sure,' Ross said. 'But don't kid yourselves too much, I was watching him very closely. He did it for Katherine. Or Katie shamed him into it.'

'Come *on*.' Justin flicked Ross's shoulder with the back of his hand. 'The guy's here, isn't he? Risking his skin for something he didn't want anything to do with. Gallantry is gallant, whatever the reason.' He looked at the commander. 'Let's go.'

The old man waved at Ross. 'Good luck.'

'Good luck, Henry.'

The commander climbed back onto the submarine. In one orderly movement of his stocky body he swung his leg over the lip, then clambered down. Justin turned to Ross.

'All right, champ?'

'All right. Don't worry about me. We're doing it at last. We're actually right here doing it.'

'If there's one guy I don't worry about it's you, Ross. Good luck, champ.'

'You're the guys who need the luck.' He tapped the Perspex windshield of the helicopter. 'My friends say it's bulletproof.'

Justin grinned at him. Then he stepped back onto the submarine's hull. He untied the painter holding the two craft together; Ross pulled it into his cabin. Justin climbed into the tower, half-way down into the control cabin, his shoulders out of the top of the hatch. He called down. 'Everybody okay?'

'Yes,' the commander said.

Justin said, 'Hatch open, commander. Start diesel engines.'

'Hatch is open, start diesels,' the commander said.

He heard the starter motor grind, then the big diesel took sweetly, doem, doem, doem. He called down above the noise, 'Steer zero zero five, half ahead.'

'Zero zero five, half ahead.'

He felt the big aft propeller take, and the submarine began to surge slowly, powerfully forward and the black water began to slide around the bulbous bow. He looked back at Ross in the helicopter, and waved. Ross was behind his controls, the setting sun on his face, the helicopter gleaming, slowly drifting beside the iceberg, in the submarine's wake. He raised his hand and waved back.

The sheer cliffs of the iceberg were sliding slowly past the submarine's starboard side. 'Three-quarters ahead,' Justin called down the hatch.

He stood in the hatch and felt the freezing air on his face, and he felt his guts turn over. Suddenly again he found it hard to realize he was actually going to do it, it felt as if this was just another underwater job they were heading for, and then, Jesus Christ, the realization all over again. Really, really, *really* going to do it at last. He called, 'Full ahead,' and he heard and felt the diesel engine throb harder.

Beyond, to the north, there were many more icebergs, scattered far and near. To the east, open sea, then many icebergs again, but they were much more scattered, miles of sea in between. And twenty-odd miles over there, behind them, unseen, the *Slava*.

He stood in the freezing hatch and looked into the darkness to the east with the binoculars. He searched the whole horizon. He could not see any lights. He called, 'Steer zero nine zero.'

The submarine turned to the east, full ahead. He stared hard through the binoculars. He shouted down into the control cabin, 'Nothing ahead for a long way, commander. We'll stay on the surface.'

He looked at his watch. It was nearly eleven o'clock. He looked around the whole horizon, three hundred and sixty degrees, with the binoculars. The sun was almost set.

He climbed down into the middle of the control cabin, leaving the hatch open. It seemed warm to him down here, and it smelled faintly of their rubber thermalsuits. The commander had his back to him at the controls. So did Hi-fi Bob Matthews. 'All right, Henry?'

'Fine.' He did not look around.

'Bob?'

Hi-fi Bob Matthews did not look around either. Just staring sullenly at his little bank of radio equipment. Justin dropped his hand on his shoulder, but Hi-fi Bob did not turn. He looked at Spider. Spider was sitting there, short, strong legs stretched out under the commander's swivel stool, his tough boy's face expressionless. 'Spider?'

'Yeah.' And Justin wondered what the kid was really feeling. His face gave away very little, almost always a mask unless he was learning something brand new. There was no excitement in the eyes now, no life in that smile. But he was not worried about Spider. And he wasn't really worried about Steve. Steve had his eyes closed, his body entirely relaxed.

Justin said, 'We can smoke until we close the hatch, Steve.'

'Thanks.' He opened his eyes and reached up and took one of Justin's cigarettes. Justin lit it for him.

'All right?'

Steve gave him his slightly languid look. 'Sure.'

Justin got down on his haunches. 'Spider, you better stick your head out of the hatch and keep lookout for a minute.' He dropped onto his elbow and shoved himself into the low connecting passage and worked his head and shoulders and upper torso into the aft chamber. Max had his eyes closed, face rigid. Craig looked at Justin, and Justin stretched out his arm and shook his young brother's foot.

Craig looked at him angrily and his voice was hoarse. 'That little son of a bitch!'

Justin shushed him. 'We don't know it was Hi-fi's fault! We don't know whose fault it was, kid – probably the goddamn manufacturers! You've got to forget it now. You've got to forget it until this job's over.'

Max said with his eyes closed, 'If you play with fire you must expect to get your fingers burned.'

Craig turned on him furiously. 'You keep your fucking mouth shut – you never liked him!'

Max said, 'On the contrary, I liked him fine.'

Craig said, 'Afterwards I'm going to knock the living shit out of that little Hi-fi son of a bitch! I'm going to knock him ten times around the deck of the *Jubilee*! That guy was the kindest guy in the whole world.'

Justin said, 'All right – afterwards you knock him ten times around the deck. Right now you're going to sink the fucking *Slava*! Now pull yourself together, Craig!' He slapped his brother's knee and shook it. 'Okay?'

Craig looked away and his face was red. Justin turned to Max. 'Are you all right, Max?'

Max opened his eyes after a moment. 'Sure. Nice trip.'

Justin knew the man was afraid but his pride would not let him admit it. He said. 'I'll come back in five minutes and we'll run through the plan again.'

'I know the fucking plan.'

'Step by step,' Justin said. 'And I'll show you how to use the weapons.'

Max sat up. 'I warn you now, loud and clear: I'm not going to kill anybody. Even if everybody's life depends on it. And I warn you of something else. I hereby disassociate myself from anybody who does. I'm here strictly on that understanding. I'll say that under oath in any court.' He looked at him. 'And I'll expect you to corroborate me. To testify on my behalf to that effect. Is that understood?'

'Fair enough,' Justin agreed. 'I give that undertaking. Nobody intends killing anybody. The whole idea of this elaborate plan is *not* to do so.'

Max looked at him steadily, the resentment in his eyes. 'And another thing I want to place on record here and now. For all the good it will do me. But I want it understood how I feel: I *deplore* terrorism. I *deplore* this modern smash-and-grab mentality of skyjacking airliners and trains and seizing hostages in embassies and so forth. It's savage. And I'm horrified to think that this operation of yours is going to be classified as that sort of thing. And probably encourage it. And, by Christ, if you guys do anything like that, if you're going to behave like those bastards, or mistreat hostages or anything like that, so help me God, I'll turn you bastards in when we get back. Katherine included. Is that understood?'

Justin nodded. He had forgotten how much he liked this guy. 'Understood. We all agree with you. Terrorism is not our intention. It is conservation.'

Max wiped his mouth with the back of his wrist and his hand was trembling. 'All right,' he said with dismissal. He closed his eyes again.

Justin reached out his hand and shook Max's knee. 'Max, I want to thank you for coming. I admire your guts.'

Max had closed his eyes. He did not say anything.

Justin worked his way backwards into the control cabin. Spider was standing on the ladder, his head out of the tower, keeping lookout. Justin could feel the cold air blowing in. He tapped Spider on the leg. 'Anything?'

'No,' Spider said down into the cabin. 'Getting dark now.'

Justin said to Hi-fi Bob's back, 'Give me the *Jubilee*, please, Bob.'

Hi-fi Bob flicked the transmission switch. 'Three to One. Stand by.' He handed Justin the microphone.

Justin took a breath and said quietly, as if he were dictating an office memo, 'All's well. We're under way. On the surface. Flat sea. Visibility good. We can't see any lights yet. There's good iceberg cover to the east though we're in clear sea at the moment. It'll be about an hour before we sight them, I should think, not until we're through those icebergs ahead. About two hours before we're anywhere near the *Slava*.' He stopped. 'Have you read that? Over.'

Katherine's voice came back. 'Loud and clear. Over.'

'Three to Two. Got that?'

'Yes,' Ross said. 'Over.'

'Any new information on the towing boats? And the *Slava*? Over.'

Katherine said, 'Nothing. Over.'

'Everything's fine aboard here. How're you, Two? Over.'

'Cold.' Justin could imagine Ross sitting there in the helicopter, floating, alone. 'Trying to think of something that rhymes with "iceberg",' Ross added. 'Over.'

'How're you, One? Over.' Katherine sounded very tense. 'All's well here. Over.'

'All right, darling. Over and out.'

He stood there a moment, then tapped Spider's leg.

'Come down, Spider.' Spider climbed down the ladder, back into the small cabin, his face red with cold. 'Take Black Bob's weapons through to Max. Show him how they work. Thoroughly. Then call me, I want to go through the plan with him again. Okay?'

'Okay,' Spider said.

Justin took the binoculars from him and climbed up the ladder.

It was indeed getting dark, just a red glow in the west outlining the range of big icebergs. There were a lot of stars. He looked at his watch. Then he pulled his tracksuit hood up over his ears.

thirty-eight

It was very cold now, completely dark, the last of the sunset gone. The Antarctic was silent except for the muffled throbbing of the diesel engine and the soft sh-sh of the sea around the bow. The big range of icebergs was only about a mile ahead now, looming dark and huge in the binoculars. At twenty minutes before midnight he saw the first lights.

Suddenly, on his horizon, the lights of the big, high *Slava* came sliding slowly out from behind a big iceberg way over there, the faraway pinpricks of her bridge lights in his big binoculars, and he felt his stomach churn. He called hoarsely down into the control cabin, 'There she is.'

His heart was suddenly pounding. He stared at her, then

looked at the compass, and his mind fumbled with the reading. He called, 'Steer zero seven zero!'

'Zero seven zero!'

He looked back at her through the binoculars, heart thudding. Now he could make out the glow of her floodlit cutting decks. Then slowly her stern lights and funnels came into view. He called down into the control cabin, 'Cruising maybe eleven miles off. Heading north, maybe northwest. We can close with her for another half an hour at least, on the surface. She'll never notice us on her radar.'

He did not wait for any answer. He did not want to hear any answer. All he wanted was for this submarine to go as long and hard and as fast as she could on the surface before she had to submerge and start using her batteries. And now that he could actually see the big bitch over there, all he wanted to do was close with her and get this show on the road. He stared through the binoculars, his mouth dry, the tense feeling in his guts – *there she is.* Seeing her now it was almost hard to believe what they were actually going to do. *Sink that ship.* He swung the binoculars looking for more lights. He could not see any, but there were many icebergs ahead. He called down the hatch, 'Spider, take over lookout.'

He dropped into the cabin. They were all looking at him, anxiously, except the commander. Justin said to Spider, 'Dead ahead there's a passage for us between the icebergs, you can see the *Slava* clearly through it. Keep us in the middle. Watch out for ice floe.' He gave the binoculars to him, and Spider went up the ladder.

'Well – there the bastards are.' He said to Hi-fi Bob, 'Give me Katie, please.'

'Three to One. Stand by.'

Justin said evenly, 'We're in visual contact. She's about ten or eleven miles off, cruising slowly north or northeast. We're still in good iceberg cover, we should be able to stay on the surface for about another hour. We'll be right on her tail in an hour and a half. Do you both read me? Over.'

Katherine's voice said. 'Loud and clear. Over.'

'Loud and clear. Over,' Ross said.

Justin said, 'No information on those towing boats? Over.'

She said, 'Nothing since last time. Twenty fifteen hours they left the *Slava*, they must be picking up your target whales about now. More or less. Over.'

'Yes.' He looked at his watch and calculated out loud, 'Thirty-odd miles at twenty knots, an hour and a half. They're there now. Say another hour to pick them up. Then thirty-odd miles back to the *Slava* at say ten or twelve knots – we should reckon on two and a half to three hours before they get back to the *Slava*, maybe less. We've got enough time.' He thought, then said, 'Got that, Two? Over.'

Ross's voice came back, 'Got that. Two and a half to three hours to countdown. Over.'

Justin wanted to say something to Katie but he could not think of what he could say on the air, and even if nobody else could hear them he was too tense to think of anything to say except that he loved her and that, by God, he was proud of her, *You're marvellous, Katie, and I love you.* Instead he said, 'All right, One. All right, Two.' He felt his eyes sting. 'Over and out.'

He clicked the machine back to receive. He handed the microphone back to Bob Matthews, then peered through the connecting passage. The red swollen look had gone out of Craig's face.

'You guys heard all that?'

Craig said, 'Yeah.' Max was out of sight, just his legs in view. 'He heard,' Craig said.

'You guys all right? We'll have soup and those sandwiches in about an hour.'

'Sure.' Craig looked at him, then took a breath and sang softly at him: 'Nothing else to do all day, but sit around and sing. Where women are your shipmates. . . . Oh Death, where is thy sting, ting-a-ling?'

Justin smiled. Okay. He straightened up, then said to the commander, 'What do you think, Henry?'

The lights of the instrument panel shining yellow and green up into the commander's face. He said, 'So far, perfect. Couldn't be luckier. These icebergs are excellent. We'll only have to dive and stay under for the very last bit.'

'Right.'

He stood there examining the instrument panel. The battery indicator registered fully charged. Couldn't be better. There was nothing to do except wait.

He turned and smacked Spider's leg. 'All right, Spider. I'll take over up there.'

Justin stood in the hatch, watching the *Slava* through the binoculars. *There she was*. The submarine was through the last range of icebergs now, out into the open sea beyond. He could not make out any more icebergs in the dark. Everything was going well. The only thing that would make it better was *one*, just one great big iceberg about five miles ahead they could keep in the radar shadow of, so they did not have to submerge, so they could save the batteries. He stared at her through the binoculars, and all he wanted to do was just keep his eyes on her and keep that diesel engine flat-out after her on top of the water. Just to go charging in there with a horsewhip and lash the living shit out of the sons of bitches, and, oh Jesus, he was glad with all his heart about what he was going to do.

His face was frozen. Say ten miles, over an hour. The wide-open black sea ahead. Just the soft muffled doem, doem, doem of the diesel engine. And the great black butcher ship with the lights over there, steaming slowly, hacking rending sawing and the yellow fumes belching. And the little submarine stealthily moving along on the surface following her, to kill her. He looked at his watch.

They would never notice the tiny tower of the submarine on their radar. Vital to save the batteries.

He lowered the binoculars and rubbed his frozen eyelids. Then lifted the binoculars again.

Three quarters of an hour later he looked around the horizon for the last time. There were no new lights. He called down into the hatch.

'Prepare for diving.'

He climbed stiffly down the ladder into the small cabin. He

275

reached up and pulled the watertight hatch down over his head. He twisted the sealer clamps.

'Top hatch sealed. Okay, Henry. Give us the oxygen.'

The commander flicked the O_2 switch, and there came the reassuring hissing sound. Then he flicked the carbon-dioxide-scrubber switch. He switched on the main electric motors and then cut the diesel engine, and the doem, doem, doem subsided into the soft whirring noise of the electric motors.

'Prepared for diving,' he said.

'Periscope depth,' Justin said. The commander repeated, 'Flooding to periscope depth.'

Henry pulled the lever and outside on the hull the big valves opened and the sea flooded into the two main tanks. He pushed the fin levers gently forward; the control cabin began to dip and the aft to slope upward behind, and the black sea began to surge and flood over the deck and then the tower. She dove gently, as sweet as a nut. Through the observation ports the sea showed black. The commander said, 'Periscope depth.'

Justin took the periscope handles and shoved the apparatus upward. And suddenly there was the Antarctic night in the eye-pieces. He twisted it a little to starboard, and there was the *Slava*, lit up like a Christmas tree, a few miles ahead, clanking rattling grinding. And it seemed he could almost smell and hear the bitch.

'Send up the aerial, please.'

The radio aerial went sliding up above the water.

'Give me Katie and Ross,' he said.

part seven

The great female blue whale lay dead, with the steel harpoon sticking out of her back, her striped bloated belly upwards, and the long steel spear sticking up out of her with the metal disc bearing the number of the catcher that killed her.

Three hours after the catcher had left her there, the calf came back, and he swam around and around her, surging and blowing and nudging her, and lifting up his flipper and trying to pull her under, and all the time making his desperate terrified heartbroken crying noises. That is what he was doing five hours later when the towing boat came to fetch her, to take her back to the factory to be butchered up.

The towing boat came ploughing through the icebergs, and the calf heard it coming, and he was panic-stricken again, for he knew now about killers. But he did not want to leave the body of his mother and he did not know where to go or what to do. Then he instinctively did what his father and mother had done for him, he went desperately galloping towards the ship and then blew to show himself and then swerved and went galloping off to the side to decoy the ship away, but the towing boat had no gun or gunner and it did not turn to chase him and he turned around and galloped back, huffing and blowing to show himself some more, but the towing boat would not turn. The men on the ship saw him and they laughed. They knew what he was doing for they had seen it all before. The towing boat churned on towards the great carcass and the calf galloped after them and ahead of them back to his mother, blowing and surging and showing himself all the way.

The ship eased up against the carcass. The seamen heaved a heavy loop of cable around the broad flukes and winched the tail up out of the water alongside the steel gunnel. The calf surged and milled and blew frantically around, once again trying to drag his mother back down under the sea.

Then the towing boat's engines churned forward, dragging the carcass through the sea, back towards the factory and the calf followed behind it. For forty miles across the sea he followed the ship that was dragging his dead mother away, all the time crying. Then he heard the terrible factory ship way ahead, and he took fright and dropped back and followed from a distance. Then finally he turned around and swam away in heartbroken fear, crying, crying, and he did not know where he was going.

The towing boat rode up to the stern of the factory ship. A heaving line was thrown from the factory's stern to the towing boat and a cable was lashed around the blue whale's tail. And then the cable was cast off and the sailors on the factory hauled the heaving line in, dragging up the end of the cable. Then the end of the cable was turned around a winch and the blue whale was dragged up to the stern of the factory. There were half a dozen other dead whales wallowing in tow behind the factory's slipway, bloated bellies up, awaiting their turn to be dragged up the slipway onto the cutting decks, to be butchered.

The reeking butchery. One hundred yards of bloody deck, with the pot holes five feet wide belching the fumes of boiling whale oil, and between the pot holes, the carnage. The reeking carnage, a quagmire of blood and flesh and fat up to the whalemen's shins, blood cascading. Mountains of animal, twice the height of a man, being torn and ripped apart, and hacked and sawed up. And behind the factory, in the icy sea were lying half a dozen other such magnificent animals with the big holes blown into their bodies and the grooved bellies pumped full of air, waiting to be butchered. One by one the whales were hauled up the iron slipway by their mighty tails by the midships steam winch, up into the blood, and one by one they were butchered up. Then the great female blue whale was hauled up.

As her giant flukes reached the top of the sloping slipway,

two Russian flenserwomen plunged their long sharp flensing knives into either side of her body, and they braced their legs and stood there, and as the great animal was pulled past them they sliced her open; and up and over her great bloated carcass ran another flenserwoman in her spiked boots, with her knife buried into the flesh like a plough, and the animal was slit open from its flukes to its dead smiling mouth. Now the ninety-foot animal was lying on the cutting deck between the rows of belching vat holes. Now steel cables were reeled from the winches. On the end of the cables were big steel hooks, and they were hooked into the ends of the skin. Then the winches heaved and the cables tightened and they began to peel the great thick skin off her. It came tearing slowly off in fatty strips ninety feet long and six feet wide, with a wrenching fatty sinewy sound, torn all the way off the great body; and then the great animal lay white and bloody and fatty and naked. And thigh-booted, oilskinned whalewomen dragged and shovelled the long strips of skin down the belching fuming vat holes, down into the great factory pots below to be boiled up into oil.

Two more big hooked cables had been placed in her vast bleeding smiling jaws, one hook into her great snout and the other into her lower jaw; and then there was the big rattling gushing hissing of the steam winches as they took the strain, and the massive smiling jaws were heaved wider and wider open with a great creaking, muscles as thick as a man's leg being torn apart and massive bones and sockets slowly wrenching. And then the jaw gave way with a mighty crack. Then the flensers were hacking through the last broken muscles. And meanwhile the flenserwomen were standing in a row down the enormous fatty bloody carcass, and they swung their great flensing knives way back over their shoulders and then swiped them over their heads, hacking deep into the raw fatty flesh, chopping it deep wide open, and with each swipe out it cascaded, the blood.

Thick red blood gushing and spurting out of veins as thick as a strong man's arm, down over the flenserwomen and onto the bloody deck in big splashes and splats, and the flenserwomen jumped back from it, then swung their flensing knives and swiped again, and out spurted more, and they swiped and swiped, hacking out great blocks of red bloody fatty flesh to be dragged off to the belching vats by the potwomen with their steel hooks. And they ran open her belly, plunging their flensing knives deep into her guts, and heaved their way up the side of her, slicing her guts open. And out they crashed into the chaos of blood and fat, intestines sloshing out into the carnage, coils of intestines as thick as a man's leg and over a thousand feet long, full of half-digested shrimps, five million shrimps in big sacs, and crashing out on top of all of it came the foetus whale.

He was fifteen feet long and he was perfectly formed already and looking exactly like his mother – the long grooves along his belly up to his sagging chin and his huge mouth smiling in death, and his little eyes closed, and his rubbery fins pressed flat against his sides. He came thudding out onto his mother's blood and guts, and the potwomen sank their hooks into his head and tail and dragged him through the blood to the rail of the *Slava*. He was too big and heavy for even four strong potwomen and the nearest flenserwoman came plodding over with her long broomstick knife. She swung it way behind her head and swiped into the rubbery foetus, swipe swipe swipe, through the middle of its spine and guts, until it was in two, with its watery guts sloshing out. Then the potwomen heaved him over the side in two big pieces, back into the sea.

And other flensing women had hacked off the female whale's jaws, and the flippers, and her fin and flukes, and these parts of her were all swinging from the derricks so the lemmers, as they are called, could swipe the flesh off them. And other flenserwomen were hacking down to the mighty backbone and ribs and skull of the animal, chopping out blocks and strips and chunks of meat, and the potwomen were dragging it over to the rows of belching pots. After twenty minutes the great whale was all butchered up and gone down into the fuming vats, and there was nothing of her left but her bloody skeleton. Now another cable was lashed around the skeleton, from the big forward winch, and the whole bloody skeleton was dragged forward under the arch of the main midships winch platform, through to the forward cutting deck, or bone deck.

And the deckwomen hooked the cables around the immense ribcage, and the winches hissed and rattled and the cables took the strain, and the fourteen-foot ribs buckled and bent and then tore off the backbone with a mighty wrenching crack, and the next and the next and the next, and other women were going into the mighty vertebrae with their big electric bone saws, sawing up the backbone into bloody chunks, and winches tore it apart and wrenched the skull off the backbone. And then the hunks of bloody fleshy skeleton were hoisted aloft on the derricks so the lemmers could better hack the last of the flesh off them, then the chunks of skeleton were dropped to the deck, and the deckwomen dragged them over to the big bone saws. Bone saws like cannons mounted on electric motors, and the saws went screaming through the chunks of skeleton and the deckwomen were dragging the chunks over to the bone-meal pots.

And the next whale was being dragged up the slipway. And all the time the rattle hissing of the winches and the swiping of the flensing knives and the screaming of the bone saws and the spurting of the blood, the stink of rich red blood, and the oil fumes belching from the pot holes, as mighty whales were turned into oil for lipsticks and shoe polish.

thirty-nine

The next hour was a long time. There was nothing to do except wait and sweat it out; sitting hunched in the two dim spheres. Unable to smoke, unable to get up and move around. And all the time the tense feeling in their guts. Nobody speaking. The periscope poking up above the icy black sea in the darkness, the submarine whirring along underneath at five knots, silent phantom. Just the whir of the electric motors in their ears. Cramped, careful movements of their bodies, shifting positions. Slowly overtaking the big carnivorous black butcher ship up there, waiting for the beeps to come suddenly from the little radio transmitters buried in the whales' chests; waiting for the periscope to show the towing boats coming ploughing across the top of the black sea, dragging the great dead animals with enough high explosive in them to blow the stern of the butcher ship clean out of the water.

Justin stood at the periscope most of the time, watching the *Slava*, turning the eyepieces through three hundred and sixty degrees, searching for lights, the lights of the towing boats. His lips were salty, he craved a cigarette. His palms were sweaty, and he wiped them on his tracksuit. Tensed up, checking his watch, the compass, calculating it out in his head over and over again. Oh God, to get it over with now.

They were only about one mile off the *Slava*, abaft her port beam. She was cruising very slowly, maybe only one knot. He could see her very well. The high black hull, the floodlit decks. He was appalled at the size of her, so big a ship to overwhelm. From down here he could see only the heads of the deckwomen and the tops of the carcasses. He stood at the periscope, minute after minute, studying her, although he knew the photographs and plans of her backwards. There, up forward, was the bridge. Aft of the bridge, the bone deck. Then the high midships winch platform, holding the big main slipway winches, with the archway underneath the tunnel. Then the rest of the cutting deck aft of that superstructure. Then the aft crew accommodations, and the funnels, and the slipway. And floating in the sea behind the slipway, dead whales.

Every ten minutes he worked it out again, how long before the towing boats would show. Katherine had advised that the towing boats had radioed the factory that they had picked up the whales. They had reported one whale missing. Now, when the submarine was one mile off the *Slava*, he figured the towing boats must be ten miles off, about one hour away. But it could be longer. The *Tretchka*, the fleet's tanker, was about twenty miles off the *Slava*, to the northwest. He could not see her through the periscope. Most of the catchers were taking their turns going alongside her to refuel. But the two towing boats were not having anything to say for themselves. The *Slava* was steaming very slowly now. He said to Hi-fi Bob, 'Give me the *Jubilee*.'

'Three to One. Stand by.'

Justin did not really have anything to say to Katherine except that he loved her. And, for God's sake, what are those Russian bastards saying? He bent over the transmitter and said to Katie, 'How're you doing? Over.'

She came in softly, strained. 'I'm fine. How are you is a better question? The catchers are still bunkering. They're talking back and forth a little, but it's all about bunkering and supplies. The *Slava*'s sending its daily reports home to Moscow. No word from the tow boats. Over.'

'Three to Two. How're you, champ? Over.'

'Fine,' Ross said. 'Over.'

'All's well here. Over and out.'

He wished to God they could smoke. He looked around the control cabin. The only people who were comfortable were the commander and Hi-fi Bob, on their stools.

'How're the batteries, Henry?' Justin said.

'Nearly fully charged still. At this speed we've still got another seventeen hours of power before we need to recharge.'

Seventeen hours. He figured it out again in his head. Say two hours before we get the limpet mines on. As soon as we're aboard the *Slava* the sub turns around; she'd still have fifteen hours of power at ten knots, a hundred and fifty miles. At ten knots she would get back to the *Jubilee* in three hours. If she had to dodge around to avoid any catchers chasing the *Jubilee*, she had plenty of time and power to find a hiding place among the icebergs to surface and recharge. He decided it was time to change back into his wet suit.

One hour later, almost exactly one a.m., Katherine's voice came crackling over the radio. 'One to Three. Tow boat number Sixteen is calling the *Slava* that she's coming to hand over her whales! Repeat, tow boat Sixteen approaching in thirty minutes to hand over her whales. Do you read me? Over.'

He grabbed the microphone and had to control himself from shouting. 'I read you! What about the other tow boat? Over.'

She said anxiously, 'He's got the thickest Ukrainian accent you've ever heard – I just couldn't get it all. Stand by.'

He stood over the radio, everybody staring at him, waiting. He asked, 'What do you see, Spider?'

Spider was craning through the periscope eyepieces. 'Nothing yet.'

He waited. *Come on, Katie!* he said to himself. He could see her sitting there desperately listening, maybe to silence, waiting for the tow boats to speak – they might not speak for ages! He wanted to shout, 'Come on, Katie! Don't keep us hanging here!' He could not say it to her because her radio was switched to transmit while she was listening on the Russian's wave band on the other radio. The seconds ticked by, then it was a minute. Then it was two minutes. He felt that if she kept them waiting any longer he would shout it anyway. Then her voice came back. 'Are you there? Sorry, they aren't saying anything. I'm listening. Do you read me? Over.'

'Yes I read you! Listen, you left the radio switched on transmit, we couldn't talk to you and you left us cliff-hanging. Don't do that again. Over.'

'Oh God, I'm sorry. I forgot. . . . Stand by!' she suddenly shouted.

The cabin was electric, desperately tense all over again. The seconds ticked by and they could hear a background noise and it seemed to last forever, then she came back. 'Yes! Yes the other towing boat! She's radioed the *Slava*, she'll be alongside in half an hour – repeat, in half an hour tow boat Twenty-one's going to be alongside the *Slava* with her whales. Do you read me? Over."

He shouted into the transmitter, 'Oh you beauty! Keep listening for the other bastard! Have you read us, Two? Over.'

'Yes I've got you, half an hour,' Ross replied. 'Over.'

The next half-hour was going to be a long time.

'Keep listening, One – and tell the bridge to stand by to destroy the evidence. Over and out!'

His mind began racing over the same calculations. Then he stopped himself and turned and looked at them.

'Half an hour,' he said.

Spider said from the periscope, 'I see her!'

Justin grabbed the periscope from him and looked, and then he saw the lights, and there she was.

Because the periscope was so low on the sea, he could only see the mastlights. Towing boat Twenty-one was coming steaming out from behind the icebergs. About five miles off, almost directly on their port beam, steaming towards the *Slava*.

'Oh, yes. . . .' Without taking his eyes from the periscope, he said, 'Tune into those whales' radios, Bob.'

'I already am,' Bob said. He turned his knobs through all the frequencies. 'Not yet. They're still too far away. I won't hear them over two miles away, they've only got tiny little batteries!'

He swung the periscope around and looked back at the *Slava*. She was one mile away on the starboard beam, large as life, floodlit and high out of the water. He swung the periscope and looked back at the tow boat. He could not yet see the other one. In half an hour at the most she would be at the *Slava*'s stern, handing over her whales. In ten or twenty minutes they should be picking up the beeps of those terrific little radios in the whales' chests, telling them which whales were which. He said to the commander, 'Take us up closer to the slipway, Henry, so we don't miss anything. Starboard, thirty degrees.'

'Starboard thirty,' the commander said. He turned the wheel. They could feel the cabin turning with it. 'Thirty to starboard she is.'

Justin checked his wrist compass. 'Too far. Give us ten to port.'

'Ten to port.'

The submarine turned underneath the sea. Now she was headed straight for the *Slava*'s stern.

'That's it. Steady now, and give us half ahead.'

He heard the electric motor's hum increase in pitch.

'Steady, half ahead,' the commander said.

Ten minutes later he saw the mast lights of the second tow boat. He could see the bridge lights of the first one quite clearly now. The *Slava* was about three quarters of a mile ahead of the submarine. Ten minutes later Hi-fi Bob Matthews called out, 'Whale beepers coming through.'

forty

She was five hundred yards off. He could see the heads of the deck labourers clearly now.

He watched the tow boats through the periscope, his heart thudding. The Twenty-one was at the *Slava*'s slipway, casting off her first whale now. From the radio beeps as the boat approached they had determined that two of the whales were ones that he and Spider and Steve had charged, A and B. The radio beeps for whale C still had not yet come through. But the third whale *must* be C.

The second towing boat, the Sixteen, was approaching the stern now, three hundred yards off, churning slowly, in front of the periscope, just two hundred yards away. She was towing three whales, the tails lashed to her gunnels. One of them had signalled itself as Justin's whale D. Another had to be the one charged by Craig and Black Bob, whale E. The third whale was unknown.

Hi-fi Bob announced, 'Whale D only! Whale E definitely isn't beeping.'

Justin said, 'E must be there.' He did not care about the missing beeps. Whales E and C must be present. As long as they exploded when the button was pressed. And even if they didn't explode, the other three would. Three was plenty. He stared through the periscope. The *Slava* was going dead slow.

He saw the sailor on the Twenty-one's bow crouch down and then cast off the first whale, he saw the cable splash into the sea. That was perhaps whale A. Then a sailor on the *Slava*'s poop threw out another heaving line, he saw the sailor on the Twenty-one catch it, then haul the second cable in. Call it whale B. He could just make out one giant fluke.

The other towing boat, Sixteen, was about fifty yards off the *Slava*'s stern now.

The third heaving line, for what could be whale C, was snaking through the air from the *Slava*'s poop, the sailor on the Twenty-one caught it.

Then Justin looked back at the Sixteen and at first he was surprised, then astonished. *What the hell. . . ?*

'What the hell's happening?' he said out loud.

'What?' the commander demanded.

He stared through the periscope at the Sixteen and his heart was suddenly thudding again. She was way past the stern of the *Slava* now, and she was steaming on, still towing her whales. He stared at her. *Where the hell was she going? Why wasn't she lying off behind the* Slava *waiting her turn to cast off her whales?* He stared at her. She was ploughing way past the slipway, then she turned slowly. And then she went up the starboard side of the *Slava*, dragging her whales.

Jesus Christ! He suddenly realized what she was doing! 'She's going to cast off her whales alongside the *Slava*!'

'*What?*'

'The Sixteen's going to tie her whales up along the *side* of the *Slava*. Not at the stern! That means the *Slava*'s going to bunker – the goddamn tanker's going to come alongside the *Slava* to give her fuel. They're using our whales as fenders!'

The commander was twisted around, appalled. 'Oh God!'

Justin met his stare, frantically thinking. 'Jesus – where's that tanker? She's coming alongside the *Slava*!' He grabbed the periscope and looked desperately again, but all he could see was

287

the great black *Slava* blocking out half the horizon. 'Jesus!'

He stared at the commander. 'If the tanker's coming along-side we're in trouble. And we can't detonate those whales along the *side* of the *Slava*'s hull. We could blow her side wide open and kill everybody! And if the tanker grinds against those whales, that could detonate them – couldn't it, Bob?'

Hi-fi Bob squinted at him, sweating. 'Yes – heavy pressure like that could click them off.'

'It could blow the goddamn tanker up! Burning oil all over the sea!'

Steve said quietly, 'Which whales are they? We can just do without them, just blow up the whales behind the slipway.'

'Craig's – plus one of ours, D. D and E.'

'*If* it's E,' the commander said. 'It might be C. The Twenty-one might have picked up E and the Sixteen picked up C. Which means we don't know *which* whale is along the *Slava*'s side – we don't know which *not* to detonate.'

Justin said, 'We've still got two whales behind the slipway that we definitely *do* know are safe to detonate – A and B. They'll be quite enough. We'll just have to use A and B only!' He said to Hi-fi Bob, 'Give me Katherine,' and to the commander, 'Half ahead around the *Slava*'s stern. Spider, take over the periscope.'

He grabbed the microphone from Hi-fi Bob and cried, 'Three to One. The tanker's coming to bunker with the *Slava* – what's your information? Over.'

She came back over, upset, 'I don't know! I must have missed it. They were talking back and forth about everybody's turn to bunker for a long time. . . . I must have missed it – I'm sorry but they talk so fast and in all these different accents. Over.'

He said, 'Keep listening. Over and out.'

He said to the commander, 'Full ahead!'

'Full ahead.'

He took the periscope back from Spider and looked through. They were four hundred yards off the *Slava*'s portside stern. The Twenty-one had cast off her last whale at the stern, and she was pulling away. 'Steer zero four five.'

'Zero four five,' the commander said.

Justin announced to everybody, 'We're going around the stern to the other side to see where that damned tanker is.'

It seemed to take a long time. As they went churning past the *Slava*, he could just see the *Tretchka*. Just the very top of her bridge lights and her mast lights on his horizon, ten or twelve miles away. He tried to make out what she was doing, coming or just lying there, but it was very hard to tell at the periscope's low level. All he knew was she was pointed towards them. And that she could do eighteen knots. And if she was coming she was going to be there in less than one hour.

forty-one

One hour at the most, maybe a hell of a lot less, before the tanker got there. They had to detonate the two safe whales and then get underneath the *Slava* and stick the limpet mines on her keel before that tanker came alongside. If the tanker came alongside, they had had it; she would stay alongside for hours. They couldn't board the *Slava* while the tanker was alongside. The submarine had only another fifteen hours of power in the batteries before they had to retreat somewhere and find cover behind some icebergs to surface and recharge the batteries on the generator. And when the tanker came alongside, the pressure of those two hulls on those detonators could click them off and blow terrible great holes in both ships with catastrophic loss of life. He looked feverishly through the periscope at towing boat Sixteen.

She was alongside the *Slava*, to starboard, casting off her second whale now. The first was trailing down the *Slava*'s side by a long cable. Now the second whale was being cast off. Now the Sixteen was churning up towards the *Slava*'s bow with the last whale. Justin could see the heads of the women deck labourers up there on the *Slava*, their flensing knives and pot hooks in the floodlights. The Sixteen was casting off the third whale now. He swung the periscope back to the tanker. He surely could not tell a difference from last time he looked, but, dear God, she seemed closer, she looked no more than eight miles off and coming big and fast. He said, 'Bob, are you sure about those whales at the stern – which they are?'

'I told you, I know two of them – A and B; I dunno about the third one because it wasn't beeping!'

Justin called to the commander, 'Dive. Fifty feet. Steer three one five.'

'Fifty feet,' the commander said. 'Three one five.'

He swung the wheel to port and pushed forward the lever. They felt her bows go down and the stern slope up and they were all straining against it. The submarine dived gently and silently down into the black sea.

'Full ahead,' Justin said.

'Full ahead,' the commander said. 'Fifteen feet ... twenty ... twenty-five feet ...' They were churning down. 'Thirty ... thirty-five ... forty feet.'

'Are you full ahead?'

'Full ahead.' He was pulling back the levers, the submarine was levelling out. She was heeling a little, so he pulled the starboard trimming lever and she trimmed up. 'Seven knots, seven and a half. . . .'

Justin took a deep breath. He said to everybody, 'We're diving under her stern. We'll probably pass smack under her propellers. We're going right over onto her other side, about a thousand yards off her port bow, out of percussion range. Then we'll detonate those two stern whales.' He crouched down to the connection passage. 'Can you hear me back there?'

'Yes,' Craig said thickly.

'We detonate those two whales. Then,' he said, 'we stick on the limpet mines. Then we board.'

'Limpet mines?' Hi-fi Bob glared over his shoulder at him. 'How have you got time to stick on limpet mines? That tanker's eight miles off – that's thirty minutes. What speed are we doing?'

'Eight, eight knots plus – that's almost flat-out with this payload,' the commander said.

Justin calculated out loud. 'Eight knots – it'll take us four or five minutes for a thousand yards. That cuts our time down to twenty-five minutes before that tanker's alongside—'

The commander cut in, 'It'll take her another good twenty minutes or so to actually manoeuvre alongside and tie up.'

Steve said, behind him, 'We should skip the limpet mines, just detonate the whales and then get aboard.'

'We've got to make the time!' Justin said. 'We've got to stick those limpet mines on because five of us are going to board this ship and we may have a second fucking great ship full of angry Russians to deal with! Those limpet mines are vital. Because if that tanker comes alongside and Russians come swarming aboard, we won't have a chance to put more explosives down in the bilges. If the Russians shoot us up, at least the limpet mines will eventually go off and sink her.'

The submarine suddenly shook and heeled. They lurched and clutched for support, the commander grabbed the trimming levers; then she steadied up. 'We're passing under the propellers.'

Justin's hands were shaky. He wanted a cigarette. He said again, 'Flat out, Henry. Everybody get ready.'

He looked at his watch. They had gone about five or six hundred yards under the black Antarctic night sea. They were all wide-eyed in the dim light. 'Craig?' he called.

'Yes?'

'When we board the *Slava* you've got another job. Cut loose those whales that the Sixteen's placed alongside the *Slava*'s hull. To stop that tanker coming alongside. Got it?'

'Yes.'

'But don't let it slow you up. We've got to keep to the schedule or the whole plan gets out of whack.'

'Don't worry,' Craig said.

But Justin worried. The plan wasn't complex, but it called for close coordination. He ran through it again in his mind. The whole idea was to get immediate control of the forward part of the ship, the bridge superstructure. From there the rest of the ship could easily be commanded; from there they could direct the evacuation of the Russians without actually going down among them.

He visualized the sketch of the *Slava* that he had drawn for use in instructing his boarding party. He had looked at it so often it was more real to him than the *Slava* herself.

The first goal was to get a lot of tear gas down into the crew spaces in the forward part of the ship. Craig was to throw two tear gas canisters down the crew hatch that stood like a sentry box on the foredeck; then he would lock that hatch by wrapping a chain around it. And Steve would hurl tear gas canisters down the two big funnels on the foredeck that sent air to the decks below.

The second goal was to storm the bridge itself. Justin and Spider would do that, one on each side.

Meanwhile Steve and Craig would have gone along the officers' deck on either side of the bridge superstructure, heading aft. They would go to the platform just behind the bridge, overlooking the cutting deck, and take cover behind the winches there, to stop anyone trying to get up to the bridge from that direction. Russians would be pouring out onto the cutting deck coughing from the tear gas thrown down the hatch and funnels, and Steve and Craig would keep them going with more tear gas, driving them aft towards the lifeboats.

Finally, Craig and Justin would go down into the officers' accommodation immediately below the bridge to clear that out and to seal the door so that nobody could get up to the bridge from inside. And when they had done that, they would have the whole bridge, the whole forward part of the ship. Then it would be in the bag. Then no one could stop them. But it would all have to be accomplished in about ten minutes.

'Bob,' Justin said to Hi-fi, 'when we go aboard, give me that radio-detonator to take with me.'

forty-two

The commander said, "Twenty-five feet . . . twenty . . . fifteen. . . ."

Justin looked at his watch. Twenty minutes past one a.m. In less than two hours the sun would start coming up. He stood crouched at the periscope, sweating.

'Ten feet . . .' the commander said. 'Nine . . . eight . . . seven . . . six . . . five. . . . Periscope depth! Hovering. . . .'

Justin slammed the periscope up and swung it around to starboard. And there was the *Slava*. About a thousand yards off their starboard stern, cruising slowly towards them. He swung the periscope to the north and looked for the tanker. There she was, steaming low in the water. She looked a bit farther away from this angle.

'Turn her around a hundred and fifty degrees, Henry! So we're facing her for the blast. Is the radio aerial up?'

'Yes,' Hi-fi Bob said.

After a long moment the commander said, 'She's turned one hundred and fifty. . . .'

'Give me Katherine.' Justin took the microphone, when Bob had connected. 'One? We're there. In position. We're about to explode those whales. Tell Cartwright to destroy all the evidence. The slides, operations table, the plans. The lot. Not a trace. Do you read me? Over.'

Her voice was husky, tense. 'Yes I read you. Over.'

'Two?' he said. 'Over.'

Ross's voice came in. 'Got you. You're about to detonate. Good luck.'

'One, any more information on this tanker? Over.'

Katie said, 'I've been trying and trying to call you. Were you submerged? Only information is she's going to bunker on the *Slava*'s starboard side – nothing else. Over.' He heard her voice shake.

'Okay.' He inhaled several times until he was steady. 'Detonating in a few seconds. Good luck, champion. We'll be calling for you in about an hour. One,' he said, 'good luck, darling. Over and out.'

He snapped off the microphone and handed it back to Hi-fi Bob. Thirty miles away over the frozen horizon Katherine closed her eyes and whispered, 'Good luck. . . . Oh God, good luck.'

Justin shouted into the connecting passage, 'Detonating in a few seconds. Brace yourselves. Face forward, knees bent. You hear me back there?'

'Yes,' Craig said. His face was pale. Max slid across the small hatch and sat beside Craig, facing forward, knees bent. He too was almost white, his eyes flickering. Steve and Spider sat on either side of the tunnel. Justin looked around the cabin.

'All right,' he said. 'Here we go. . . .' He turned back to the periscope and peered into the eyepieces, at the butcher ship. He said hoarsely, 'Ready?'

There was a ragged yes. 'Ready,' Hi-fi Bob said. He had his fingers on the detonating buttons, his glasses halfway down his nose, breathing through his mouth. Justin stared at the *Slava.*

'Blow them,' he breathed. And they blew.

An eruption of white sea out of the blackness, high and wide in all directions, higher than the funnels. And in the middle of it, massive whale bodies suddenly heaving up, blown to bits. And other whales heaving up out of the sea beside them. The sea bellied up around the stern of the *Slava,* the percussion impacting right under her. She lurched and her stern rose and hung there in the great eruption of sea and blood and guts. And the screams of whalewomen clutching and crashing and sprawling on the decks in the blood.

For a long moment it all seemed suspended, then the stern thundered back down, and the blood and guts and sea came raining down. He saw it, heart pounding, through the periscope. Then came the muffled thudding sound of it through the sea and he shouted, 'Hold tight,' and then the shock waves hit them.

The shock waves came throbbing through the sea and hit the submarine with a thud that threw them backwards and sideways, and the cabin jolted around them. Justin hit his forehead on the periscope. The commander shouted something and heaved on the trimming levers and the whole submarine was staggering, shuddering. Then the main shock wave passed and the submarine was just shuddering; then suddenly she was almost steady again and Justin shouted, 'Full ahead. Steer zero three zero!'

The motors whirred up and the submarine began to surge forward and he stood with his eyes against the periscope and his heart was pounding and he shouted to everybody, 'Going for the keel now! We'll be diving in a few minutes!' and he said to the commander, 'Periscope depth! All the way until we get almost right up against her. Spider?'

'Yes!' Spider almost shouted.

'Switch on your thermalsuit.'

'It's on.'

'Max?'

'Yes?'

'Get ready to come here into the control cabin. Spider and I are coming down there in a minute.'

forty-three

The high black hull loomed closer and closer through the periscope, five hundred yards . . . four hundred . . . three hundred, looming bigger and bigger, black and floodlit. The *Slava* had stopped engines. He could see the crowd of whalemen and women gathering, clamouring around the stern. Whalemen hurrying down the long cutting decks towards the stern, people coming out of the aft accommodations onto the lifeboat decks, crowding around the stern rails. She was two hundred yards off now. He swung the periscope and looked for the tanker; she was moving towards them six or seven miles off and he whispered to the submarine, 'Faster, you bitch!' It seemed to take a long time to get one hundred yards off . . . seventy-five . . . fifty. The

hull of the *Slava* rose massive and more massive. Forty yards
. . . thirty . . . twenty-five. . . .

'Dive,' he said. 'Fifty feet!'

'Fifty feet – flooding!' The bows suddenly sloped down and
for an instant the black yellow sparkling waterline danced across
the periscope, then it was gone. 'Ten feet . . .' the commander
was counting, 'fifteen . . . twenty. . . .'

Justin's mouth was painfully dry. He looked up through the
topside observation port at the dull reflected lighting of the
surface; it was growing dimmer and dimmer. 'Thirty feet . . .
thirty-five. . . .' Suddenly the dull surface light went out
altogether as if snuffed, and they were under the *Slava*'s hull
and all was blackness above.

'Hover!'

'Hover,' the commander said. He flicked the levers and the
motors rotated in their pods in opposite directions, and the
movement slowed, then ebbed to a stop under the hull of the
ship, held hovering stationary by the propellers whirring in
counter directions.

'Hold her there!' He turned and crawled through the connecting passage to the aft chamber. Spider Webb was already
tanked up, his face mask on top of his head. Craig was crouched,
holding Justin's tank and harness ready. Justin dropped onto his
knees and hefted it on. Then he sat down and pulled on his
flippers. The four limpet mines lay ready on the deck. 'Are the
timers set?'

'Yes,' Spider said. 'Sixty minutes.'

'Open the hatch.'

Craig wrenched back the levers of the lock-in–lock-out hatch,
and the circular steel plate dropped away, swinging back on its
hinges. And there was the black Antarctic sea, staring at them
through the circular opening. The sea did not enter the submarine because of the air pressure in the sub. Down there was
nothing but icy blackness. Up above, the great steel hull. Justin
pulled his hood up over his head, wrenched on his mask, sucked
once for airtightness. He snapped open his demand regulator
and the compressed air flooded into his mouth. He looked at
Spider, gave him the thumbs up, and nodded.

Spider slid on his buttocks to the edge of the circular hatch and his legs went into the water up to his knees. He slid off the edge of the hatch feet first into the blackness, just his head showing. Then he reached out and slid a limpet mine over the hatchrim and into the water with him and hugged it to his chest. His other limpet mine was in a satchel around his neck. He looked at Justin wild-eyed once, then his head disappeared underwater, and he was gone in a flood of bubbles.

Justin entered the water in one movement. He reached out and slid the limpet mine over the lip of the hatch and clasped it to his chest. Then he ducked his head and let himself go.

The freezing water hit his face, but he did not feel it. There was pitch blackness everywhere except the dull glow from the submarine's forward portholes. Then the short beam of light appeared, shining down into the blackness from the flashlight that Craig was holding down onto the sea through the hatch. Spider was on the other side of the submarine's bulk, and Justin could not even see his flashlight. He kicked away from the side of the submarine, then kicked to drive straight up. He flicked on his flashlight. The beam went ten feet into blackness, then petered out into nothing. He could see particles floating in the grey flashlight beam, shreds of whale flesh. He went up with his arm outstretched, looking, his other hand clutching the limpet mine. He rose for fifteen feet, then suddenly there was the *Slava*'s hull looming down at him. He let his flashlight touch it, then he twisted and swam to its lowest point and found the keel. Next he began to swim down the keel towards the propellers.

He swam as fast as he could, his breathing roaring in his ears. The vast blackness of the keel pressed down on the blackness of the water. Riveted steel plates were above him, the bulge of the hull stretching on into infinity, blocking off all surface light from the factory stern. Then suddenly, invisibly, the keel curved upward and away, and then a moment later, a good way ahead, there was a scattered diffused glow of lights and big black shapes, which were whales. Some of the light was slowly moving, powerful searchlights being beamed down into the water. He could suddenly see the big bent shapes of the rudders and the two big propellers, blurred. He held his flashlight up against the keel. Then he saw the long shapes of the stern tubes and drive shafts emerging out of the black steel, and he was under the engine room.

He swam to one stern tube, stopped, treading water hard, and shone his flashlight up at the hull. He stroked it with his fingertips. It was fairly clean. He lifted the limpet mine up to the steel, then against it, and felt the magnets clamp it on. He gave it a tug, it was firm. Then he wrestled the other limpet mine out of the satchel and hugged it to his chest, then he turned and swung his flashlight back across the keel, and started swimming again.

He swam across the keel, flashlight up, then he was at the other stern tube. He clamped on the second mine and tugged it. It held firm. He looked back once at the lights around the stern, the big blurred shapes of the whales. Then he turned and swam forward.

He held his flashlight up to the hull, following a line of rivets. He looked back again, and the lights at the stern were gone. Only blackness again. On he swam. He could see no light ahead. Then he saw the glow of Craig's flashlight beaming down into the blackness, then the glow of the submarine's porthole lights. Then the blurred bulk of the submarine materializing almost ahead of him, and it seemed he was never so relieved to see anything in his life. He dived down six feet under the hull, kicking his legs hard; then he looked up and there was the broken dancing circle of light in the hatch just above him. He kicked hard and eased up to it. He burst through it with a splash and spat out his mouthpiece.

'Spider?' he gasped. And there crouched Spider stripping off his suit, smiling at him.

They heaved and wrestled him in.

'Seal the hatch!'

'Good work, Spider!' He ripped off his hood and mask and wrenched off his wet suit.

'Good show both of you!' the commander called.

Justin got into his tracksuit and then snaked through the tunnel to the control cabin. They were all grinning at him.

'Go!' he said. 'Get all your gear together! Craig!' he shouted 'Pass the bags through!'

forty-four

The submarine whirred away and soon he could see surface light through the top observation port. They were clear of the hull of the *Slava*. 'Twenty feet . . .' the commander was saying, 'eighteen . . . sixteen . . . fourteen . . . twelve. . . .' Justin stood at the periscope, ready, his head back, looking up at the observation port, his lips and jaws tingling. 'Eight . . . seven . . . six . . . five – periscope depth!' The periscope broke through the water back up into the night. He swung it around, and thirty yards back there were the black bows of the *Slava* towering up, and above them the bridge and its lights.

'Hard to starboard,' he ordered. 'Slow ahead.'

The submarine churned around under the sea, back towards the *Slava*'s bow. 'Steady!' Justin panted. 'Steady as she goes! We're twenty-five yards off – ease her up now!' He rotated the periscope and looked aft; there was a big crowd of whalemen gathered on the *Slava*'s stern now, looking down at the whales in tow; he could hardly see the bridge from down here. 'Fifteen yards off now,' he rasped. 'Dead slow now. We're no more than twelve yards off now. We're coming in nicely. . . .' He swung the periscope again and looked aft. There was nobody hanging over the rails looking forward at the bow. 'Five yards more,' he called. 'We're almost up against them! Four . . . three . . . two. . . .' Now the periscope showed only the hull towering up above it.

'Surface!' he shouted.

'Surface!' the commander said, and the compressed air flooded into the main tanks and the submarine rose under the *Slava*'s bows. 'Plug in your earphone receivers,' Justin shouted. 'Gas masks ready. Hatch!'

Spider snapped back the watertight levers and flung back the hatch. He climbed up the ladder and flung open the top hatch and stepped up and out. Justin thrust the roll of nylon net up through the hatch to him, and Spider grabbed it. Then Justin went up the ladder after him. He looked up, and all he could see was the sweep of the *Slava*'s steel bow plates reaching up up up. He looked towards the stern; he could not see around the curve of the beam. There was nobody looking over the rail. From the stern, where all the whalemen were crowded, he could hear the rumble of excited voices. His heart was beating in his ears.

Spider tossed him one corner of the wide nylon ladder, and Justin found the line attached to it. 'Throw,' Spider whispered, and they threw the rubber-coated hooks up into the night, and Justin prayed *Please God, make them catch*. He saw both hooks sailing up into the night, trailing the net, then arcing over at the top of the throw. They fell beyond the rail with a dull clang.

They wrenched them tight and the net hung.

Steve came up out of the hatch, his gas mask around his neck, his weapons over both shoulders. Craig was up after him. 'Go!' Justin whispered. They both grabbed the net and climbed up onto it. It swung against the hull under their weight. They started clawing their way up. Spider was half a length behind them. Then Justin.

Max came up out of the hatch, his eyes wide. He looked wildly up at the bow, then reached back down the hatch and Hi-fi Bob heaved the first sack of spare ammunition up to him. He swung it up. Then the next sack was heaved up to him. Then the big radio, which he slung on his back, with two megaphones.

The whole net ladder was swinging crazily under the clambering. Craig was almost at the top. He stuck his head over the gunnel; then Steve put his head over, too. The foredeck was clear. They looked up at the bridge and there was not a face showing. Craig beckoned down to the others. Then he swung up over the rail, and Steve scrambled after him, followed by Justin and Spider.

Justin ran across the deck, close against the bridge housing, to the starboard side. He looked back and saw Steve running for the big forward air funnels with his tear gas canisters in his hand. Craig was already chaining the crew's hatch. Max was bent over the rail, hauling up the rope with the two sacks of ammunition from the deck of the submarine. Justin pulled on his gas mask. Spider was at the portside bridge companionway. He waved and then he and Justin both went bounding up the two companion-ways to the bridge.

They ran up the companionway, onto the officers' deck, then up the next companionway, tear gas canisters in their hands. Justin burst up onto the open bridgewing and he saw Spider dash onto the opposite wing at the same moment. In the middle was the wheelhouse. He saw a look of amazement on the face of the helmsman, then terror. A young officer spun around astonished, agape. Behind him the captain was coming out of the radio room. In one movement Justin pulled the pin of the tear gas bomb and flung it skidding across the bridge into the wheelhouse. Suddenly there was tear gas hissing and billowing everywhere and the Russians were reeling back, gasping and choking. Justin leaped into the wheelhouse through the fumes and hit the young officer.

Hit him hard with a karate chop on the side of the neck, and the man sprawled. Spider was onto the helmsman. Justin charged after the captain into the radio room and grabbed him by the lapels and hit him on the side of his neck. He crashed, choking. Justin seized him by the collar and dragged him out of the radio room into the wheelhouse to the wheel. He wrenched his wrists through the big steel spokes and snapped the handcuffs on. He saw the radio officer come staggering out and Spider appear from nowhere and slug him. There was grey tear gas everywhere, the sound of coughing.

'The helmsman!' Justin shouted into his gas mask radio. The helmsman was crawling towards the door to the bridgewing. Justin went after him. He grabbed him by the collar and yanked. He dragged him back to the wheel, rammed his wrists through the spokes, and handcuffed him. Spider had handcuffed the young officer to the wheel and he was dragging the coughing radio officer over. That was all of them. There was a big overhead fan in the wheelhouse. He snapped it on. He heard a crash of glass: Spider was in the radio room, swiping with a fire axe at opposite windows to let out the gas. He slung down the axe and ran out to Justin on the bridge.

Justin looked down onto the foredeck. Craig had cut loose

two of the three whales alongside the *Slava*'s hull. He had been unable to cut loose the third one because it was tied to a midships bollard; they would get it later. He and Steve were guarding the officers' deck outside the wardroom. Justin was triumphant – they had the bridge!

Max came running up the companionway, the big radio on his back, lugging the sacks and a megaphone. Justin ran down the companionway to the officers' deck, Spider following him. Craig was guarding the door to the wardroom. He kicked it open. Empty. He pushed through the furniture, Craig behind him. He entered the officers' alleyway and flung a tear gas cylinder ahead of him.

He kicked open the first cabin door. It was empty. He kicked open the second door; it was the captain's quarters, also empty. Then the next door burst open and a man looked out furiously, then fell back, gasping in the tear gas. Justin leaped at him, grabbed him, and pulled him out into the alleyway back into the wardroom. There were stairs leading up to the radio room. He shoved him up the stairs, threw open the door. Max took the man and handcuffed him.

In the officers' alleyway Craig opened the next door, which was ajar, and found a young man; gas poured in and he began coughing. Craig dragged him into the alleyway. Justin was pulling a man out of the next cabin, and they all bumped into each other. Craig and Justin shoved the men up the stairs on top of each other, up to Max. Gas was billowing everywhere. Justin ran back down the alleyway, flinging open the doors. The rest of the cabins were all empty. He turned. Craig was looking at him, grinning inside his gas mask. They had the whole bridge superstructure now.

At the end of the alleyway a staircase led below. Justin ran down it. He pulled a tear gas canister out of his pouch, then swung open the door.

There was another alleyway, leading in both directions. Opposite him were administration offices with typewriters and desks. Tear gas was fuming down this alleyway, the gas Steve had flung down the air funnels on the foredeck. He dropped another canister in the alleyway for good measure, then slammed the door, locked it, and went back up the stairs into the ward-room. He grabbed a dining chair, then clattered back down the stairs, and wedged the chair under the door handle. He ran back up to the wardroom and locked the door leading onto the outside deck. All the portholes were shut. Now the whole place was sealed. He dropped another canister. Anybody who tried to break up to the bridge would have to fight their way through thick tear gas everywhere. Impossible without gas masks and axes.

He turned and raced up the stairs, back into the radio room, with Craig after him. The room was clear of gas now. Out in the wheelhouse the Russian officers and the helmsman were crouched handcuffed to the wheel, faces red with coughing and tears. Justin tore off his mask.

'Where's the public-address system?' he asked Max.

'There.'

He could hear the noise of panicked people fleeing the tear gas that was billowing through the forward crew accommodation below. He snatched the public-address microphone and pulled out his notebook. He scrabbled it open, hands shaking. Then he spoke into it slowly, in Russian:

'Attention everybody. Attention everybody. I am speaking from the bridge. This ship has been captured. We have your captain and six of your crew as hostages. We are about to blow up this ship and sink it. I repeat, we are about to blow up this ship and sink it. In order to avoid injury and death we order you to proceed immediately to your lifeboat stations and abandon ship in an orderly fashion. Once you are in your lifeboats you will be safe because you will be picked up by your tanker and other catchers, which are nearby. I repeat you will be safe and unharmed if you proceed immediately to your lifeboats and abandon ship in an orderly manner. But any resistance will be met by force. Coxswains of lifeboats are ordered to make sure everybody is present.'

Justin yelled at Max, 'Tell them to open fire.'

Max ran out onto the bridgewing. He shouted down to Steve and Craig, 'Open fire!'

Suddenly there was the terrible racket of Steve's and Spider's machine guns cracking the night wide open, for two seconds, then the screams of whalewomen in the shocked silence, then the next burst of gunfire for another two seconds to impress them, then the screams again.

Justin shouted to Max, 'Get hold of Katherine!'

He dashed out onto the bridge. There was the tanker, just two miles off, steaming towards them. He turned back into the wheelhouse. Max was crouched over the radio saying, 'Jonah to One. Stand by!'

Justin took the microphone from him. 'We're aboard and we've captured the bridge!' he said. 'The tanker's still coming, about two miles away. Order her to stand off! Repeat, order her to reverse engines immediately and turn about and stand off or we'll open fire on her. Tell her we've captured the ship and we're about to blow it up – there is no chance of saving the *Slava*. If the tanker comes near she'll be blown sky-high too. Tell her to stand ten miles off and stand by to rescue the lifeboats. Do you read me? Over.'

She came back breathlessly, 'Yes, I read you. But for God's sake hear this – all the fleet knows about the explosion. The *Slava* radioed all the fleet – it even radioed Moscow – and the tanker is coming to help and so are some catchers. If I radio the tanker that you've captured the ship, all of them will come. Do you read me? Over.'

He shouted back at her, 'Yes I read you. Tell the tanker what I said, to stand off or we'll open fire on her – we'll blow her and all her oil to Kingdom Come. Do as I say. Over and out.'

He dashed back out onto the bridgewing and glanced at the tanker. She was still coming. He looked around the black horizon and he could see the distant lights of four catchers, then another far astern. Down there on the cutting decks, men and women were stumbling through the blood and blubber, coughing and retching, tears streaming, clutching oilskins and life belts and blankets. Down aft on the lifeboat decks there were hundreds of them crowding and shouting. He hurried back into the wheelhouse and repeated the abandon ship order. Then he went back to the bridgewing.

The tanker was about one mile off now. He raised Max's

automatic gun to his shoulder like a rifle and he opened up in front of her bows. Opened up in a sudden burst of machine gun fire, da-da-da-da-da and the din of it filled the night and he bellowed, 'Stand off!' He swept the rifle down the hull of the ship at the waterline – da-da-da-da, water spurting and the bullets clanging against the steel. 'Stand off – stand off you murdering bastards.'

Then he saw their signal light flashing and then Max was shouting at him from the wheelhouse. 'Okay! Katie says okay, they're stopping. Stop firing at them. Stop!'

He stopped, joyful. Yes, she was reversing engines, and he wanted to bellow and whoop in triumph. Then Max was shouting at him again. 'She's radioing all the catchers to come, Katie says. The *Tretchka*'s alerting all the catchers to come to the *Slava*!'

Justin bellowed at him, 'Hold the bridge! Use the riot gun.'

He wrenched his gas mask on, then went down the bridge companionway. He ran down towards the winch platform at the back of the officers' deck, above the cutting deck. He crouched down next to Steve behind a starboard winch. Spider was behind the winch on the portside. Justin looked down on the pandemonium.

It was beautiful, absolutely beautiful! The tear gas that Steve had thrown down the forward air funnels was billowing out onto the deck and whalemen and women were pouring out onto the cutting deck, faces white in the glaring floodlights, men and women in oilskins and bath robes and pyjamas moving through the hulks of bleeding meat, coughing their way aft to the lifeboat decks, fleeing the gas. Max's voice was rasping over the loudspeakers, stumbling through the abandon ship order. On the lifeboat decks there was a great jam of men and women. Most of the lifeboats had been lowered from their davits down to the deck level already, and men and women were climbing into them. And down there on the cutting decks their carnage lay abandoned – and, Jesus Christ, Justin had never been so glad about anything in all his life. He shouted into his gas mask radio to Steve and Spider, 'Fire a burst in the air to hurry them up!' And there was gunfire in the night again.

He shouted to Steve and Spider, 'Keep them moving! Use more gas to hurry them up. Fire over their heads if you think it necessary. Just for Christ's sake don't hit anybody!' Then he said into his radio, 'Craig, meet me up on the bridge, we're going through the ship.'

forty-five

He ran up the companionway onto the bridge and into the wheelhouse. The hostages looked at him in fright. With the bridge windows all open and the overhead fan whirring to keep the tear gas out, they were cold. Justin pulled off his gas mask and clapped Max on the back. 'All right, Max?'

He grabbed the Russian captain's wrist. Craig came running up onto the bridge, pulling off his gas mask. Justin barked, 'Hit him hard if he tries any funny business!'

He unlocked the captain's handcuffs, freed him from the wheel, then snapped the handcuffs on both wrists again in front. He said to Max, 'Put on your gas mask and go down to the officers' accommodation and grab some blankets for these guys.'

The captain stood there glaring at him; he was a big man with a large moustache and furious red eyes. Justin pulled out his notebook. He recited in Russian, 'Sir. We are taking you with us now as our hostage. We are going to go together through every part of the ship to make sure that everybody has evacuated. It is in your interests and in the interests of your whole crew to co-operate with us to prevent injury. This ship will be blown up shortly and we have no time to waste. Do you understand?' The captain of the *Slava* just glared murderously at him. Justin pulled out his .38 and jabbed him fiercely in the ribs. 'Do you understand?'

He flinched and nodded, hate in his eyes. Justin said, 'Give him a mask.'

Craig pulled a spare gas mask out of Max's sack. He wrenched it over the captain's head so it hung down under his chin.

Justin slapped him on the shoulder. 'Let's go, captain!'

Taking his elbow, Justin pushed him out onto the bridge-wing. Craig now had his gun jabbed in his back. They clattered down the companionway. They ran him, stumbling, hands manacled in front of him, to the forward crew hatch. The captain was panting and snorting. Craig unlocked the chain around the steel door, flung it open. Gas flooded out. Justin shoved his gas mask up and wrenched the captain's mask up over his face. 'Sorry, sir!' He beamed at him through his gas mask. 'Let's go!'

He went down the steel steps first, gun out, dragging the captain's wrists with one hand. Craig was bringing up the rear with his gun. They went into the alleyway. There was tear gas fuming everywhere, flowing out of the ventilation like smoke. There were crew cabins all the way in both directions. Most of the doors were open. He ran up the alleyway, flung open a closed door. The cabin was empty, everything in disarray, blankets strewn on the floor where women had scrambled out of their bunks. They were all women's cabins – hairnets, brushes, combs, clothes, photographs in frames. He continued down the alleyway, dragging the captain, throwing open doors, looking into each cabin.

Craig was down the other end of the alleyway, searching. All the cabins were empty. They ran on, throwing open doors. Halfway down was another junction of alleyways. They hurried down each alleyway, flinging doors open, looking in. They were all empty.

They came to the messrooms and galley and the recreation room. Benches overturned, pots, crockery, food spilled every-where. Tear gas hung in the air like steam. There were big posters with Communist slogans on the bulkheads.

At the end of the alleyway the door opened onto the cutting deck. He could see the slough of blood and fat and flesh in the floodlights out there and hear the clamour. Max was still bel-lowing over the public-address system. Justin slammed the door and bolted it on the inside. Near the door was another flight of steps that led down to more crew accommodation below and the factory itself. He jerked the captain towards it and they clattered down. The accommodation was entirely women's. They ran through, searching. All was abandoned.

At the top of the alley they threw down two more gas bombs. At the bottom of the alley was a big steel door. Justin stopped, panting into his gas mask. This was it. This door led down into the factory itself. He looked at Craig. Craig took a breath and shook his head. Now they were starting on the dangerous part.

From here onward Steve's original tear gas would not have penetrated, because the factory was served by different ventilation funnels. And in the factory there were plenty of places for men to hide and lie in ambush. He motioned Craig to stand back. Then he flung open the big steel door and the roar of the gigantic machinery hit them. Then both flung in a tear gas canister, then another.

The canisters went hurtling through the hot roaring factory, spewing out their gas above the big vats. Justin held the captain flat back against the alleyway bulkhead. He saw the tear gas fizzing up grey everywhere, all over the factory; then he saw a dozen men suddenly staggering out of hiding. They ran reeling through the avenue of the vats, heading aft. He pointed his .38 pistol above the vats and fired six shots, the cracking reports echoing through the vast steel hall, and the coughing Russians trampled over each other to get up the steel ladder at the aft end and into the aft accommodation.

Justin pushed the captain, making him climb down the forward ladder into the factory. Then he followed him. At the bottom of the ladder he grabbed the captain by his collar and wrenched him around in front of him. Then they started down the avenue between the vats. Then there was a crack of gunfire.

Gunfire suddenly ricocheted through the vast steel hall, and the captain jerked and fell on his face, and Justin fell on top of him, and Craig tripped on top of both of them. All of them sprawled in a heap in the middle of the avenue, and the gunfire was cracking everywhere. 'Take cover!' Justin roared into his gas mask. He scrambled up and seized the captain and thrust him across the steel deck to shelter behind a vat. Craig was scrambling after him. Justin waited there, listening through the hammering of his heart for the gunfire. He wrenched the captain up to his feet.

'*Are you all right?*' He was all right.

Justin looked at Craig. He was crouching, unhurt. The gunfire had stopped. Justin peered over the top of a pipe. He could see nobody. The gunfire had been inaccurate. Anybody could have hit them in that open avenue. The gunman was blinded by the tear gas and had just fired wildly to terrify them. Justin replaced the clip in his pistol and fired three shots at the steel door at the top of the aft ladder. They clanged and ricocheted.

Then he pulled the captain down the back of the vat, to the bulkhead. There was a narrow space between the vats and the bulkhead, all the way down. They could not be seen from the door. They went hurrying down this narrow path, dragging the captain. There was no more gunfire. Just the roaring of the still operating machinery. They came to the aft end of the factory hall and stopped behind the last vat. Justin looked around the corner. There was no one.

Next to the aft ladder was the steel door leading down to the engine room. It was closed. No tear gas would have penetrated down there. And that was where men would be working trying to repair the steering gear. Justin jerked his head at Craig and pulled the captain's wrist, and they ran for the engine-room door. He flung his arm out to hold Craig and the captain back flat against the bulkhead. He pulled out another gas bomb. Then he grabbed the door handle and opened it to throw his tear gas bomb inside. He stopped in midthrow. The great watertight door behind the ordinary steel door was closed!

Closed. The engineers down there had closed it and there was no way to open it without the big crank handles, and the limpet mines were going to explode right under their feet.

He stared horrified at the door, then looked around wildly for the handles. They were not there. They were inside the goddamn engine room! Jesus Christ, these idiots had sealed themselves in, and they were going to get themselves blown to bits. He looked desperately at Craig. The only way to warn them was to get back up to the bridge where there would be a telephone to the engine room and get the captain to speak to them on the telephone. And the only way to do that was to get Katherine on the radio to order him to do so. And this goddamn captain wasn't going to help them to do any such thing – this captain would blow the whole of Russia to Kingdom Come before he cooperated.

He grabbed the captain by his lapels and fiercely shook him and pointed at the door and rotated his hand to ask him to indicate the handles. The captain just glared at him. He grabbed the captain's gas mask and took it off so he began to cough and choke and struggle. Justin roared in English through his gas mask, 'Where are they?' He shook the man again, then bellowed at Craig over his gas mask radio, 'I've got to get up onto the aft cutting deck and throw tear gas down the engine-room air vents! Hold him.'

He turned and raced up the aft ladder. He stopped at the top, checked the pin on the gas bomb, his gun in the other hand, shaking. If that bastard with the gun was waiting, he did not know what he was going to do, except that sure as hell he wasn't going to let one man kill a whole lot of men. Then he wrenched on the door handle to fling it open and hurl the gas bomb in ahead of him and the door shook in his hand.

The door was also locked, from the other side. He stood staring at it, teeth clenched, fury flooded into his face. *Those bastards have locked their own comrades down in the factory deck!*

He had thirty-odd minutes before those limpet mines went off and blew the engine room. He shouted down at Craig over the gas mask radio, 'The fucking door's locked! We've got to run the gauntlet and get up to the air vents on the aft cutting decks!'

He plunged back down the steel ladder, past Craig and the captain, and started running back up the avenue to the forward ladder. He looked back and saw Craig running after him with the captain. He climbed up the ladder, burst through the door, and ran up the alleyway, up a flight of steps, and came out next to the messroom. He opened the door to the cutting deck and looked over the mass of bones and whale flesh.

He could see the whalemen milling on the lifeboat decks. Four of the lifeboats had already been lowered to the sea, and men and women were crowding into the others. He crouched at the door a moment trying to get his breath back, then he went through the door and ran out into the floodlights. He ran down the bloody deck towards the midships winch platform and he got ten paces and his feet skidded out in front of him in the fat and he crashed.

Crashed on his back in the deep blood and fat, and his head smashed the deck, and all he saw was red-black stars. He lay there flat on his back a long shocked instant, gasping, furious. Then he struggled onto his knees, covered in blood, his arms up around his head, expecting that Russian with the gun to shoot the living shit out of him.

All he could see was blinding floodlights, and all he could hear was Max yelling abandon ship over the loudspeakers. He shouted up to Steve and Spider, 'Shoot those aft floodlights out!' And then suddenly there was Craig, lurching out of the doorway onto the cutting deck with the captain, and there was a burst of gunfire, and Craig lurched and fell with the captain. The two of them crashed headlong onto their gas masks at full run and skidded across the deck.

'Kid!' Justin cried. He staggered up and ran at him. All he knew was the horror of seeing his brother shot down before his eyes. He dropped to his knees beside him. 'Craig!'

Craig began struggling up, his mask smeared with blood. And then Justin saw that the aft floodlights had been shot out. The gunfire he had heard had been Spider's.

He pulled Craig up and ran him and the captain, slipping through the blood and fat, towards the shelter of the midships winch superstructure, and they dived behind it.

'Running spikes!' Justin said. Craig held the captain while Justin wrestled on his own spikes, fixing them over his shoes. He got them on then he grabbed the captain up by his collar and yelled at Craig, 'Throw smoke bombs ahead of us up onto those lifeboat decks!'

Then he shouted into his gas mask radio at Steve and Spider, 'We're going to throw tear gas down the aft ventilation funnels to clear the engine room. They've locked themselves into the engine room. Fire smoke bombs ahead of us now, fire smoke screens ahead of us. Do you read me?'

He looked for the tanker and he could not see it. Craig was putting on his running spikes.

'Ready!'

'Cover me!' Justin rasped. He pulled the captain in front of him, and he heard Steve's and Spider's gas guns thud. Then smoke and gas were hissing up all over the place on the aft lifeboat decks, and he started to run.

He ran through the whale flesh towards the smoke with the captain by the scruff of his neck in front of him. His spiked shoes gripped the wooden deck, but the captain was slipping and sliding. They ran through the archway of the midships winch superstructure, and Craig was right behind them. Up among the lifeboats, smoke was billowing. He took the captain by the collar and shoved him aft along the bloody whale carcass towards the big air funnels on the starboard side. Craig was running for the portside air funnels.

A breeze was blowing the smoke away. Justin ran down the side of the great gaping pot holes shoving the captain in front of him, his heart pounding in his ears. For ten paces he ran him like that, then the captain skidded and slipped. His feet shot out underneath him and he fell onto his chest, and Justin fell down on top of him, and they went skidding on their chests straight towards a gaping, belching vat hole. For a long terrible moment he saw the gaping vat hole careering towards them, the captain's manacled hands outflung and ploughing up the gore in front of him. Then the captain gargled a scream of terror and his hands passed over the edge of the vat hole and his head, then his trunk, disappeared.

Disappeared over the rim, down into the vat hole, and his legs came kicking up wildly, and Justin grabbed them. Flung his arms desperately over them, bellowing to Craig, and he ploughed to a stop at the very edge of the vat hole, spread-eagled, clutching the captain's legs; and there was the captain of the *Slava* headfirst down the belching pot hole, legs kicking wildly, screaming into his gas mask and Justin writhing in the blood and fat on top of him, trying to hold him, to get him back up and get the hell out of there before that mad Russian sniper shot both of them. And

312

every time Justin managed to get up onto his knees, the captain kicked.

'Stop kicking, for Chrissake!'

And then Craig was beside him and grabbed the captain by his belt and heaved, and Justin got back up and they both heaved. And the captain came back up out of the vat hole. Justin yanked him back up onto his feet and dragged him stumbling through the smoke the last ten yards across the cutting deck.

They smashed up against the aft bulkhead. Then Justin heaved himself off it and stumbled to the starboard air funnel, which fed air to the engine room. He lurched against the funnel, ripped the pin out of a gas bomb, and hurled it down the funnel. It was done. He was dizzy with exhaustion, covered in blood.

Craig was flinging open the aft accommodation door. He hurled a gas bomb down the alleyway through it. Then he started down the alleyway. To make sure those engineers got out of the engine room. And to check the aft accommodation.

Craig was shoving the captain ahead of him down the alleyway. Justin ran panting after them. Craig disappeared around the first corner. Justin lurched after him and met him coming back. 'Other way,' Craig croaked. They turned back down the alleyway. The cabin doors were all gaping. Steps led down to the accommodation below. He leaned there a long moment, trying to get his breath back and slow the hammering of his heart. Then he started down the steps. There was more accommodation, cabins abandoned everywhere.

At the bottom of the alleyway was the steel door leading down into the aft end of the factory. He ran for it. He tugged back the big iron bolt and heaved the door open. Tear gas billowed up into the alleyway from the factory below, and he nearly got trampled to death. A blind struggling rush of Russian engineers was fighting its way up the companionway, coughing and shoving. The front one bumped into Justin, and they both fell down. Justin struggled up, he seized the engineer and shoved him up the alleyway. Then he tried to fling himself against the bulkhead to get out of the way of the others; then they were all over him. All over him – fighting blindly, and he was steamrollered up the alleyway by a multitude of weeping Russian engineers. He shoved a man past him, then there were red-black stars as his head hit against the bulkhead. Something smashed into his solar plexus and he lurched forward and there were more stars as somebody hit him on the side of the head, and then they were all over him again. Feet knees shins, gasping spluttering, all he knew was that he was somehow at the bottom under a tangle of reckless Russians who did not care whom they trampled to death to get away from the tear gas, and he was yelling into his gas mask, '*Jesus Christ, you bastards, get off!*'

He somehow flung the nearest pair of legs off him and tried to yank his truncheon off his belt, to just lash out at anyone, and then everybody was getting up. Then all he saw was the backs of recklessly retreating Russians. And then there was Craig lurching out of a cabin doorway with the captain. Justin heaved himself up against the bulkhead, then he said into his mask, 'Check out the engine room!'

He ran to the engine-room door and looked down inside. There was machinery everywhere. Tear gas was spewing out of the ventilation ports. He went down the steel steps, then he rested. Then he went searching among the huge cylinders, with his truncheon out. Craig was following with the captain. But there was nobody else down there. He looked at his watch – twenty-four minutes before those mines went off. They had wasted nearly ten minutes on the engine room.

He clambered back up the steps into the factory, and then he saw something way down at the factory's forward end. He stopped and stared, panting. 'Oh Jesus! . . .'

It was a body. Sprawled at the bottom of the ladder at the other end of the factory. He stared at it, then he turned back down the steps. He began to run down the long avenue between the vats, his steel spikes slipping on the steel. He knew he should take them off but did not have the will to stop and do it. He skidded to a stop at the bottom of the ladder and knelt and shook the body's shoulder, and it coughed and vomited. He heaved it over onto its back. It was a young woman, and his eyes widened at the gash on her forehead and the blood all over her face. He whispered, 'Oh Jesus! . . .'

forty-six

She was out cold. He hoisted her up, grunting, then took her over his shoulder in a fireman's lift. He staggered there, thinking wildly, *What the hell do I do with her now? Can't take her aft, they'll get me.* The only place was the bridge, with the others.

He turned and started pulling himself up the ladder rungs. He got to the top, then went along the alleyway. There was still tear gas everywhere, and she was choking over his shoulder. He stumbled up the steps with her to the messroom; his legs were trembling but he knew if he stopped now he could not start again. He climbed the last companionway, which led up to the foredeck. The blood was pounding in his head, his legs were buckling. He got through the doorway into the clean ice cold night, then staggered across the foredeck towards the bridge. At the bottom of the bridge companionway he slumped her down into a sitting position on the steps, and he thought he was just going to topple with exhaustion. He held her like that somehow and he tore off his gas mask to get the fresh air on his sweating face. He held her by her shoulders with his head down, waiting for the trembling to go out of his legs and the hammering out of his heart. Then he looked up groggily and saw a blood-stained face with a pair of big blue wild eyes glaring at him. Then a clenched fist heaved sideways at the corner of his eye from nowhere.

That wild-eyed Russian whalewoman bitch he had personally lugged up from the bowels of the ship to save from death had suddenly come around and slugged him one! A left hook on the ear. He fell back stunned, outraged, clutching the side of his head yelling, 'Jesus Christ, lady!' And then the lady was lunging at him, and he saw another left hook coming. He did not have the slightest notion of how to combat a Russian whalewoman and he did not want to find out now, all he wanted to do right now was get rid of her and get the rest of her fucking comrades off this fucking ship. He threw up his arm blindly to block her blow and his other hand grabbed the top of her head. Her cap flew off and yellow hair flew all over her bloody face. He grabbed a handful and got a headlock on her, and he got his other arm round her waist, and then he howled as her teeth sank into his hand. His other hand came up to give her a karate chop, and she vomited all over his stomach.

Suddenly he had had enough. He yanked her off the steps and over his shoulder, vomit and all, and he went clumping up the companionway to the bridge. Now she was kicking and scream-ing and pounding his kidney with her fist. He got to the bridge and let go of her, and she fell in a heap at his side. 'Max!' he yelled, 'lock her up to the wheel and watch out!'

Craig came scrambling up the companionway with the cap-tain. He looked at the Russian woman and panted, 'Hey, she's good-looking.'

And the Russian woman heaved herself halfway up and screamed and kicked Craig on his shin.

Justin dashed back to the winches overlooking the cutting deck, he dropped down behind Steve's winch. He looked over the top at the afterdecks.

'How they going?'

'Six in the water.'

There were six lifeboats in the sea already, jam-packed. They were rowing out into the black night. He looked for the tanker again. She was still lying there, about a mile and a half off. He looked at the catchers – they were a lot closer but the nearest was still two miles off.

From this position he could not see astern of the *Slava* be-cause the funnels blocked his view. He looked back at the life-boats. Two more lifeboats were being lowered down to the water. The last two were in their embarkation positions, people getting into them. There were only about forty people left, crowding on the lifeboat decks – they could all get into the last two lifeboats. He crouched there a moment longer, getting his breath back and taking in the scene.

Almost the whole goddamn ship evacuated and they still had twenty minutes in hand before those mines went off. And another sixty minutes thereafter before this ship finally went down. And so fucking what if those catchers were steaming in from all sides! Maybe they had an automatic rifle each and a few pistols but nothing else except their harpoon guns. He crouched there, grinning at Steve. It was clear of tear gas here. The breeze was blowing from them towards the stern. He pulled out his little two-way radio and snapped in to Ross and the commander and to Katherine.

'Jonah to One, Two, Three. It's all happening. It's almost happened! Ross stand by for evacuation. Come in one at a time and report. Over.'

L.C. came in, frantic, 'Stay there, Jonah! Katie's listening to the Russians, she says it's terribly important. Stand by, for Christ's sake, don't disappear.'

Back on the *Jubilee* Katherine was clutching her earphones with one hand and with the other was scribbling notes, her pencil trembling. David Cartwright stood in the bridge doorway, watching nervously, L.C. was sitting beside her, poised over his radio. Then she turned and grabbed L.C.'s transmitter and said, 'For God's sake, Justin, hear this – the catchers are all talking to each other about wiping you all out. For God's sake, do you read me? They're coming to storm the *Slava* and wipe you out. They're going to storm up the slipway and they're going to encircle the whole ship. Do you read me? They've got guns. Each catcher has one automatic rifle and some pistols, and they've got some gas masks from their fire-fighting suits. Repeat, they've got fire-fighting gas masks. I don't know how many. Do you read me? They're coming to kill you.'

He snapped back at her, 'I read you. The last ones are getting into the lifeboats now. Ross, come in high at five thousand feet and hover out of range. We're going to plant the additional explosives in the factory now and throw the bombs down the vats. Over and out!'

He said to Spider, 'Get up to the bridge and help Max get the hostages into one of those lifeboats on the bridge. If anybody resists, hit him hard and throw him into the boat bodily.'

He switched the radio to Max on the bridge and said, 'Get ready to get the hostages into the lifeboat. Spider's coming to help you. Slug anybody who resists. Tell Craig to get his ass down here with those thermal bombs! Over.'

Max shouted, 'Those two catchers astern are side by side now! They're passing things to each other, I think it's guns. And another catcher's steaming up to join them, about five hundred yards behind them. Over.'

He looked at the stern but he could not see the catchers because of the funnels. He shouted out, 'Yes I read you. Get those hostages into the bridge lifeboat. But only lower them half-way down, so that they're stranded in mid-air. We'll lower them all the way when we're safe.'

He turned to Steve and pointed at the midships winch super-structure. 'Get up onto that winch platform and cover the slip-way! They're going to try to charge up the slipway. Shoot the shit out of them with your riot gun.' Steve got up and swung down the ladder onto the cutting deck.

Craig came running down from the bridge lugging the big canvas sack of explosives. 'Come on!' Justin shouted.

He shoved his gas mask over his face and leaped down onto the cutting deck. Craig followed. 'Put on your gas mask!' Justin yelled. He turned and ran for the door into the forward accom-modation.

They entered the alleyway, then flung themselves down the steps to the lower accommodation deck, then ran for the steel door leading down into the factory. Justin flung it open. Tear gas hung thick. They hurried down the ladder to the factory. Justin tore open the canvas sack, pulled out the limpet mines.

'Do the starboard side!'

They knelt together, setting the timing dials, fingers shaking. Then Justin ran for the portside bulkhead and clamped the first limpet mine against the steel. It was well below the waterline, and the explosions would be lethal to the *Slava*.

Up on the bridge Max and Spider were shoving the hostages into a lifeboat. Down aft, the final mob of whalemen and women were boarding the last lifeboat.

The midships winch superstructure divided the long cutting deck and dominated the whole stern and slipway. Underneath it was an arch of tunnel, through which the whales were dragged from the first part of the cutting deck to the forward part. Steve crouched up there on the superstructure behind the big main winch, a great powered barrel which, when cable was wrapped around it, could drag a whale up the slipway and into the first cutting deck. Below Steve was a whale carcass and beyond it the slipway. On either side of the carcass was the row of gaping vat holes. Flensing knives and pot hooks lay abandoned everywhere. He could see right down the slipway into the sea, to the bodies of the whales in tow. Out there on the black sea the crowded lifeboats were pulling away from the ship. The catchers and the tanker had most of their lights off now. There was a stiff breeze blowing across the ship. Steve lifted his gas mask to test the air for tear gas, and it was clear. The breeze had blown it all away. There was no need for him to shoot off more; the last lifeboat was nearly loaded. Then he felt the wind change.

Suddenly the wind changed direction, strongly, and he got the stinging whiff of tear gas, and he wrenched his gas mask back on. The wind was coming from the south now, straight from the stern, and it was bringing the remainder of the tear gas with it. The last of the crew, mostly women, were climbing into the lifeboat. Then he heard a shout, and he looked and saw a huge Russian woman gesticulate, and then she got out of the lifeboat.

He saw her scramble onto the deck, shouting at her comrades, waving her big arms. She went lumbering towards the companionway, bellowing at her comrades to follow her. Then she stopped and picked up a flensing knife and raised it above her head like a banner. Half a dozen women climbed out of the lifeboat and came shouting and jostling after her. Now they were picking up flensing knives also, and the whalewoman was stumping down the companionway towards the cutting deck.

Steve watched them come down the companionway brandishing their flensing knives, and then he stood up from behind his winch, to show himself. He raised his riot gun. The leading whalewoman was now on the cutting deck. She saw him and stopped, they all stopped behind her. Then her face split wide in a grin, and she shook her flensing knife at the man standing up there. The others behind her yelled, and then they surged on down the companionway to join her on the cutting deck.

For a long moment Steve stared at them. He watched them

come out onto the cutting deck, waving their knives and pot hooks, the wet blood flashing on their black oilskins in the yellow floodlights. Then his mind reeled and went cold-blooded, and a smile came over his handsome face. He stood there a moment longer, legs apart, then he ripped off his gas mask and roared at the whalewomen surging towards him, 'Get back to your lifeboat, women.' Then he lifted his riot gun up high for them to see, and then he put it down on the platform. And then Steve leaped off the winch platform, fifteen feet down onto the cutting deck.

He landed on his feet on the deck at the dead whale's tail. He stood there, crouched a little, in the middle of the tunnel under the winch platform. His hands were at his waist, bunched into fists. The leading whalewoman stopped at the beginning of the cutting deck, astonished. Her comrades stopped behind her. She eyed Steve, not moving. Then he crouched a little lower and he yelled, 'Bare hands, ladies.'

The Russian whalewoman stared, then her big bloodstained Slav face screwed up and she bellowed to the night in Russian, 'He's mine – leave him to me.' Then she lumbered forward at him. She came charging, a six-foot woman with big shoulders and enormous breasts under her shiny black oilskins, one two three four five bloody strides along the whale carcass. Then she lifted the long flensing knife high above her head, and for a moment it looked as if she was going to hurl it down too and tackle this male with her bare hands. Then she swung the great curved knife back behind her shoulders like an axe and she charged him, big booted legs pounding and her breasts bouncing and the terrible flensing knife flashing; she came screaming at Steve and he stood his ground. He crouched with his feet spread and his hands flat and rigid, ready for a karate chop. The huge whalewoman came pounding at him, her knife way over her head, and when she was three strides away she swiped. Slashed the flensing knife whistling flashing over her head with all her might, and Steve sidestepped.

The knife whistled past him into the wooden deck, and Steve thrust out his foot and the charging woman crashed into it, and she spread-eagled in the slough of blood. Steve bounded after her and grabbed the flensing knife and swung it around his head and hurled it into the night. Then he bounded at the whale-woman as she scrambled up and grabbed her by the back of her collar and by the seat of her baggy pants and shoved her head down, and he ran her. He ran her head down, bellowing, out-raged, legs pounding out of control, down the side of the whale carcass back towards her comrades, one two three four five strides, then he shoved her with all his might towards them. And the whalewoman went hurtling out of control, sprawling onto her stomach and crashing into them. Then they were all climbing over her and charging Steve.

Seven furious whalewomen with flensing knives and pot hooks scrambling over the prostrate body of their comrade; they charged along the whale carcass, pushing each other to get at Steve to kill him and then storm the bridge and kill everybody and recapture their ship for the motherland. And now the original whalewoman was back on her feet and trying to fight her way through her comrades to get at Steve and tear him apart.

Steve stood his ground again. He roared, delighted, 'Now, now, ladies – back to your lifeboats.'

And the leading woman charged him with her flensing knife in front of her like a lance. Steve waited until she was two paces in front of him, then he sidestepped again. And his hand came down in a karate chop on the woman's arm and his other hand grabbed the long handle and wrenched the knife away from her. He danced backwards, nimbly brandishing the long handle like a stave, and he whacked the whalewoman a sharp blow on her buttocks as she staggered past him. Then he whirled and blocked the next flensing knife with the handle of the one he held, roaring, 'Get back to your lifeboats, you stupid women!'

And he swiped the next flensing knife clean out of the woman's hands with a smash of wood and he spun and whacked her on the shoulder, and the next shrieking woman was onto him with a pot hook. Great steel hook whistling through the air at him and he blocked it so that it cartwheeled out of her fist, then he jabbed the butt of his handle into her stomach. And the next one was onto him. Also with a pot hook, leaping at him, and another flensing knife was swiping through the air at him and Steve was right on the very edge of a vat hole shouting, 'Get back to your lifeboats!' And he blocked the pot hook with his flensing knife handle and he ducked and danced sideways, grinning, shouting, and the flensing knife whizzed over his head. And he was about to skip away from the vat hole and dodge the next flensing knife, and the whalewoman got him.

The woman who got Steve Gregorowsky lashed out with her spiked boot and got him on the knee. He lurched off balance, and the flensing knife got him. The stock of the flensing knife crashed onto his shoulder and Steve lurched again and the original whalewoman came bursting through her comrades, her great ham fist up like a club, and she smashed it down on his neck. Steve fell, and the woman fell on top of him. He fell onto his side with the woman on top of him trying to club him again with her fist, and Steve bucked to throw her off him, and the flensing knife came down.

The knife chopped into Steve's neck, and the blood spurted out over the whalewoman, into her face. And Steve bucked and threw her off him, and he got to his knees, shocked, spouting blood, and he drew his fist way back behind him and hit the whalewoman a wild glancing blow on her head. And then the pot hook got him. The pot hook came down behind him as he staggered up from his knees, and it smashed through his collar-bone, and the whalewoman wrenched and Steve staggered backwards. He twisted the pot hook out of his shoulder and yanked it from the whalewoman with a roar and hurled it away, then another flensing knife got him. A whalewoman screamed and rammed her flensing knife into his side and Steve faltered and then he grabbed the handle with his good hand and pulled it out and the whalewoman howled and charged again, and it sank into Steve's guts up to the hilt, and he fell back against the whale, with the long flensing knife sticking out of his guts and the whalewoman leaning on the handle, screaming into his face. Steve tried to heave on the handle of the flensing knife to pull it out of his guts, and the next flensing knife got him. It swung forward and down and chopped off his arm.

The flensing knife slashed through the point of Steve's shoulder and chopped his arm clear off. For a long terrible instant he stood there leaning onto the flensing knife buried in his guts. Then his legs buckled and he pitched forward, and the whalewoman roared triumphantly and wrenched the knife out, and he collapsed onto his knees.

He knelt there with his head hanging down and the blood spouting out of his guts and both his shoulders. The whalewomen stood over him and raised their knives way over their heads to chop him down, and then Steve began to get up. He groaned deep and tried to get his arm to go for his knife and he was trying to get it straight in his head, *No animal can kill me and man is an animal*. . . . All he knew was the shocked astonishment and that his arm was not there to go for his knife, there just simply was no arm any more because there it was lying on the deck in front of him. And then he tried to get his other arm to go for his pistol, and he got halfway up off one knee with his head hanging down, and the whalewoman screamed and her flensing knife flashed over her head and the blade came down and chopped his head off.

Steven Gregorowsky's head crashed onto the deck and then his body fell forward with the blood spurting out of his neck. And a whalewoman kicked the head furiously and it went rolling through the blood, and then another kicked it, and it went skidding towards the edge of the slipway, and then it rolled down. The head went tumbling down the slipway leaving a long trail of blood, then it splashed into the water at the bottom with a plop, and it was gone.

The whalewomen shrieked in glee, and then they were waddling back to the chopped-up body, and one sunk her pot hook into its thigh and then another swiped her pot hook into its chest, and they were all shouting as they dragged the body to the rail. In Russian they yelled, 'One . . . two . . .' and they swung it backwards and they bellowed, 'Three,' and they heaved and Steven Gregorowsky's body went hurtling through the blackness, and it crashed into the freezing sea. And then there was the thud of a gas gun and the whalewomen were suddenly choking, gasping, and Craig Magnus was on the forward cutting deck with his gas gun up to fire again, and the whalewomen went stumbling back towards the lifeboats.

Up on the lifeboat decks the rest were scrambling frantically back into the lifeboat, and then Justin burst up onto the forward cutting deck behind Craig. And he saw what was happening and he looked up wildly onto the winch platform for Steve and he could not see him.

'Steve!' he shouted into his gas mask. 'Steve!'

He went running towards the whale carcass, looking for Steve. 'Steve,' he shouted into his gas mask, and then he saw the man's arm lying on the deck. Then there was gunfire from out there in the blackness.

'Max!' he cried desperately into his radio. 'Max, lower the hostages' lifeboat to the water. Then send Spider to the tunnel winch platform to take Steve's place. Do you read me?'

part eight

forty-seven

The catchers were steaming towards the *Slava*. She lay drifting, the limpet mines ticking murderously, her lights shining yellow on the dark water, the tear gas drifting away from her in the breeze. The lifeboats were pulling away into the darkness from the terror of the ship. They were jam-packed with men and women in their oilskins, clutching blankets about them, faces red and swollen from the tear gas, terrified, angry, but most of all terrified; the last lifeboat holding the women who had butchered Steve Gregorowky was almost on the water now. Behind the slipway floated the bodies of seven dead whales; one of them – probably whale C – was still loaded with seventy-five pounds of explosives, which had not yet been detonated. There were also the three whales that tow boat Sixteen had laid alongside the *Slava* as fenders. Craig had cut two of them loose and they were floating out there in the darkness; the other still lay next to the *Slava*'s hull. Of those three, two – D and E – were full of explosives, but there was no way of knowing which two they were.

Out there in the night were the lights of the tanker and four smaller vessels. The tow boats Sixteen and Twenty-one were astern with the Eleven – in the dark they all looked like catchers. The Five was lying off the *Slava*'s starboard beam. They were all about a thousand yards off, waiting.

*

The Russians were waiting for the last lifeboat to get into the water before attacking. They had radioed back and forth desperately, trying to make a plan to save their mother ship. They were taken completely by surprise, completely unprepared. They reasoned that the saboteurs had come in some very fast small boat that they had not noticed on their radar screens. Another theory was that the saboteurs were crew members bribed by the American CIA or the Chinese. Another was that they had dropped out of the sky from a helicopter. They had had no radio communication from the attackers since the first report of the explosion, except for the woman's voice ordering the tanker to stand off. The tanker was highly inflammable and was standing well off, but the whole fleet of catchers was steaming flat-out towards the *Slava* now. To pick up their comrades in the lifeboats, to get their weapons together, to do something about this crisis.

They were shouting back and forth to each other over their radios, informing each other about their automatic rifles, their pistols, their fire-fighting masks. The Eleven had steamed up to join tow boats Sixteen and Twenty-one to put their weapons and gas masks together. Nine seamen had volunteered to storm the slipway while the Five gave them cover by firing on the *Slava* with an automatic rifle. It was the Five that had opened fire as Justin found Steve's arm lying on the bloody deck.

The staccato of machine-gun fire came from out of the blackness, and the clanging of the bullets hammering across steel and ricocheting off into the night, and Justin ran for the cover of a winch. He crashed down behind it, looked over his shoulder. Craig was running across the deck. 'Get your head down!' Justin shouted. Craig came down onto his haunches beside him. The firing suddenly stopped. Justin pulled off his gas mask and looked at his watch. Then he said, 'Is that lifeboat on the water yet?'

'Yes.'

'And the hostages?'

'Yes.'

'Set the thermal bombs for twenty minutes.'

The machine-gun fire opened up again, the terrifying killer-hammering everywhere. He looked down the cutting deck and down the slipway, and he saw the black bow of the Sixteen ploughing towards them out of the night, about five hundred yards off, the sea breaking off the sharp bow and the flashes of wild gunfire coming from her bridge. Then the Five gave another run of automatic fire to rake the ship and scare them, and it succeeded. Justin saw Spider leaping down onto the cutting deck, then running for the tunnel winch platform. 'Head down!' Justin shouted at him. He worked at the timing dials on the thermal bombs – twenty – twenty – twenty. Craig was squatting, setting his bombs. And all the time the clattering of the guns. Justin got his dials set, then lifted his gas mask to his mouth and shouted into the radio at Spider up there on the tunnel winch platform: 'Spider, catcher approaching slipway now. Shoot the hell out of them with your riot gun and if that doesn't work shoot them in the legs. Hit the guys with the gas masks first. Got it?'

'Yes,' Spider shouted. 'Where's Steve?'

Justin shouted into his radio, 'Max? Give the catchers out there a blast. Keep the bastards' heads down. Do you read me?'

'Yes.'

'Give it to them!' he yelled, and he looked around at Craig and shouted, 'I'm going!'

He ran doubled up across the deck and skidded to a stop at the first vat hole, his heart thudding, and dropped the first thermal time bomb down the big black hole. Then he turned and scrambled doubled up under the gunfire and skidded to a halt and dropped the next one down. Abruptly the firing ceased. He stopped at the next vat hole and threw the third bomb down, then raced through the tunnel. He looked towards the slipway as he ran and saw the prow of the Sixteen four hundred yards off and he knew that on her foredeck were a dozen desperate Russians ready to leap aboard and come storming up the slipway. He ran past the next three vats throwing the bombs down them, then slid to a stop at the last vat hole. Craig was on the opposite side of the deck throwing down his last thermal bomb. Justin turned and ran back through the tunnel of the midships winch platform. He looked back down the slipway and pulled his riot gun off his shoulder. The gunfire was still stopped. The catchers were probably waiting for the Sixteen to get up to the stern before opening up again to cover their boarding party. There was suddenly no sound but the pounding in his ears. He turned and raced up the ladder onto the midship's winch platform. He scrambled around behind Spider's winch.

'Where's Steve?'

'Dead, Spider. Forget him for now.'

'Dead . . . ?'

'Forget it, Spider. The guy's dead!' He looked down the slipway. 'I'm going to blow up that last stern whale as they approach the slipway.'

Spider stared at him.

Justin pulled out the radio detonator and uncovered the dial. He looked at the Five, then down the slipway. He could not see past the funnels, what was happening astern. Back there the Twenty-one was still waiting, about a thousand yards off. The Sixteen was still steaming towards the stern and was about two hundred yards off now. The Eleven was a few hundred yards behind the Sixteen. They were obviously going to steam up to the slipway, one behind the other, and send their men storming up in two waves.

He wished to Christ he was up there on the bridge where he could see the catchers better, but from the bridge he would not have been able to see down the slipway at all. He crouched there with the radio-detonator, waiting for the prow of the Sixteen to come into the frame of the slipway and he wished he knew which whale it was that had not yet been detonated astern. He was almost sure the whale was C. But maybe C was the one alongside the *Slava*'s hull, or one of those whales floating out in the darkness, which Craig had cut loose. He would blow them all up if necessary, but those lifeboats full of women were out there, and he might blow a boat full of women clean out of the water. And if that whale at the stern didn't explode, they were going to have a gunfight. And a lot of human beings were going to get killed, including maybe himself. He set the detonation dial for whale C, and his fingers were shaking. Then suddenly a terrible din of ships' horns shattered the black night. All the catchers and the tanker were blasting on their hooters WHOOOOP WHOOOOP

WHOOOOP to create a horrifying din as the Sixteen approached the *Slava*. And then all the catchers opened fire again, and all hell broke loose.

From all sides came the cacophonous da-da-da-da and the crashing of bullets on the steel everywhere, amid the deafening blasting whooping of the hooters. And then all the catchers were steaming at the *Slava* with guns blazing and hooters blaring WHOOOOOOP.

Justin looked down the slipway and he knew he had made a mistake – he should have been by those funnels down aft where he could see everything and shoot up those catchers *before* they even got near the slipway. Then he saw the bow of the Sixteen just come into the frame of the slipway about thirty yards off and he hollered, 'Heads down and hang on!' and he braced himself against the explosion and flicked the detonator switch. And there was the explosion, but no impact.

There was no impact; the stern of the *Slava* did not heave up out of the sea to send those Russians aboard the Sixteen crashing to the decks, but four hundred yards out there a great plume of sea went shooting up into the blackness. And in the shock of it the gunfire stopped, and he wanted to yell to the skies, 'Yes, you bastards, the sea's full of whales like that!' Then the gunfire opened up again more furiously than before. He looked down the slipway and the Sixteen's bow was still ploughing towards it. His fingers fumbled the dial to frequency D and he snapped the switch over again, and again there was no eruption behind the slipway. But out there in the blackness another explosion went up.

Jesus Christ, it was right in front of the Five as she came steaming and hooting and blazing towards the *Slava*, and her bows stood up out of the black exploding sea, and for a long terrible beautiful moment the whole vessel hung poised half out of the water, then crashed down. And, dear God, if there was one thing he wanted at that moment it was a whole pod of whales charged to the eyeballs with high explosives to blow this whole whaling fleet all over the Weddell Sea.

More gunfire. And now the Sixteen was ploughing between the great bloated whales towards the stern, she was right between the whales now, and her volunteers were crouching, ready to jump, and he snapped the detonation switch for whale E, and the sea exploded in the slipway.

Exploded in a great crash of sea and blood and guts right there in the slipway, and there was the giant thud and crash and eruption of it and the mass of other whales heaving up. Whale E exploded right under the Sixteen's bow, and it rose up out of the sea, upwards and sideways, and the boarders were thrown with her, in all directions amid the flying blood and guts. And the stern of the *Slava* lurched up also, then the Sixteen smashed back down into the sea and the blood and guts rained down everywhere. And, oh God, it was absolutely beautiful to see and he snapped on his two-way radio and shouted jubilantly, 'Jonah to One. Tell the bastards that every whale is loaded with high explosives and we'll blow the living shit out of everyone who tries to board the slipway – we'll blow them all to Kingdom Come. And tell them that the ship is going to explode in fifteen minutes and they'll be killed anyway. Tell them we'll shoot the shit out of them as they come up the slipway. Do you read me? Over.'

Katherine said, 'I read you. Over.'

'Ross – where the hell are you?' he called into the radio.

Ross's voice came back above the chopping of the helicopter's propellers. 'I'm ten miles off you at five thousand feet. I can see the *Slava* clearly – I'll be overhead in ten minutes. Repeat, in ten minutes I'll be hovering over the bows at five thousand feet. Do you read me? Over.'

And the gunfire opened up again, and the hooters were blasting and there was ricocheting everywhere again, and Justin shouted back to Ross, 'Go flat-out now! We'll hold them until you're overhead, then retreat back to the foredeck fast! Radio us when you're overhead and we'll tell you when to come down! Repeat, radio us and hover overhead out of range until we tell you to come down! Over and out!'

The Eleven was almost at the *Slava*'s stern. She was out of his sight behind the funnels and aft accommodations. Spider called, 'Shall I go down to the funnels and let them have it before they get to the slipway?'

The gunfire from the Five stopped.

'No. We command the whole slipway from here – they'll be

sitting ducks. We'll let them have it with the riot guns as they come up.'

The gunfire started again. Justin and Spider lay there behind the big main winch, bullets crashing whining all over. They could still not see the Eleven yet; Justin looked up at the sky for the helicopter but he could not see it yet either. He snapped his radio to Max on the bridge and shouted, 'Max, do you see the Eleven? What's she doing? Over.'

He listened for Max, but there was no answer.

'Max, do you read me? Repeat, what's the Eleven doing? Over.'

And suddenly the remaining aft lights went out, the whole stern of the *Slava* was plunged in darkness, and then gunfire opened up from the lifeboat deck.

forty-eight

It may be that Justin Magnus made his mistake in not stationing Spider Webb on the aft lifeboat deck to shoot up the Eleven with tear gas and the riot gun as it approached the *Slava*'s stern. It was a decision made in the wild crashing of gunfire; if he had sent Spider down there he would have split up his men; if Spider had got wounded, somebody would have had to go get him, through the gunfire while the helicopter hovered over the foredeck, liable to get shot up itself. Whereas from his position on the midship's winch platform he dominated the slipway, and Russian seamen storming up it would be sitting ducks for the riot guns. To send Spider down to the aft lifeboat deck was an unnecessary risk.

What definitely was a mistake was Justin's assumption that the Russians would have to board the *Slava* via the slipway. They did not do so. Under the cover of gunfire from the other boats, the Eleven steamed up under the overhang of the *Slava*'s high stern, and six men scrambled up the catcher's mast rigging and jumped onto the *Slava*'s stern rails. They knocked out the aft lights and they opened fire.

Six Russian seamen were suddenly shooting at the floodlit midship's winch platform and at the bridge, and all Justin Magnus knew was that they were aboard and shooting at them from out of the blackness just forty yards away, among the funnels. There were bullets everywhere and he could see nothing to shoot back at and then all he knew was the fury that it had gone wrong. Those crazy bastards were going to be aboard this ship when those bombs blew up, and Jesus Christ he did not want to shoot up Russian seamen with wives and children and mothers and fathers! He didn't want to kill anybody let alone ordinary seamen who weren't trained to fight. He was furious at their stupid bravery and outraged that they were risking everybody's lives for nothing, and he filled his lungs and roared into the chaos, 'You stupid bastards get off this goddamn ship!' And he roared at Craig and Spider, 'TEAR GAS,' and there were the ragged thuds of their three guns going off. The canisters flew down onto the afterdecks. 'TEAR GAS!' he yelled. 'SMOKE!' He rammed another canister into his gun and roared, 'Get back you crazy Russian bastards!' And there was only the thud of guns and the chatter of gunfire.

He yelled at Craig, 'Get back to the foredeck! Tell Ross to stand by to pull us out any minute!'

'What about you?'

'Cover us as we retreat! We'll pull back one at a time!'

Craig turned and scrambled on his hands and knees behind the winches for the vertical ladder. Justin shoved the barrel of his riot gun over the top of the winch and rammed a clip of real bullets into the magazine and let fly to make a noise. Spider was firing his gas gun, crouched behind his winch. Craig ran across the cutting deck, got to the ladder, and dashed up it for the bridge. Justin gave the funnels another burst, then he scuttled on his belly to the other side of the platform, to Spider's winch. Spider was on his stomach at the corner, firing into the dark. Justin crawled behind him and poked his gun around the side of the winch. He wished to God he knew what he was firing at. He looked back over his shoulder and saw Craig's flashlight blink once from the bridge and he whispered, 'Thank God,' and yelled at Spider, 'Up to the foredeck!'

Spider did not hear him in the gunfire and he slapped him on the shoulder. 'Get up to the fucking foredeck! Keep me covered when you get there!'

Spider went. Justin gave the aft a burst of gunfire to keep the Russians' heads down while Spider made it – *Just as long as we keep their heads down until the helicopter comes down on the foredeck and lifts us off. They'll try to storm the bridge, but two of us can hold them down on the forward cutting deck with tear gas and smoke bombs. Please God, just keep the bastards from getting up onto the bridge while Ross brings the helicopter down.* He looked feverishly at his watch: nine minutes before the mines and the thermal bombs went off. He fired another tear gas canister into the dark and he wanted to yell at them, 'In nine minutes this ship will blow up. Get back you crazy bastards or you're going to get blown up too.'

He looked over his shoulder again, and there was Spider's flashlight blinking. He rammed another gas canister into the gas gun and let it fly into the dark afterdecks, then he turned and raced for the ladder.

He ran low across the deck towards the bridge. He heard the gunfire from the officers' deck covering him. Then he was climbing the companionway. *Please God, not one in the back now as I go up – not one in the back now, please God!* The bullets were smacking against the steel around him – *just five more seconds, please God* – and he climbed the last steps and threw himself down behind Craig's winch. He lay there, thanking God. Spider was behind another winch on the starboard side of the officers' deck. The Five was four hundred yards off, an automatic rifle firing, but she was too far away to be accurate. The Sixteen and the Eleven were lying a hundred yards off the stern.

He shouted to Craig, 'Hold them on the cutting decks with tear gas! Then use the riot guns.'

He stood up and ran forward. He ran onto the bows and tore off his gas mask and snapped on his radio.

'Where are you, Ross?'

forty-nine

Three Russians in fire-fighting gas masks leaped down from the aft decks, then ran for the cover of the tunnel winch platform. Justin heard the gas guns go off. The Five was still blazing at them. They were the bastards he was worried about when they saw the helicopter. The Five could come steaming up and shoot Ross out of the sky while those Russians down there on the cutting deck came storming up onto the bridge and shot the rest of them. He shouted into the radio, 'Jonah to Two. Where are you, Ross? Come down on the foredeck with both nets lowered. Repeat, come down now on the foredeck with both nets lowered and hover. Do you read me? Over.'

Ross's voice came back. 'Two to Jonah. Down to foredeck both nets lowered. Over.'

'Max!' Justin shouted. 'Shoot up that catcher as soon as the helicopter shows.' He could not see him.

He grabbed the megaphone Max had left on deck and ran across the foredeck, then down the officers' deck, to Spider's winch. He looked down onto the cutting decks, and all he could see was smoke and tear gas. The Eleven and Sixteen were still lying a hundred yards behind the stern. He shouted at Spider, 'Get back to the bow for takeoff. Keep us covered!'

There was tear gas hissing all over both cutting decks, but the wind was blowing it in long drifts across the deck out to sea. The Russians were somewhere down there behind the tunnel, firing at the whole bridge. In five minutes those bombs in the vats would explode all around them. He tried to lift his gas mask and bellow in Russian, 'Brave Russians, you must now abandon ship. This ship is about to blow up,' but the sting of tear gas made him pull his mask back on. He looked up into the sky and saw the blurred shape of the helicopter. Coming down out of the blackness five hundred feet up there. Oh God, they were going to make it!

He shouted at Craig, 'Get to the bow. Cover your side from the bow.' Then he tore off his gas mask again and managed to bawl into the megaphone, 'Brave Russians! This ship is about to blow up! You must abandon ship immediately!'

The helicopter was just up there, just two hundred feet up, and any minute now those explosives would go off and those brave Russian bastards would be running for their lives. He tried to shout to them over the megaphone again, and he got as far as '*Brave Russians,*' and suddenly from nowhere came the blur of a brave Russian scrambling up the ladder on the starboard side that Craig had just left. All Justin saw was a crouched black blur, then the blaze of a gun firing up at the bridge. Then the terrible flash of realization: *The factory – they're coming through the factory. They've got gas masks!* The bastards had got through.

He swung his riot gun and fired and the big rubber bullet flew and the man was knocked sideways, flying back into the blackness. And then there was another gas-masked figure coming up the ladder two yards from him, and he spun around with a roar of murder in his throat and bounded at him and kicked him with all his might. Swung his leg and kicked him with all his might in the chest, and the man fell crashing backward, arms outflung, and the next man was coming up the ladder towards him and he hollered, 'Get back you stupid bastards!' and tried to kick him, and the Russian grabbed for his leg and seized it. He kicked with all his might but the Russian hung on to his leg, and Justin kicked with all his might again, and Jesus it was wonderful to feel the bastard just disappear, then there was a burst of gunfire. And suddenly two men were racing forward across the deck from the midship's winch platform, firing with their pistols, and another figure was coming up the other ladder on the starboard side and he felt only desperate need to shoot the bastard before he shot him, and he fired and the man crashed. He swung the riot gun on the two men racing across the deck and fired two shots and both shots missed and the men threw themselves into the shelter of the winch overhang.

He crouched on the forward winch platform, gasping, waiting for them to show themselves at the ladders. He waited, shaking, and it was suddenly almost quiet with just the sporadic firing of the Five and the thudding of his heart in his ears. Then he turned and started to run for the corner of the foredeck. He looked around as he ran and saw a figure coming up the top of the ladder. He spun and fired, then he ran on for the corner, and there was the crash of the gun behind him and the sledgehammer blow on his shoulder.

And he was falling onto his stomach, and there was only the terror of the next bullet ripping into his body. He rolled over, and there was the dark figure running up through the blackness. Justin gave a strangled roar and raised his riot gun, firing from his waist. The man lurched and for an instant he seemed to hang poised in midcharge, stopped by the blows of the rubber bullets, then he went sprawling. Justin got up, shocked and bloody, and a hand grabbed the back of his collar and yanked him around the corner. And there was Spider hurling a smoke bomb. Craig was at the other corner and Justin heard Spider yell in his ear, 'Are you all right?'

He was leaning against the bulkhead saying to himself, *I can stand! I'm not dead.* His left shoulder was wet with blood and he moved it to see if it worked and, my God, it even painfully worked! And there was the helicopter chopping hovering just twenty feet above the deck and the roar and wind of it was deafening. He pulled off his gas mask and croaked out, 'Get aboard.'

'You get aboard – I'll hold them!'

Justin shoved him and roared, 'Do as you're fucking told!'

He dropped to his knees and stuck his eye around the corner. All he could see was the smoke and tear gas being swept down the narrow officers' deck by the wind of the helicopter blades, and the sprawled stunned body of the Russian. And the Eleven and the Sixteen steaming up the portside.

The boats had seen the helicopter. All three of them were steaming fast now for the *Slava*'s bow. The Five was four hundred yards off out there, steaming flat-out on the starboard side. Craig had his gun up firing at her. Justin shoved his gun up to his wounded shoulder and fired a wild burst at the Eleven and the Sixteen. They were almost level with the *Slava*'s stern, a hundred yards down there. He looked over his shoulder at the helicopter hovering just fifteen feet above the *Slava*'s bow, her

nets hanging, and Spider was clambering wildly up. Justin
staggered across the foredeck to Craig and slapped him on the
shoulder and roared, 'Get aboard!'

He looked wildly around for Max and he realized he had not
seen or heard or thought of Max for Christ knows how long and
he yelled up at the bridge, 'Max! Maaaax!'

He turned and ran for the corner and up the bridge companionway. For the first time he felt the agony in his shoulder;
his whole body suddenly felt wounded and his left arm did not
want to work. He heaved himself up the steps, one-armed on the
handrail. He got up onto the bridge and looked for Max, but he
could not see him. 'Max!' he shouted. Then he saw legs
sprawled out of the opposite bridgewing.

Max was on his stomach and a big black pool of blood was
running out of the wound in his neck. Justin stumbled to him
and fell to his knees and heaved him over onto his back, and, oh
God, the blood. Blood pumping out of the big hole right through
the carotid artery on the left side of the neck, the face red in
blood and deadly white, eyes sodden with blood. 'Max!' he
croaked, and he jabbed his thumbs on both sides of the big hole
in the artery to choke off the blood. The man was still breathing,
gurgling bloody noises. 'Craig!' he shouted, but it was drowned
by the roaring of the helicopter and the gunfire. 'CRAIG!' But
it was nothing against the helicopter, and he whispered, 'Oh
God Jesus, give me strength!'

He wrenched Max's lifeless arms over his left shoulder and he
heaved himself up. Max hung deadweight, lolling, pumping red–
black blood, and Justin thought *Jesus Christ* and he somehow
threw his arm, up through the pain, around Max's neck and his
fingers groped for the big pulsating hole in his neck. They
jabbed right inside the hole, then he somehow got his index and
forefinger parted, pressing the carotid. He looked at the Five.
She was steaming flat-out towards the *Slava*'s bow, only three
hundred yards off now. He stumbled through the wheelhouse,
dragging Max. The Eleven and the Sixteen were steaming up the
portside of the *Slava*, about halfway up. Justin staggered, cursing
and praying, and he had no idea how he was going to get Max
down the companionway. He rasped 'please God' and buckled

down and heaved Max up over his back. Then he turned around, his back to the steep companionway, and he grabbed the handrail and backed down the first step, hanging on desperately. He went clutching, gasping down the ladder. He got halfway down, and slipped and fell crashing over backwards on top of Max. He got up whimpering, 'Dear Jesus, don't let anybody shoot me now,' and he grabbed Max's wrist and dragged him towards the bow and bellowed, 'Craig!'

Craig had been by the helicopter's nets when he spotted Justin. He came running. He grabbed Max's wrist and wrenched him, sliding, dragging, over the foredeck, into the roaring wind of the helicopter rotors. Spider was kneeling in the back of the copter, looking down. Justin went lurching up the deck after Craig.

Spider now was blazing at the Five. The Five was bearing down rapidly on the starboard bow, spurts of gunfire coming from her bridge. Justin reeled around as he ran and hurled one more tear gas canister behind him down the officers' deck, then he followed Craig.

Justin ran stumbling backwards towards the helicopter, his gun at his hip. *Christ, this was the most treacherous and the easiest part of the whole operation. All they had to do was get Max up into that helicopter, and if anybody came out onto the bridge now, they had been warned. NOBODY IS GOING TO STOP US THEY HAVE BEEN WARNED WE'VE DONE IT AND NOBODY IS GOING TO STOP US NOW AND THERE'S EXACTLY TWO MINUTES BEFORE THOSE BOMBS GO OFF AND BLOW UP THIS WHOLE FUCKING SHIP.*

He looked up at the helicopter hovering just up there, and Ross was shouting something, and Spider was halfway down the net and had grabbed Max by his belt. Craig had him around the thighs and they were heaving him up on the swinging net and the helicopter was heeling hard over to port with all the weight on that side. Then Justin looked back and saw how close the Eleven was.

fifty

The Eleven was steaming full speed close to the *Slava*. From the middle of the foredeck he could see only her crow's nest above the *Slava*'s high gunnels. The Sixteen was fifty yards behind her, out into the sea. The Five was a hundred and fifty yards off on the other side. The three boats were racing for the *Slava*'s bow to try to get the helicopter, and Justin gave a roar and raised the machine gun up to his bloody shoulder and fired a burst of real bullets at the Five. He looked at the Eleven and all he could see was her flying bridge and he gave that a burst of fire, then he turned and ran.

He ran for the bow, into the rotor blast. He saw Spider lying on his guts half-out of the helicopter heaving Max up the net bodily by the belt and Craig was clinging halfway up the net, shoving Max's legs, and the net was flapping. Justin slung his riot-gun strap over his shoulder and grabbed at the nets with both hands. The helicopter dipped under his weight and he yelled, 'Get him up!'

The helicopter was bucking and Spider was still half-out, heaving Max up, and Craig was still shoving and Justin looked back at the Eleven and she was fifty yards from the bow down there. Then there was the crack of a pistol.

The helicopter's windshield shattered in front of Ross's face, then pistol fire was blazing from down in the darkness, and Justin saw the figure behind the harpoon gun, behind the big bales of nylon line stacked up around it, and the harpoon was aimed upwards. The Eleven was just thirty yards away now – thirty yards and the harpoon's horizontal range was fifty, and Justin clutched the net and shouted, 'Go, for Chrissake!'

The helicopter roared, hacking, straining slowly up.

The Eleven was just twenty yards down there, her great harpoon gun pointed upwards and the crack of the pistol coming from her bridge. And on the other side the Five was just fifty yards down there with her harpoon gun up also, and he bellowed into the icy black and the cracking of the gunfire, 'GO ROSS FOR CHRISSAKES!'

The helicopter was slowly lifting off the foredeck; it rose, rocking, with Justin desperately clutching the net in the roaring wind. Max was halfway into the cabin now. The foredeck of the *Slava* was dropping very slowly away, and Justin heaved with his bad arm and tried to pull himself up and Spider was tugging Max into the cabin and then Craig stretched down to Justin. Justin heaved with his good arm, and his foot groped for the next rope in the net, and the foot entangled. He kicked and wrenched it free and then tried to grope upward with his bad arm, Craig reaching down, yelling at him, 'Stretch! Come on!'

In another ten feet they would be out of range – and then there was the big thud of the cannon and the harpoon flew.

It flew upward, a hundred pounds of steel with the big explosive head flying viciously up into the night at the helicopter and at the wounded man clinging. Justin looked down, and for a long terrible time the harpoon flew straight for the belly of the helicopter, to blow them out of the night sky and send them crashing down into the Antarctic sea. The harpoon flew murderously upward, many times faster than the helicopter was rising, and it was going to hit it – and if it missed the guts it was surely going to hit the nets, hit them and entangle them and wrench them down, yank the helicopter down out of the sky and plunge it into the icy black sea. The killer harpoon flew for the helicopter and it was going to hit it at the top of its trajectory, then the big barbed head slowly levelled out and turned.

It turned just under the nets, and then curved downward and hurtled away into the blackness. And Justin was still clinging, bloody, gasping, and Craig was hanging out of the helicopter clutching onto his wrist, and the helicopter was chopping harder, higher, faster upwards, and the foredeck of the *Slava* was dropping away, and there was only the incredulous triumphant joy. The only thing left was to get up this net and into the helicopter, and he held Craig tight and heaved, and there was the crack of the pistol, and the bullet hit him.

fifty-one

The bullet that got Justin Magnus struck him in the top of his thigh and smashed through his pelvis and entered his abdominal cavity. For a long shocked instant he did not feel anything except the blow, like a sledgehammer in his back, then came the thud of agony in his guts and the letting go of everything.

Letting go, the stunned agonized unclutching of his hands, and the crumpling of his knees, his head flung back, to go falling spinning through the blackness down into the icy black Antarctic sea. Justin Magnus let go of everything, and Craig held him.

Held him fiercely by the wrist shouting, 'Get him! Get him!' And Craig hauled frantically, trying to lift him bodily up out of the air, and then Spider was writhing on his belly and leaning down the nets, and the helicopter was heeling way over. Now Spider was hanging headfirst down the net, and he grabbed Justin's wrist from Craig and he roared, 'Get underneath him!' Craig was already scrambling down the swinging net. He got his arm around Justin's legs and he heaved, clutching the net, and Spider pulled with all his strength, and the limp bloody body inched up. They wrenched and heaved up the net, then Spider got him by the armpits and dragged him up into the helicopter.

'Justin!' he cried above the roar. 'Justin!'

His eyes were open and he tried to speak and he choked and coughed and tried to clutch his guts. Craig pulled him up into a half-sitting position and held him by the shoulders and he coughed and retched, he dragged his wrist across his face, then clutched his guts again. Then he looked at Craig and he tried to smile and say something. What he tried to say is 'We made it,' but it would not come out. Craig held him tight by the shoulders and Spider pulled the radio headset onto his head so they could hear him, and he tried to smile again and he rasped, 'We made it, didn't we?'

They held him as he choked and coughed again and Craig shouted, 'We made it, Justin! We made it because of you! You made it, Justin!'

Ross shouted over the intercom, 'Where's he hit?'

'It's gone into his guts – he's got pain in his guts.'

'Is he coughing blood?' Ross shouted.

'No – not yet.'

'How's Max?'

'I've got him!' Spider shouted. 'I'm holding his neck, I've stopped the blood.'

'Is he still breathing?'

'Yes!'

Ross shouted, 'Justin, do you hear me? You're going to be all right, champion – you're going to be all right! You're not coughing blood so it hasn't got your stomach, champion! You're going to be all right, we're going to fly you and Max to Chile. We can be in south Chile in eight hours, champion, and we'll get you to a doctor. Do you hear me, champion?'

Craig shouted, 'Don't fly the decoy route! Fly straight back to the *Jubilee* and refuel!'

And Justin rasped, 'No!' and it was choked off in another spasm of coughing; then he choked out, 'Give me Katie.'

Ross shouted, 'Two to One. Do you read us, Katie? We're on our way. We made it, Katie, we're on our way! Here's Justin. Stand by!'

He passed the microphone back over the seat and Craig held him tight and put the microphone to his mouth. Justin tried to take a breath and to grin and he rasped into the microphone, 'Katie, everything is going to be all right. Everything is fine. . . .' And he started to cough. Craig rammed his hand over the microphone so she would not hear him coughing, then he shouted into the microphone, 'Everything's fine, Katie. Over and Out!'

From the sub, miles ahead and far below, came the voice of Henry Thorogood. 'Three to Two. Is there anything we can do?'

'Nothing now,' Craig said, his voice quavering. 'We just don't know.'

With each cough the agony in his guts slugged harder, and he knew he might die. Knew he might die the long, slow agonized death of peritonitis, the blood pumping into his torn-up guts and the massive agony of the infection. All he knew through the slugging agony was that he did not care about the dying, it was even almost funny, he was recklessly wildly triumphant about what he had done and he was reckless of the dying; the dying was just some sort of bad joke, *Justin Magnus goes and blows up the Russian whaling fleet and gets himself shot up the ass at the very end*. And all he cared about at this agonized moment, all that made him angry was that he might not live and lie and love with Katie again, and even that was sort of funny – Justin Magnus hadn't had the sense to fall in love with the most beautiful, wonderful girl until just before he gets himself killed. In a terrible way it seemed heartbreakingly funny, then through the agony it was not funny at all, it was heartbreakingly tragic, because he might never have her glorious golden body again, never again her wide laughing mouth and her big blue eyes and her running into his arms and the superb feel of love in her arms and the laugh of love in her eyes, *never again my darling, my lover, my champion, my magnificent woman*. And through the pounding agony in his guts this was what he wanted to do more than anything else, to give her something, give her something, anything just to try to make her happy, try to make her laugh, to try to tell her he loved her, and that he was sorry he had been so stupid as not to fall in love with her long ago, just to reach out again and touch her, and he gasped into the intercom to Ross, 'Give me Katie!' and he whispered to the others, 'Switch off your intercoms—'

Ross said hoarsely, 'Two to One. Katie, stand by for the boss.'

Justin took an agonized breath and said, 'Katie?'

'Yes, I read you.'

And he felt the tears burning in his eyes and he did not know what to say, how to make her know and feel what she already knew and felt, he just wanted to touch her, love her, hold her tight to him, and all he wanted to say was, 'I love you, Katie, and I don't want to die, I want to live for you, Katie, but I'm afraid I'm going to die, my darling, and isn't that the worst joke you ever heard? Would you believe that a fucking Russian shot me in the ass just as we finally made it. Katie, you are my life and I will live through you somehow, if there is any way at all, I will come and live through you, with you, in you, and we will go on living together, and we will go on that way seeing we didn't have the goddamn sense to fall in love ages ago and then I had to go and get myself shot, do you hear me, Katie? We will go on and we will make beautiful pictures and write beautiful books about beautiful things and I will be you and we will live together and save the beauty of the world, I will be in your heart and body and soul and we will live and learn and laugh together my glorious darling Katie, so I am not really dying I am coming to live with you.' But he did not know how to say these things, all he said was, 'Katie . . . everything is going to be all right. . . .'

And he tried to take a breath to try to make a bad joke of it and he began to cough and Craig took the microphone from him and shouted, 'Katie! Hand the radio over to L.C. L.C., do you read me? Over?'

And Katherine shouted desperately, 'Tell me what's happening!'

And then L. C. Singleton's voice came on, 'I read you – I've got it now. For Christ's sake tell me what's happening! Over!'

'Get Katie down to her cabin and keep her there!'

And she snatched the microphone back from L.C. and shouted, 'Like hell you will! Tell me what's happening! Give me Justin! Justin, do you hear me? Do you hear me, darling? Over!'

And Justin held his guts and took the microphone from Craig and he drew an agonized breath and he said, 'Katie. . . .' And he did not know what to say except that he loved her and that he was sorry for making a mess of their lives, and he said, 'Katie . . . I love you – and everything's all right, my love. Do you read me? Over.'

She cried, 'Yes, my love, I read you! I love you, darling, I love you with all my heart and soul. What's happened, my darling, tell me what's happened, have you been hit? Over.'

'It's nothing, Katie, I'm all right—' and the agony kicked in his guts and he cried out, and Ross shouted, 'Give me the transmitter!' and he grabbed it.

'Katie – yes he's hit. He's been hit in the guts, but he's not coughing blood. Now for God's sake hold on to yourself tight until we get back! I don't want him to try to talk any more now! Do you understand? Over.'

The microphone was shaking in her clenched hand and her eyes were tight shut and her face was ashen and the sick horror of it was hammering in her chest, and she hung on tight with all her strength and then she said, 'Yes, let me talk to him. I don't want anybody else to hear. . . .' She did not switch over, so that Ross could not argue with her, and she took a big sobbing breath and said, 'Justin? I love you. . . . It won't be long my love. . . . I'll look after you. I'll look after you forever and ever, my darling. . . . And, oh God, my darling, forgive me for being weak – forgive me, my darling, and give me your pain now. Give me your pain now and let me carry it. Let me take your pain away from you, my love, oh dear God, let me do that. . . . But I'm here, my darling, and I am praying for you – oh God, I will pray for you. Don't try to talk now, darling. Don't try to say anything – just hang on and know that I love you and I'm here waiting for you. All right, my darling. Over. . . .' And the heartbreak and the desperate fear broke up into her throat, and she choked and she dropped her head, and she wept.

And two thousand feet below Justin in the Antarctic blackness there was a great thud in the bowels of the butcher ship.

fifty-two

There was a massive thud so the whole sea shook, and then came the flames. Sheets of fire erupting from the bloody deck. The steel vats suddenly burst into the big factory hall below in an explosion of flying steel and whale oil and flame. The flames went leaping upwards out of the rows of big vat holes, high into the night, and lit up the sea and the tanker and the catchers. And underneath the ice-black sea the limpet mines exploded, blasting up into the bowels of the killer ship. And the sea went gushing through the ragged holes into the engine rooms, and the explosion burst the whale oil storage tanks, and burning oil raged up into the ship's exploding guts.

The helicopter was at two thousand feet, and they did not hear the explosion above the roaring of the helicopter, but Craig shouted, 'Justin – look!' and he gripped him around the shoulders and he tried to heave him across his knees so he could look down and see it also, shouting in his ear, 'Justin!'

And then they were all looking, and they saw the beautiful sky-high sheets of flame and there was a kind of shocked triumph and incredulity in the roaring helicopter, as if they could not really believe what they had done down there, and through it all a kind of awed horror for the destruction they had wrought. Craig held his brother tight across his knees and Justin saw what he had done, and through his agonized triumphant awe came the horror for those brave Russians down there, the horrified remorse for those human beings in those terrible sheets of flame, and he wanted to bellow, JUMP YOU CRAZY BASTARDS – JUMP INTO THE SEA. And in the glare of the flames he thought he saw a man leap into the freezing sea, and then another, and through the pain he tried to roar, Jump! That's right jump! But it just came out in a choking rasp and he looked desperately for more men jumping and he wanted to cry out, Oh God, make them jump! Then the enormity of it overwhelmed him and his head slumped down and he was just gasping, choking, crying.

Oh God, why did I use the thermal bombs – just to impress them. Oh God . . .

And the heartbreakingly beautiful Antarctic sunrise was in their eyes, and the helicopter was high above the pillars of flame now, and somewhere way over there in that sunrise the *Jubilee* was steaming through the icebergs.

And far away over there in the sea, among the icebergs that were beginning to turn pink, the blue whale calf was swimming, swimming, alone, feeding on the plankton, his big mouth open and his eyes alert, watching for danger. And as he swam he was making his calling noises, calling calling for other blue whales, but he did not hear any answers. The blue whale calf was very frightened, and very lonely, and he knew very well about death now. But he also knew naturally that he had to stay down at the Antarctic for a long time yet to feed his great growing body because he knew that when the summer ended and the Antarctic seas began to freeze he had to go north, and it would be a long time before he could come back and feed on the abundance again. The blue whale calf swam, calling, calling, but he did not hear any answers, and it was probable he never would, because there were so few blue whales left in all the oceans, and there were many millions of cubic miles between them, and all the time his heart was crying out.

Jack Higgins
The Eagle Has Landed 80p

The order: 'Bring me Churchill out of England' – Adolf Hitler
16 September 1943

The plan: To kidnap the Prime Minister during a quiet weekend
at a country house in Norfolk.

The people: Kurt Steiner and his handful of crack paratroopers
an embittered woman spy, an IRA gunman and a Free Corps
traitor.

The date: 6 November 1943 – the most audacious mission ever
conceived is poised to strike . . .

The Last Place God Made 70p

World War I ace Sam Hannah was down to pushing ancient planes
across the worst jungles in the world.
Mallory was one of the new generation who would rather fly
anything than not fly at all. Mallory needed a job and Hannah
needed a partner.

Two men in patched-up planes . . . against the savage Huna
Indians of Brazil's Rio das Mortes – The River of Death.

'High octane adventure' NEW YORK TIMES

The Savage Day 70p

Simon Vaughan fought a dirty war in Korea, so the British Army
eased him out. Ex-Major turned adventurer, firearms specialist
with the best of gun-running connections, and half-Irish as a
bonus . . .

Now they offer to get him out of the Greek prison if he'll take on
the IRA in Belfast . . .

'First class . . . packed with action, atmosphere and ingenuity'
BELFAST TELEGRAPH

'Among the greats of the high adventure storytellers'
EVENING NEWS

Colin Forbes
Avalanche Express 80p

'When the luxury Atlantic Express pulls out of Milan Central Station it has aboard the highest-ranking defector ever to leave the Soviet Union.
In the care of British and American agents, he is pursued across the Continent by the massed network of the Soviet's European agents. A blizzard is roaring across Europe and airlines are grounded. Tension mounts unbearably as *Avalanche Express* develops to its spine-chilling conclusion' LONDON EVENING NEWS

The Stone Leopard 75p

'A real cracker ripping through Europe. The heart of the story is a plot which could destroy the Western world. The action is based on the threat to a President of France from a mysterious and vicious resistance leader from the past. Hard, bitter and compulsive: and the ending . . . Wow!' DAILY MIRROR

Year of the Golden Ape 70p

Racing at Concorde speed from the Middle East through Europe to California, a ruthless battle of wits reaches unparalleled tension as mercenaries hijack a giant British tanker, arm her with a plutonium bomb and sail into San Francisco harbour.

Target Five 70p

No quarter is asked or given when a top Russian oceanographer defects across the Arctic icefields with plans of their submarine network. The Americans send in dog teams and an unconventional trio under Anglo-Canadian agent Keith Beaumont. The Russians use everything they have in an increasingly bloody life-or-death struggle to win him back . . .

Wilbur Smith
Cry Wolf 80p

Two men, one girl and a batch of decrepit armoured cars running
the gauntlet of an Ethiopia in the grip of the Wolf of Rome –
'Mussolini has all the guns, aircraft and armour he needs. The
jolly old Ethiop has a few ancient rifles and a lot of two-handed
swords . . . It should be a close match!

'Another cracker . . . Africa, arms dealing, armoured cars, strong
men with stronger women all combine beautifully for real
entertainment' DAILY MIRROR

The Eye of the Tiger 80p

'A blood-and-cyclone story . . . action follows action, menace
mingles with violence and horror and Harry Fletcher with blonde
and brunette . . . Mystery is piled on mystery . . . death on brutal
death as Fletcher hunts the Mozambique Channel for the ocean's
unknown treasure. A tale to delight the millions of addicts of the
gutsy adventure story' SUNDAY EXPRESS

Gold Mine 75p

'The rock face exploded . . . It killed every man in the gang, and
immediately afterwards the monstrous burst of water that poured
from the face picked up their mutilated remains and swept them
down the drive.'

'Set in South Africa today, a brutal tale of violence, greed,
chicanery and lust amid the gold dust' SUNDAY EXPRESS

The Sunbird £1·25

An action-packed novel of African adventure – a screaming
nightmare of blood and flame and smoke, shining black faces and
sweat-polished bodies . . . From the drama and excitement of
modern Africa the chief characters are projected into the battles,
romance and tragedy of their Carthaginian past.

Peter Benchley
Jaws 70p

The acclaimed bestseller . . . one man against a giant killer shark and a town that won't face the truth!

'Pick up *Jaws* before midnight, read the first five pages, and I guarantee you'll be putting it down breathless and stunned – the final climax is even better than the beginning – as dawn is breaking the next day' PETER GROSVENOR, DAILY EXPRESS

The record-breaking film, produced by Richard Zanuck and David Brown for Universal, stars Robert Shaw, Richard Dreyfuss and Roy Schneider.

The Deep 75p

'Entertainment . . . adventure . . . and underwater chill . . . Two honeymooners . . . sunken Bermudan treasure . . . A sinister black revolutionary and a traitor concealed among the good guys . . . Slow cruising sharks . . . ocean-floor manoeuvres and needle-toothed moray eels darting suddenly from the reef cavities in which the treasure rests' NEWSWEEK

Coming shortly : the Columbia Pictures film starring Robert Shaw, Jacqueline Bisset and Nick Nolte ; directed by Peter Yates.

Alfred Coppel
34 East 75p

34 East – the longitude which holds the key to tomorrow's Middle East peace, where an international force sits in the desert, edgily uncertain of the peace they are there to guarantee . . . As the American Vice-President arrives in the zone to renew the international treaty, a series of appalling catastrophes shatters any illusion of a pact – and the unthinkable becomes the actual . . .

'One of the best political thrillers I've ever come across' FINANCIAL TIMES

'For sheer driving power, irresistible momentum and mounting tension, this book has no equal' COLIN FORBES, author of *Target Five*

Jack Bickham
Twister 80p

Twister is a tornado – the most devastating force ever to emerge
from the world of the elements . . . it moves across America leaving
a trail of devastation and death . . . no life touched by the Twister,
as it wreaks a billion dollars worth of damage, will ever be the same
again . . .
'Blends fact and fiction in a tale that will chill'
PUBLISHERS WEEKLY

Kit Thackeray
Crownbird 70p

Four men and one woman with a plan to change the face of
Africa . . . where the stranglehold of the Chinese is daily more
threatening . . . Their mission – on orders from Whitehall – is an
'adjustment', violent if necessary, of the power politics of the Dark
Continent.

Zeno
The Four Sergeants 75p

Sicily 1943 : A sabotage operation behind enemy lines, to blow a
bridge behind a Panzer Division and smash Axis withdrawal
strategy. The men – a hand-picked Airborne platoon – include a
section of German Jews . . . soldiers who can never allow themselves
to be taken alive . . .
'In the war yarn class, this book rates high . . . tense, authentic'
SUNDAY TELEGRAPH

You can buy these and other Pan Books from booksellers and
newsagents; or direct from the following address:
Pan Books, Sales Office, Cavaye Place, London SW10 9PG
Send purchase price plus 20p for the first book and 10p for
each additional book, to allow for postage and packing
Prices quoted are applicable in the UK

While every effort is made to keep prices low, it is sometimes
necessary to increase prices at short notice. Pan Books reserve
the right to show on covers and charge new retail prices which
may differ from those advertised in the text or elsewhere.